THE HUMAN BODY
IDENTIFICATION MANUAL

Your Body and How it Works

Chief Consultant
Professor Ken Ashwell BMedSc, MB, BS, PhD

GLOBAL BOOK PUBLISHING

Managing Director	Chryl Campbell
Publisher	Roz Hopkins
Editorial Director	Sarah Anderson
Managing Editor	John Mapps
Project Editor	Dannielle Viera
Chief Consultant	Professor Ken Ashwell
Cover Design	Stan Lamond and Kylie Mulquin
Designer	Stan Lamond
Design Concept	Kylie Mulquin

Illustrators	David Carroll, Peter Child, Deborah Clarke, Geoff Cook, Marcus Cremonese, Beth Croce, Hans De Haas, Wendy de Paauw, Levant Efe, Mike Golding, Mike Gorman, Jeff Lang, Alex Lavroff, Ulrich Lehmann, Ruth Lindsay, Richard McKenna, Annabel Milne, Tony Pyrzakowski, Oliver Rennert, Caroline Rodrigues, Otto Schmidinger, Bob Seal, Vicky Short, Graeme Tavendale, Jonathan Tidball, Paul Tresnan, Valentin Varetsa, Glen Vause, Spike Wademan, Trevor Weekes, Paul Williams, David Wood

Indexer	Marie-Louise Taylor
Proofreader	Marie-Louise Taylor
Publishing Coordinator	Jessica Luca
Administrative Assistant	Kristen Donath

First published in 2010 by
Global Book Publishing
Level 8, 15 Orion Road, Lane Cove,
NSW 2066, Australia
Ph: (612) 9425 5800   Fax: (612) 9425 5804
Email: rightsmanager@globalpub.com.au

ISBN 978-1-74048-058-1

Printed in China by Toppan Leefung Printing Limited
Color separation by Pica Digital Pte Ltd, Singapore

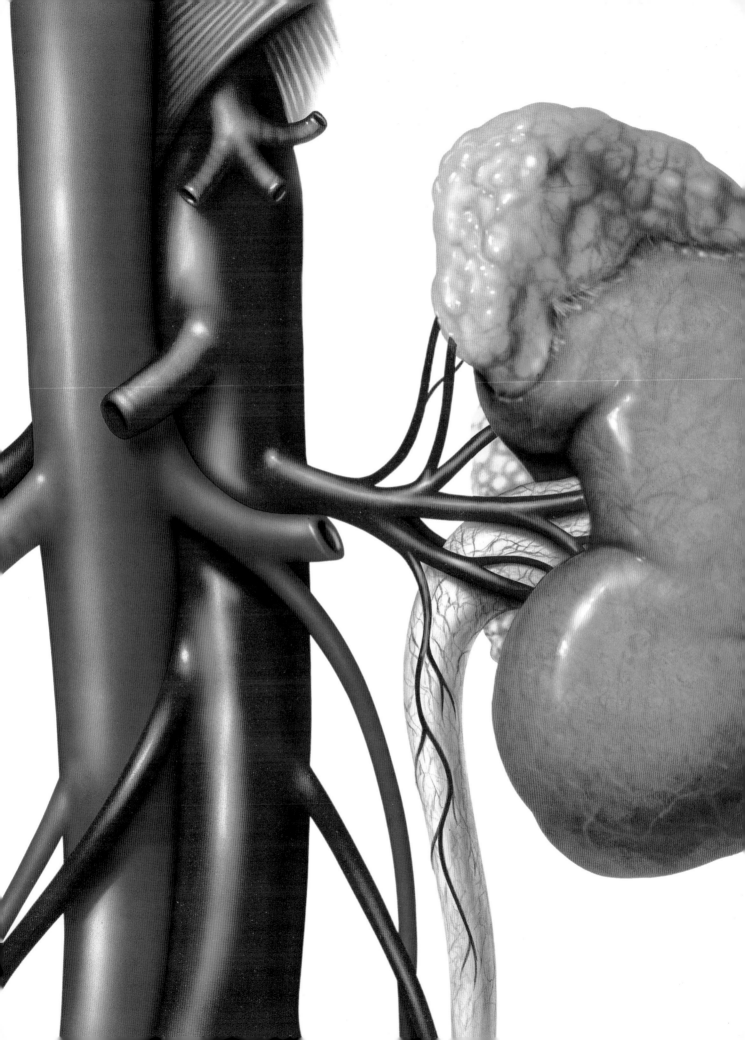

c o n t

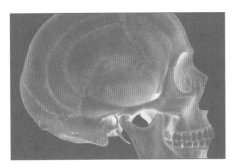

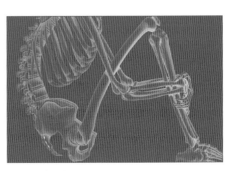

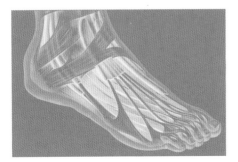

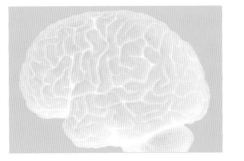

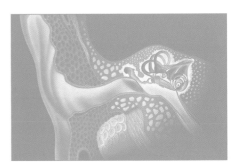

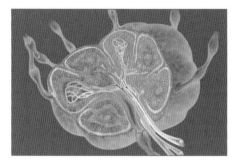

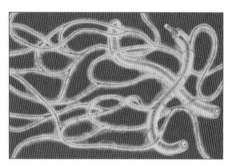

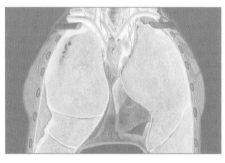

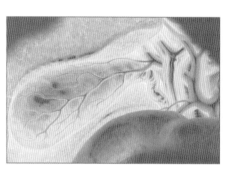

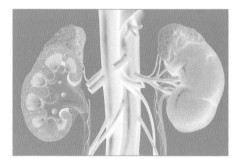

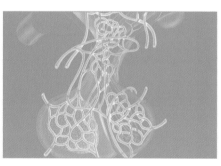

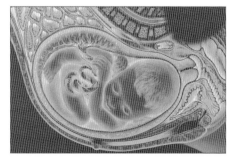

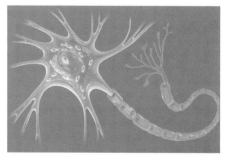

How This Book Works

The Human Body Identification Manual is a stunning pictorial handbook that reveals the marvels of the human body. By concentrating on graphic elements, this comprehensive book allows people with an interest in human anatomy to visualize the various parts of the body and their special links to each other quickly and easily.

Divided into 15 chapters, the book begins with an overview of the body systems and regions, followed by an introduction to cells and tissues. Subsequent chapters identify the structures and functions of the major body systems, from the skeletal and muscular to the endocrine and reproductive. A handy glossary and an extensive index complete the book.

The book features over 500 anatomically correct illustrations with clear and informative labels. Short but instructive captions explain physiological processes, microscopic structures, and other difficult anatomical concepts. As well as showing the location and name of hundreds of body parts, the color illustrations also reveal the unique composition of the human form.

In some instances, the illustrator has removed one part of the body so that another may be viewed more clearly: for example, in some of the illustrations of the abdominal organs, the liver has been peeled back to show the gallbladder. This is also true of some of the lung illustrations.

Many illustrations are supplemented by a locator diagram, which indicates where the organ is in relation to the rest of the body or shows the position and orientation of a cross-section illustration. The appearance of an organ often depends on the angle from which it is viewed, and for this reason some of the illustration names include an orientation such as Front View, Side View, or Rear View.

For ready reference, each chapter features an individually colored border along the side margins of its pages. The chapter name appears within the colored border on the left-hand page, while the body region or part appears within the colored border on the right-hand page. This helps readers to find the body system and region or part that they are looking for with ease.

Because of the nature of the subject matter in *The Human Body Identification Manual*, technical terms are unavoidable; however, the language and style of the text have been made as interesting and accessible as possible.

Illustration headings
Illustration headings give the name of the body part. The orientation is included if necessary, and right or left limbs are also identified here.

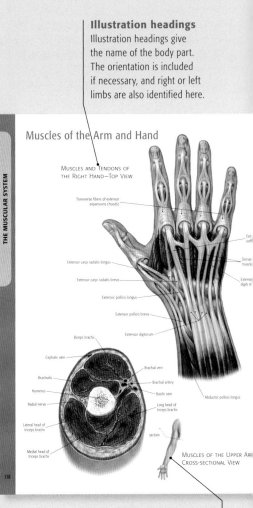

THE MUSCULAR SYSTEM

Muscles of the Arm and Hand

MUSCLES AND TENDONS OF THE RIGHT HAND—TOP VIEW

Transverse fibers of extensor expansions (hoods)

Extensor carpi radialis longus

Extensor carpi radialis brevis

Extensor pollicis longus

Extensor pollicis brevis

Biceps brachii

Cephalic vein

Brachialis

Humerus

Radial nerve

Lateral head of triceps brachii

Medial head of triceps brachii

Ext indi

Dorsa muscl

Extenso digiti m

Extensor digitorum

Brachial vein

Brachial artery

Basilic vein

Abductor pollicis longus

Long head of triceps brachii

section

118

MUSCLES OF THE UPPER ARM CROSS-SECTIONAL VIEW

Locator diagrams
Locator diagrams are included to show where in the body the particular organ or part is found, or to establish the body region from which a cross-section illustration has been drawn.

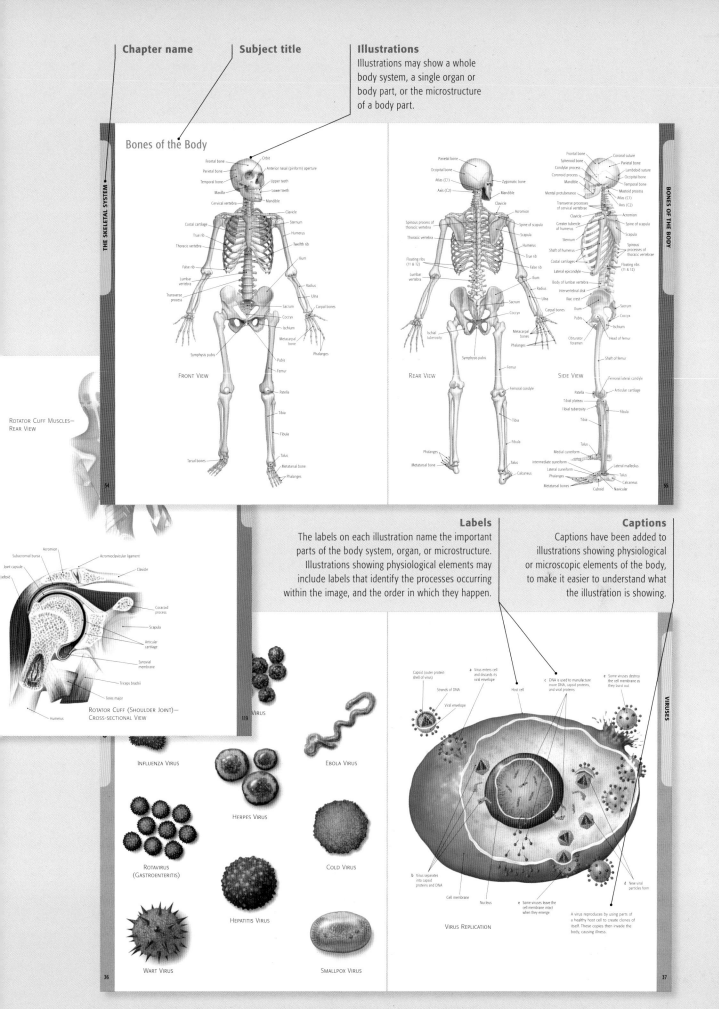

Chapter name

Subject title

Illustrations
Illustrations may show a whole body system, a single organ or body part, or the microstructure of a body part.

Labels
The labels on each illustration name the important parts of the body system, organ, or microstructure. Illustrations showing physiological elements may include labels that identify the processes occurring within the image, and the order in which they happen.

Captions
Captions have been added to illustrations showing physiological or microscopic elements of the body, to make it easier to understand what the illustration is showing.

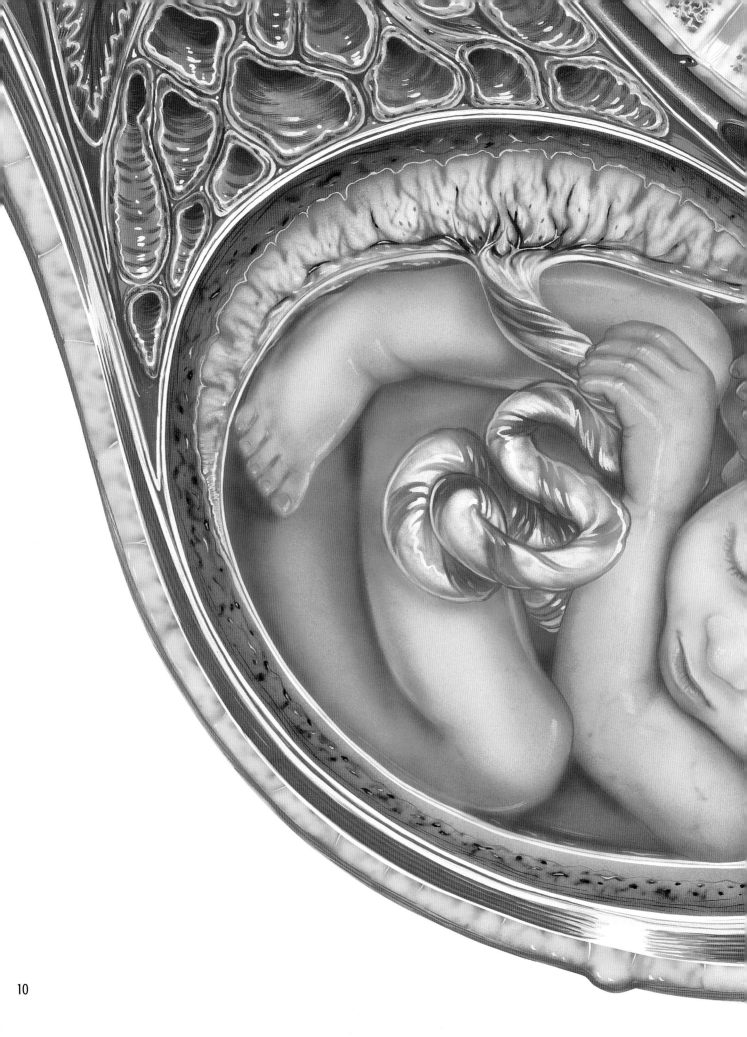

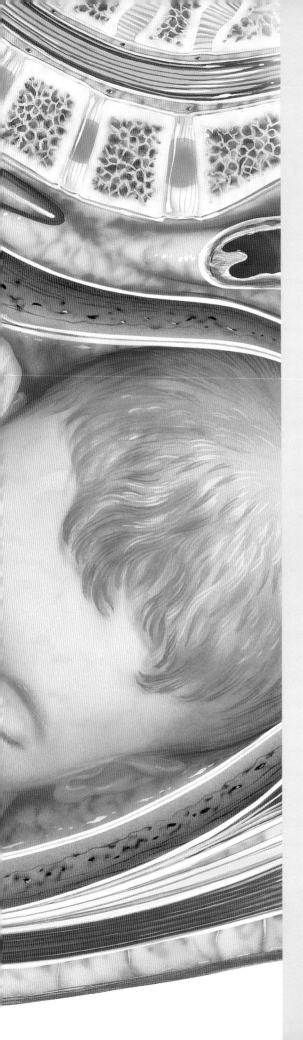

Foreword

Beneath the surface of our skin lies a complex system of muscles, internal organs, nerves, arteries, veins, lymph nodes, joints, and bones; a world of exquisite detail that we all rely on for our health and vitality, but one to which few of us ever give more than a passing thought. Although some of these internal structures can be felt through ridges and elevations on the skin's surface, most people would have only a vague idea of what lies just below their skin.

In this book, the intricate world of human internal structure is brought to life in beautiful, realistic, full-color illustrations that range from the molecular, through the microscopic, to the naked-eye level of magnification. The large-scale panoramic diagrams of the whole body in realistic poses allow the reader to quickly identify key anatomical features and their relationships to each other, while more detailed images focused on discrete body regions provide a seamless progression from the large to the small scale. Hundreds of muscles, bony features, arteries, veins, and nerves have been illustrated and labeled on full-page, full-body images, so the reader can relate these structures to the external features of the body. The figure legends provide pertinent detail on the orientation and focus of each illustration.

This book will not only be useful for students of biology, physical education, osteopathy, chiropractic, podiatry, massage therapy, nursing, physiotherapy, and medicine, but will also be a valuable addition to the home library of those interested in the internal structure of the human form. The accessible, easy-to-understand nature of the images makes the book suitable for anyone who wishes to discover the wondrous workings of their own body.

Naturally, the focus of this book is upon normal structure. It is not intended for the self-diagnosis of disease or abnormality. Readers with concerns about changes in their body should see a medical professional for appropriate diagnosis and treatment.

Professor Ken Ashwell BMedSc, MB, BS, PhD
Department of Anatomy,
School of Medical Sciences, Faculty of Medicine,
University of New South Wales, Sydney, Australia

Body Overview

Overview of the Body Systems

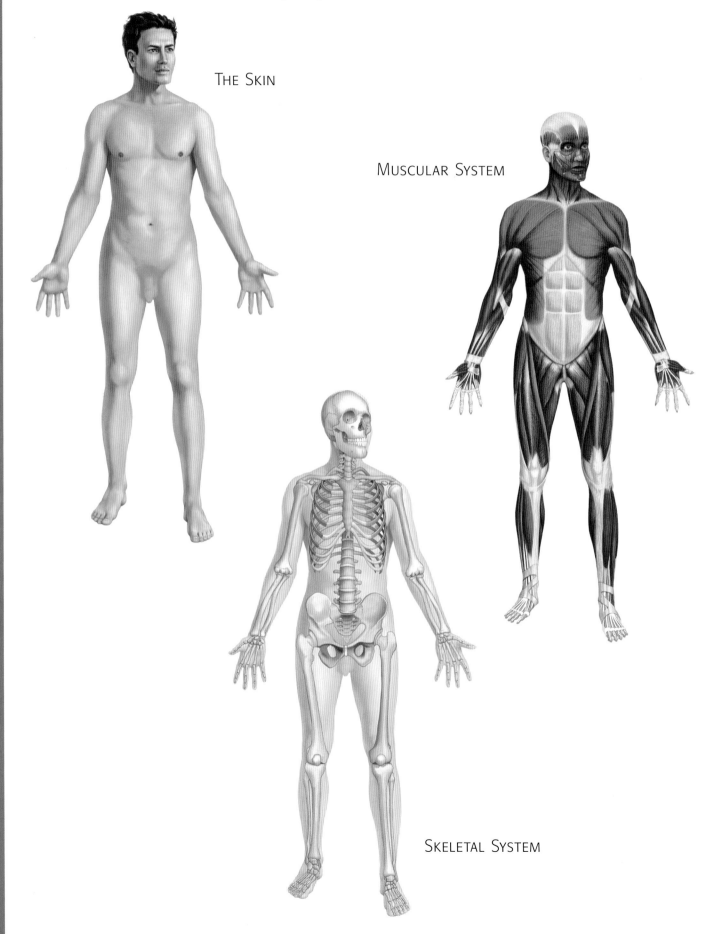

The Skin

Muscular System

Skeletal System

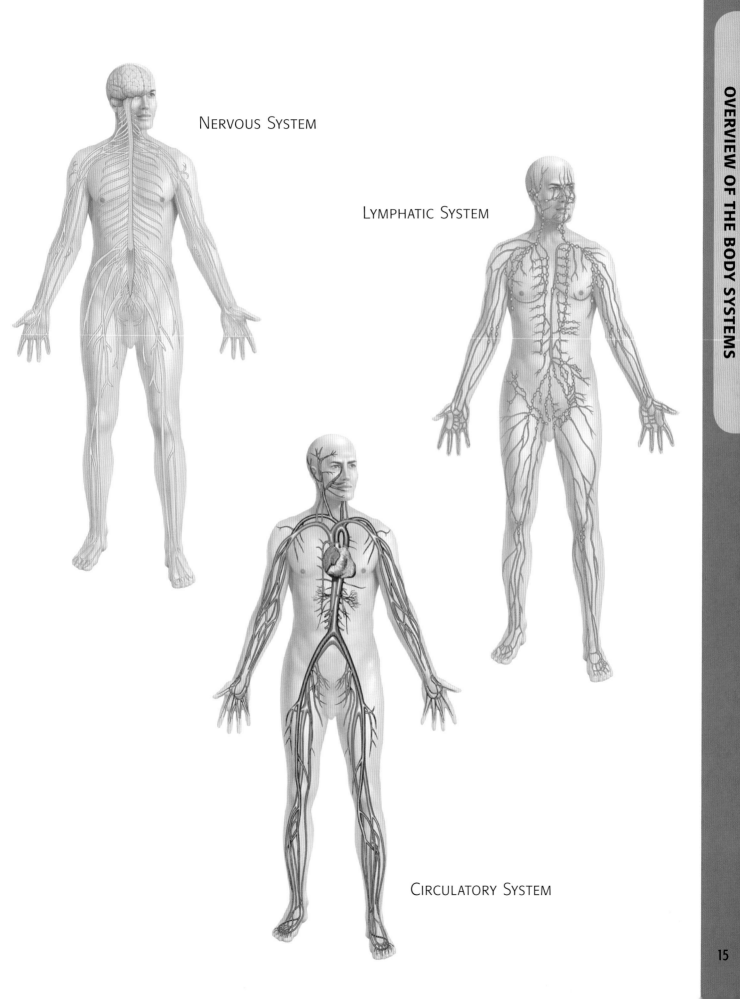

NERVOUS SYSTEM

LYMPHATIC SYSTEM

CIRCULATORY SYSTEM

Overview of the Body Systems

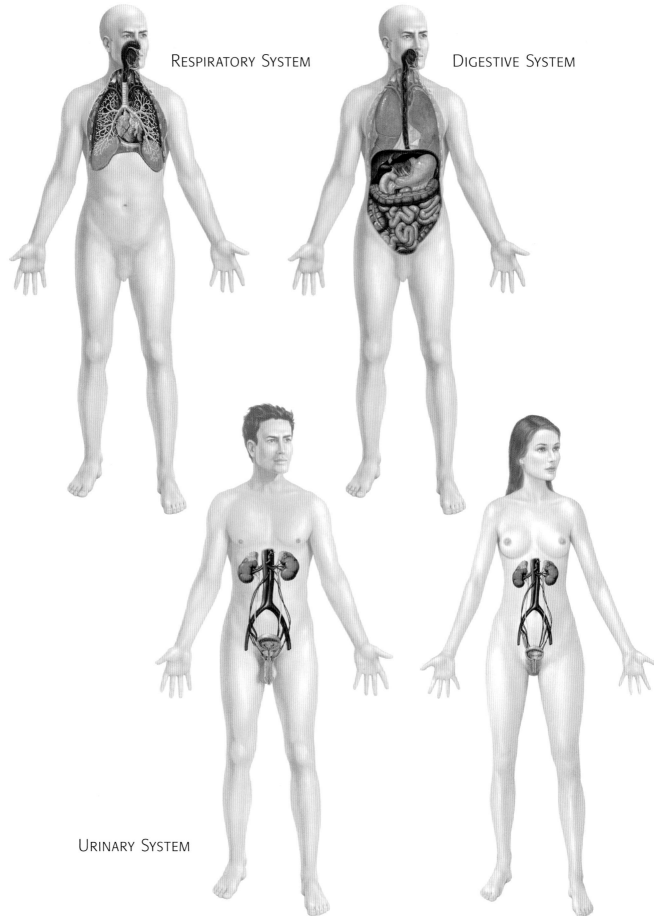

RESPIRATORY SYSTEM

DIGESTIVE SYSTEM

URINARY SYSTEM

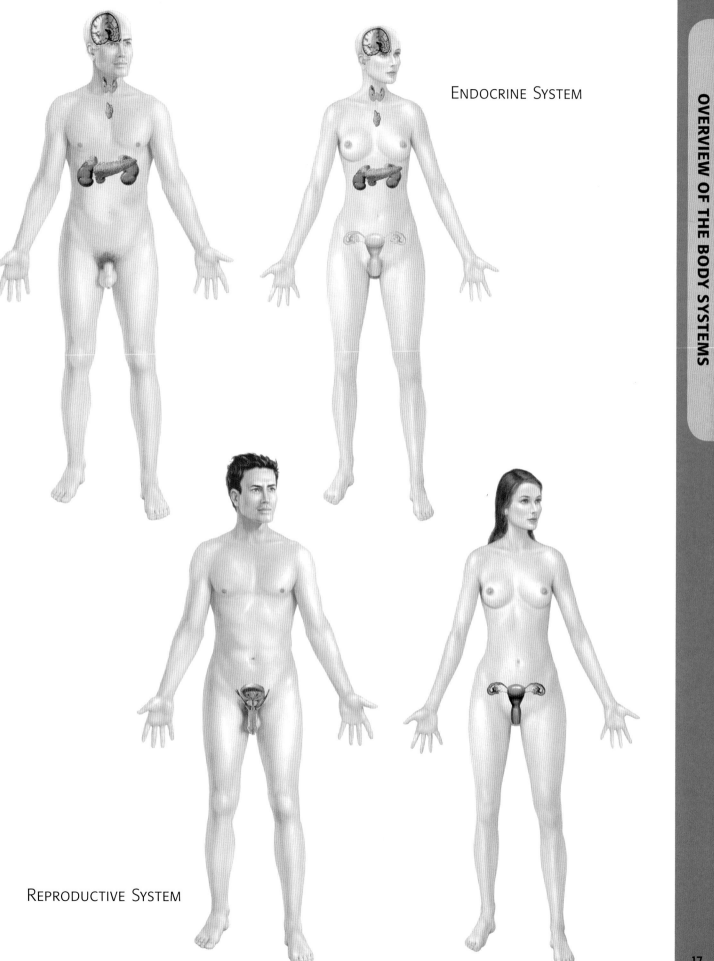

ENDOCRINE SYSTEM

REPRODUCTIVE SYSTEM

Body Regions

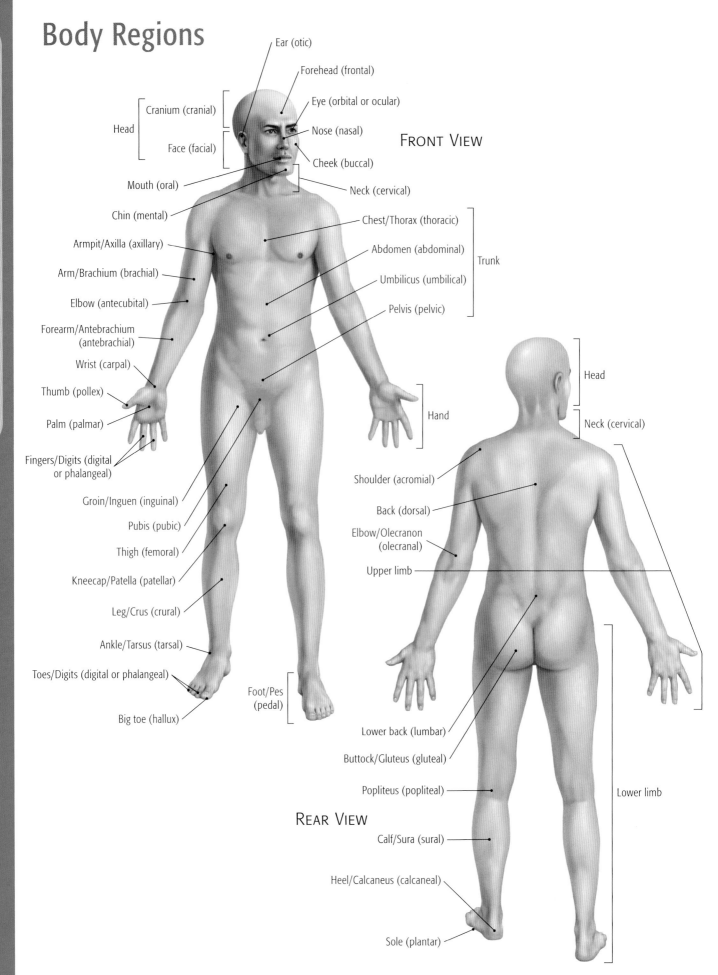

Ear (otic)

Forehead (frontal)

Cranium (cranial)

Eye (orbital or ocular)

Head

Nose (nasal)

FRONT VIEW

Face (facial)

Cheek (buccal)

Mouth (oral)

Neck (cervical)

Chin (mental)

Chest/Thorax (thoracic)

Armpit/Axilla (axillary)

Abdomen (abdominal)

Arm/Brachium (brachial)

Umbilicus (umbilical)

Trunk

Elbow (antecubital)

Pelvis (pelvic)

Forearm/Antebrachium (antebrachial)

Wrist (carpal)

Thumb (pollex)

Head

Palm (palmar)

Neck (cervical)

Fingers/Digits (digital or phalangeal)

Hand

Shoulder (acromial)

Groin/Inguen (inguinal)

Back (dorsal)

Pubis (pubic)

Elbow/Olecranon (olecranal)

Thigh (femoral)

Upper limb

Kneecap/Patella (patellar)

Leg/Crus (crural)

Ankle/Tarsus (tarsal)

Toes/Digits (digital or phalangeal)

Foot/Pes (pedal)

Big toe (hallux)

Lower back (lumbar)

Buttock/Gluteus (gluteal)

Popliteus (popliteal)

Lower limb

REAR VIEW

Calf/Sura (sural)

Heel/Calcaneus (calcaneal)

Sole (plantar)

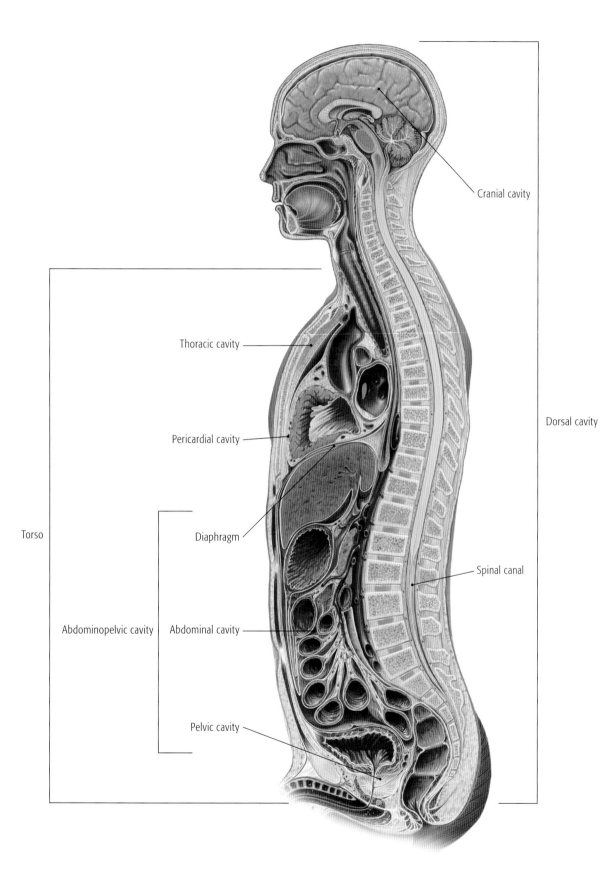

Cranial cavity

Dorsal cavity

Thoracic cavity

Pericardial cavity

Diaphragm

Torso

Abdominopelvic cavity

Abdominal cavity

Spinal canal

Pelvic cavity

BODY CAVITIES—CROSS-SECTIONAL VIEW

Body Shapes

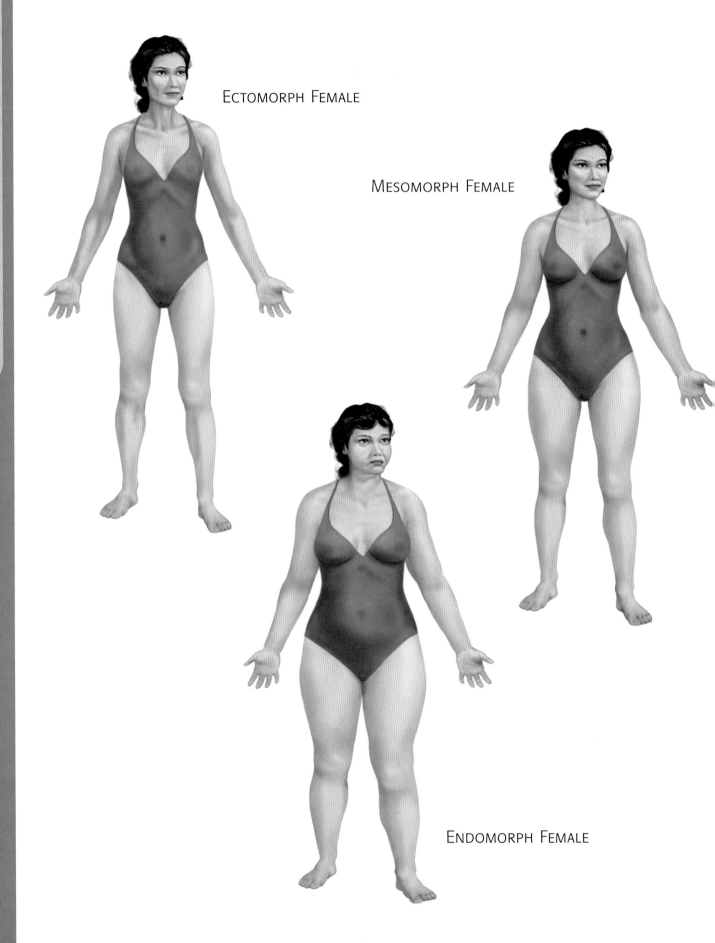

ECTOMORPH FEMALE

MESOMORPH FEMALE

ENDOMORPH FEMALE

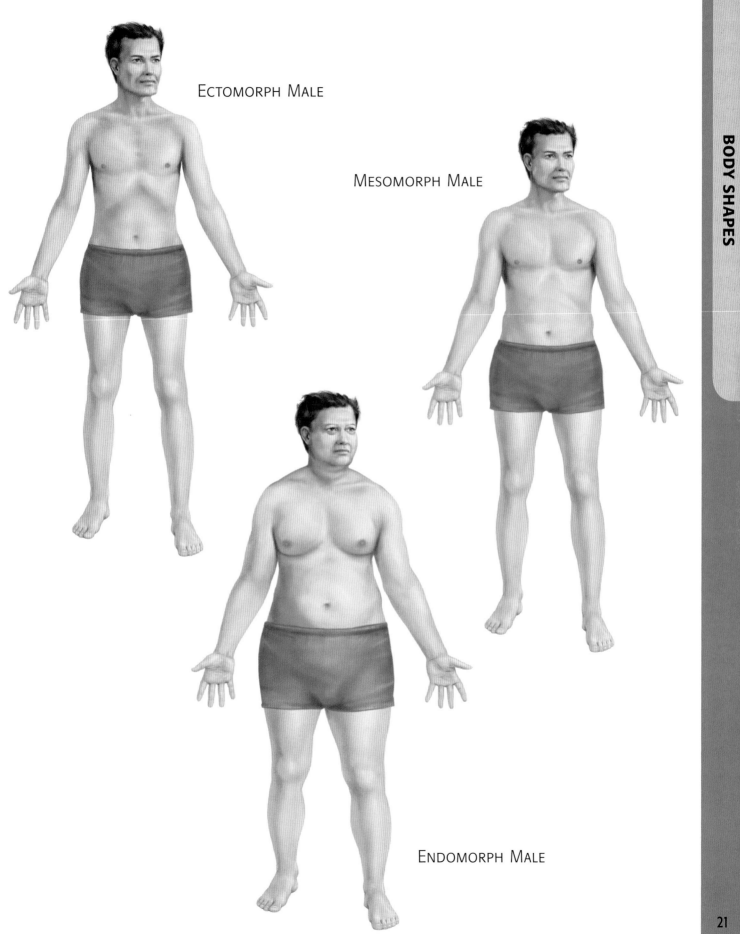

Ectomorph Male

Mesomorph Male

Endomorph Male

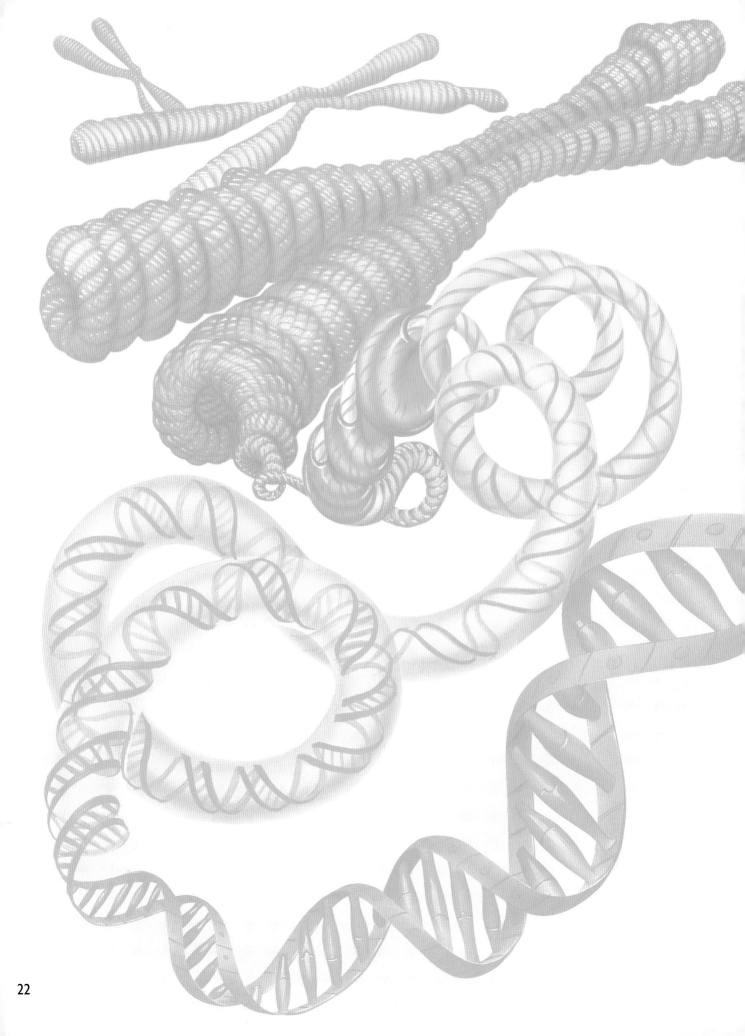

Cells and Tissues

Cell Structure and Major Cell Types

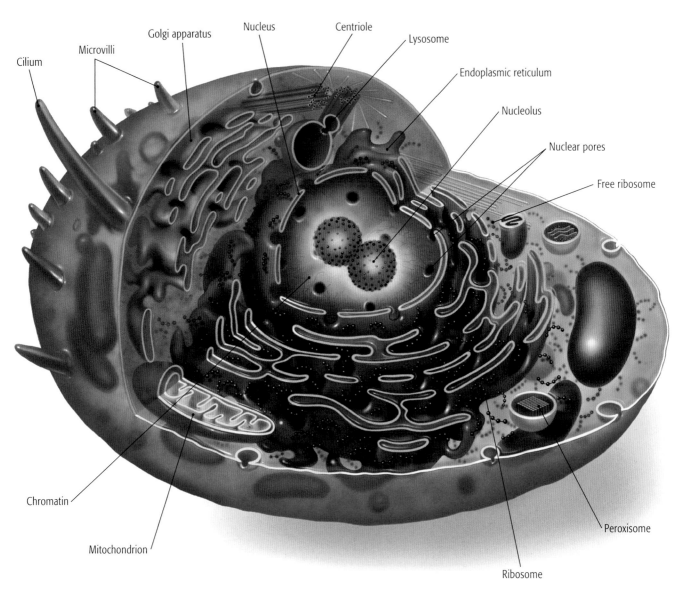

CELL STRUCTURE

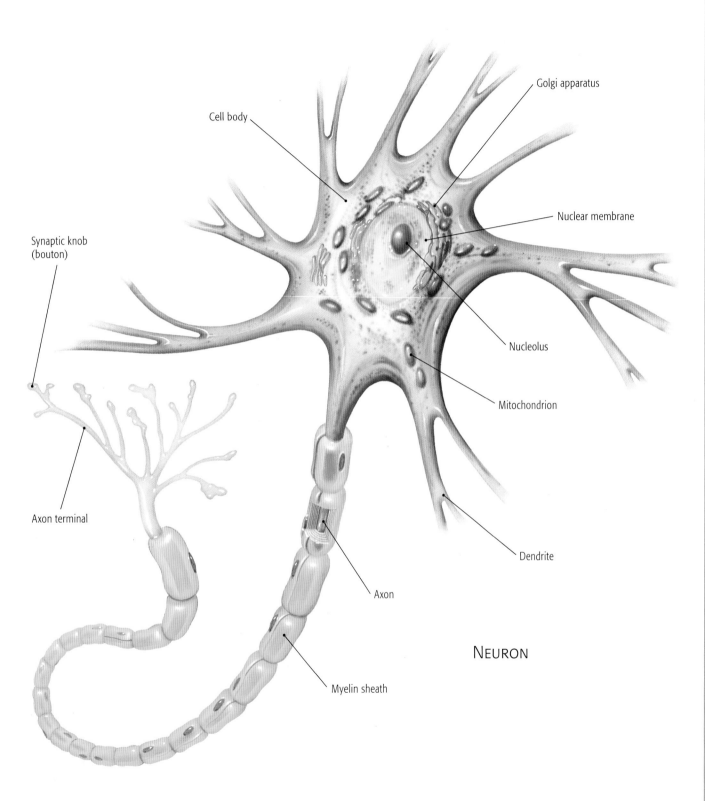

Cell body

Golgi apparatus

Nuclear membrane

Synaptic knob
(bouton)

Nucleolus

Mitochondrion

Axon terminal

Dendrite

Axon

NEURON

Myelin sheath

Blood Cells

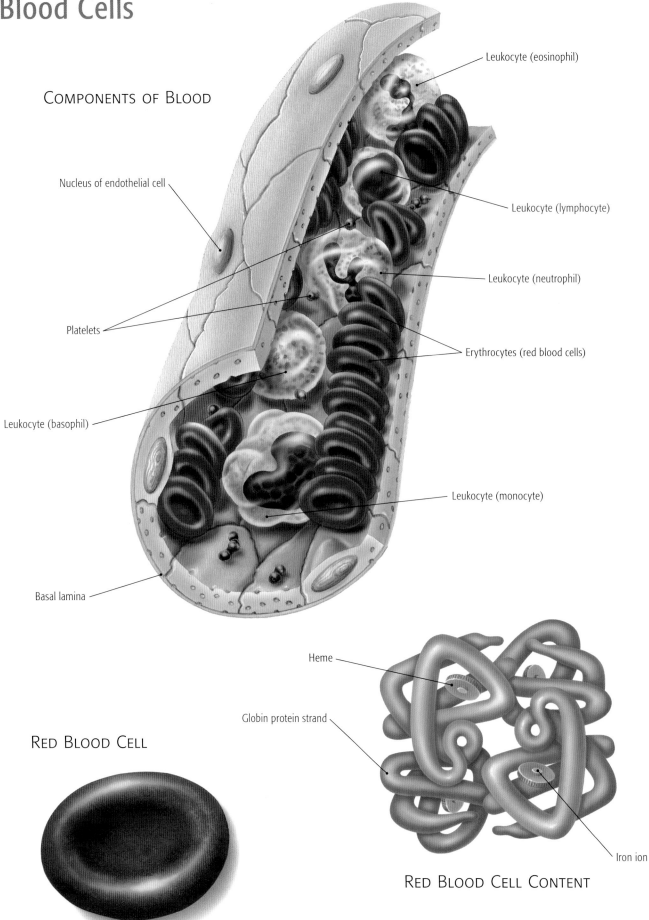

COMPONENTS OF BLOOD

Leukocyte (eosinophil)

Nucleus of endothelial cell

Leukocyte (lymphocyte)

Leukocyte (neutrophil)

Platelets

Erythrocytes (red blood cells)

Leukocyte (basophil)

Leukocyte (monocyte)

Basal lamina

Heme

Globin protein strand

RED BLOOD CELL

Iron ion

RED BLOOD CELL CONTENT

Monocyte

Macrophage

Neutrophil

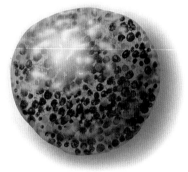

Basophil

Eosinophil

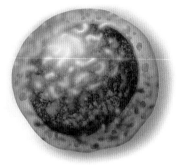

Lymphocyte

WHITE BLOOD CELLS

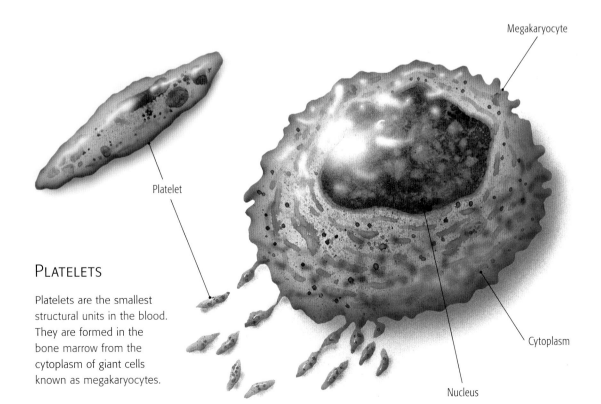

Megakaryocyte

Platelet

Cytoplasm

Nucleus

PLATELETS

Platelets are the smallest structural units in the blood. They are formed in the bone marrow from the cytoplasm of giant cells known as megakaryocytes.

Healing

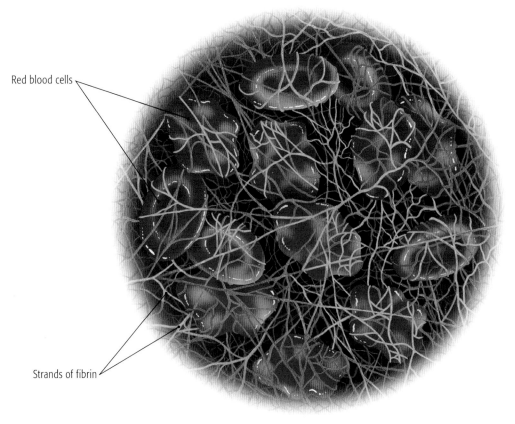

Red blood cells

Strands of fibrin

BLOOD CLOT

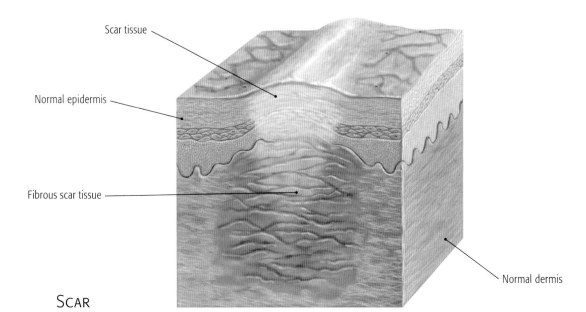

Scar tissue

Normal epidermis

Fibrous scar tissue

Normal dermis

SCAR

BLOOD CLOTTING

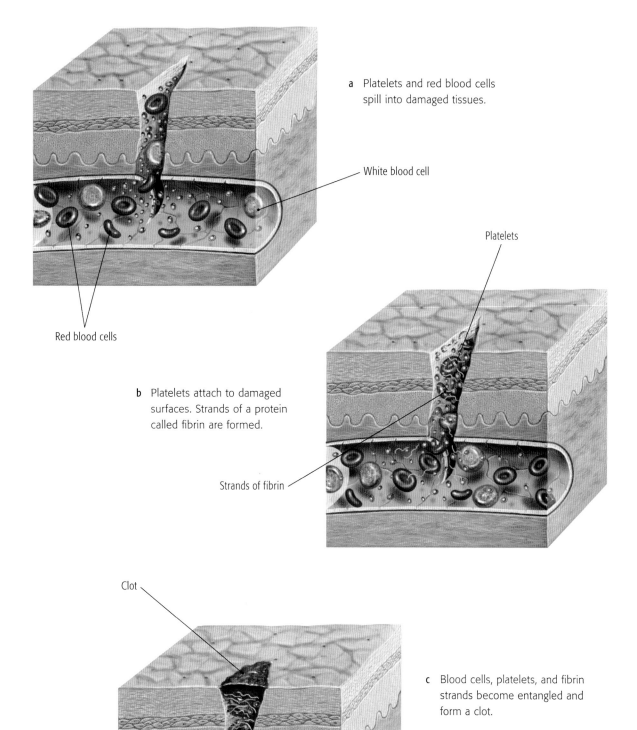

a Platelets and red blood cells
   spill into damaged tissues.

White blood cell

Red blood cells

Platelets

b Platelets attach to damaged
   surfaces. Strands of a protein
   called fibrin are formed.

Strands of fibrin

Clot

c Blood cells, platelets, and fibrin
   strands become entangled and
   form a clot.

DNA

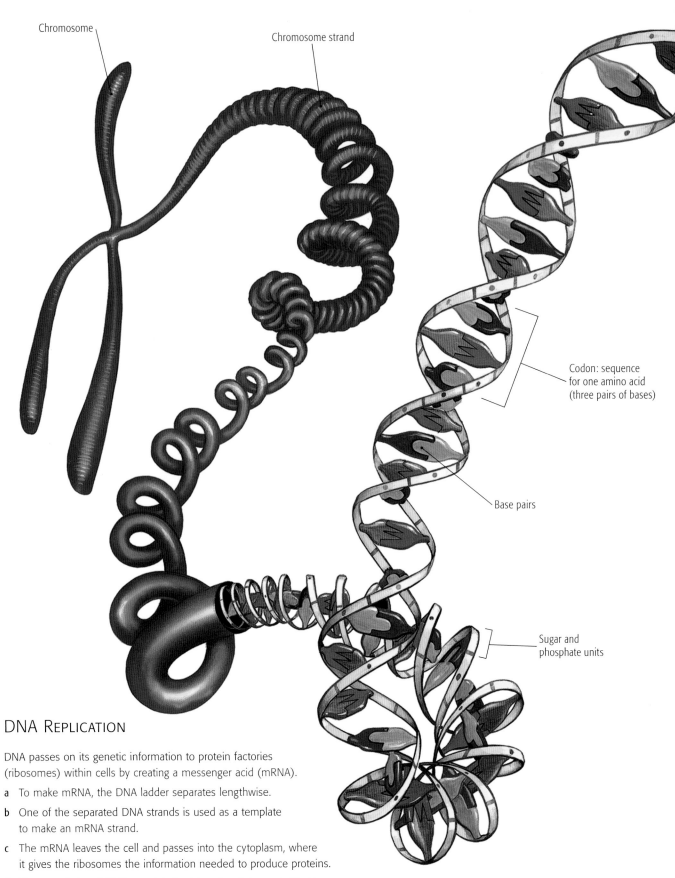

Chromosome

Chromosome strand

Codon: sequence for one amino acid (three pairs of bases)

Base pairs

Sugar and phosphate units

DNA REPLICATION

DNA passes on its genetic information to protein factories (ribosomes) within cells by creating a messenger acid (mRNA).

a To make mRNA, the DNA ladder separates lengthwise.

b One of the separated DNA strands is used as a template to make an mRNA strand.

c The mRNA leaves the cell and passes into the cytoplasm, where it gives the ribosomes the information needed to produce proteins.

d The two chains of DNA now join back together into a spiral ladder.

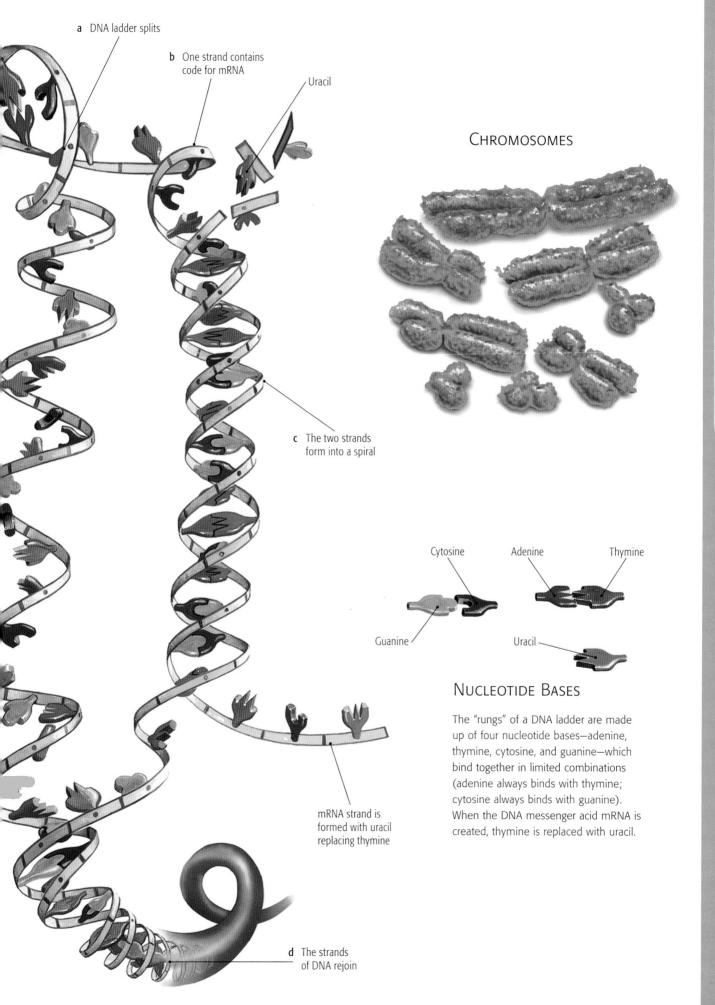

a DNA ladder splits

b One strand contains code for mRNA

Uracil

CHROMOSOMES

c The two strands form into a spiral

Cytosine Adenine Thymine

Guanine Uracil

NUCLEOTIDE BASES

The "rungs" of a DNA ladder are made up of four nucleotide bases—adenine, thymine, cytosine, and guanine—which bind together in limited combinations (adenine always binds with thymine; cytosine always binds with guanine). When the DNA messenger acid mRNA is created, thymine is replaced with uracil.

mRNA strand is formed with uracil replacing thymine

d The strands of DNA rejoin

Genes and Heredity

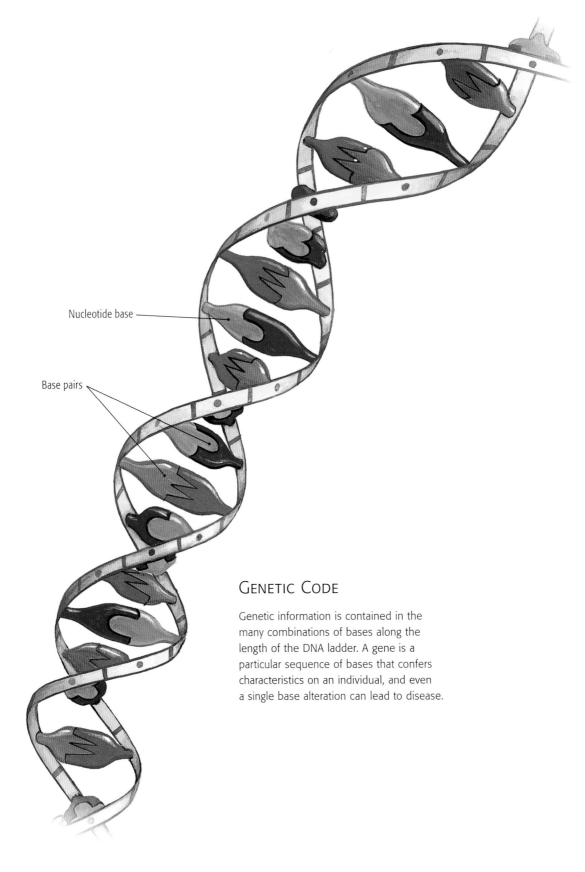

Nucleotide base

Base pairs

GENETIC CODE

Genetic information is contained in the many combinations of bases along the length of the DNA ladder. A gene is a particular sequence of bases that confers characteristics on an individual, and even a single base alteration can lead to disease.

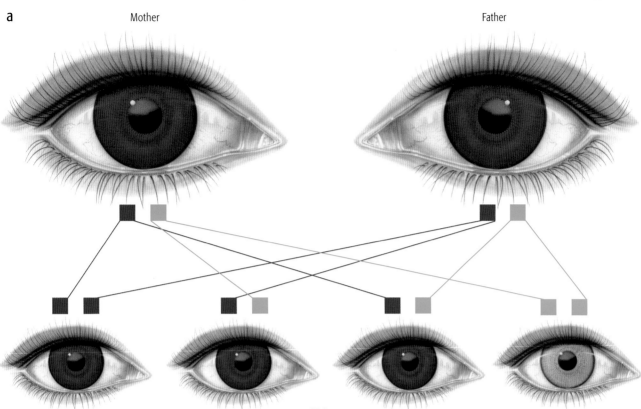

a Mother   Father

Children

Dominant and Recessive Genes

Some features, such as eye color, are determined by a single gene. The gene for brown eyes is dominant over the gene for blue eyes. Two parents with brown eyes can only have a blue-eyed child if the child inherits a recessive blue gene from both parents (**a**). If one parent with brown eyes has two dominant brown-eye genes, all children will inherit at least one dominant gene and will have brown eyes (**b**).

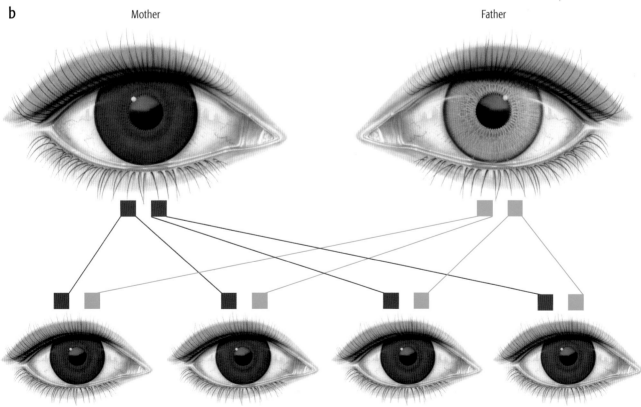

b Mother   Father

Children

Bacteria

Bacteria are simple organisms of microscopic size. Many are beneficial and live in harmony with humans. Some are harmful and can cause and spread infections such as cholera, syphilis, and food poisoning.

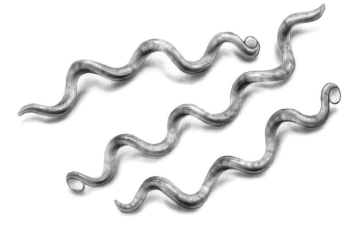

TREPONEMA PALLIDUM
(SYPHILIS)

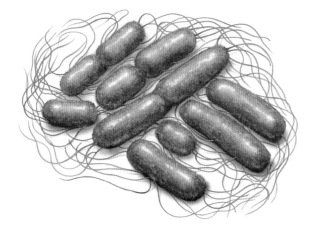

BORRELIA BURGDORFERI
(LYME DISEASE)

CLOSTRIDIUM TETANI
(TETANUS)

SALMONELLA
(FOOD POISONING)

E. COLI
(FOOD POISONING)

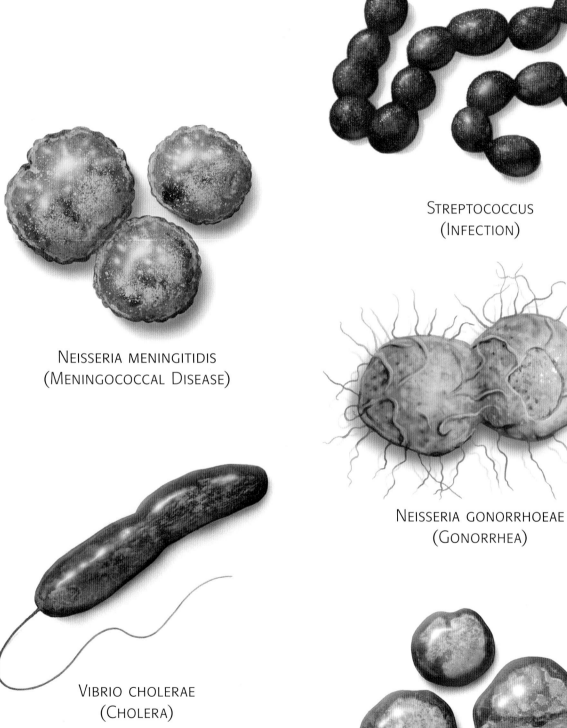

STREPTOCOCCUS
(INFECTION)

NEISSERIA MENINGITIDIS
(MENINGOCOCCAL DISEASE)

NEISSERIA GONORRHOEAE
(GONORRHEA)

VIBRIO CHOLERAE
(CHOLERA)

CHLAMYDIA TRACHOMATIS
(CHLAMYDIA)

Viruses

These tiny organisms are much smaller than bacteria and vary considerably in shape and structure. Some viruses cause acute disease lasting for only a short time and others cause recurring or chronic disease, while others do not cause any disease.

POLIO VIRUS

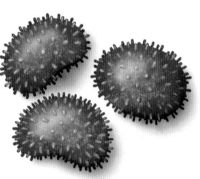

INFLUENZA VIRUS

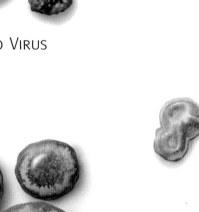

HERPES VIRUS

EBOLA VIRUS

COLD VIRUS

ROTAVIRUS
(GASTROENTERITIS)

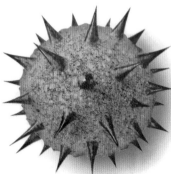

WART VIRUS

HEPATITIS VIRUS

SMALLPOX VIRUS

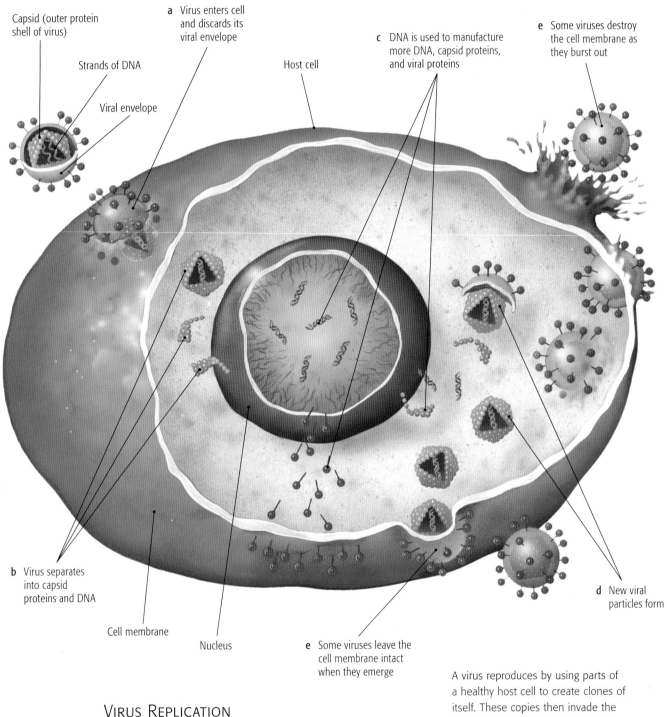

Capsid (outer protein shell of virus)

Strands of DNA

Viral envelope

a Virus enters cell and discards its viral envelope

Host cell

c DNA is used to manufacture more DNA, capsid proteins, and viral proteins

e Some viruses destroy the cell membrane as they burst out

b Virus separates into capsid proteins and DNA

Cell membrane

Nucleus

e Some viruses leave the cell membrane intact when they emerge

d New viral particles form

A virus reproduces by using parts of a healthy host cell to create clones of itself. These copies then invade the body, causing illness.

VIRUS REPLICATION

Immunity

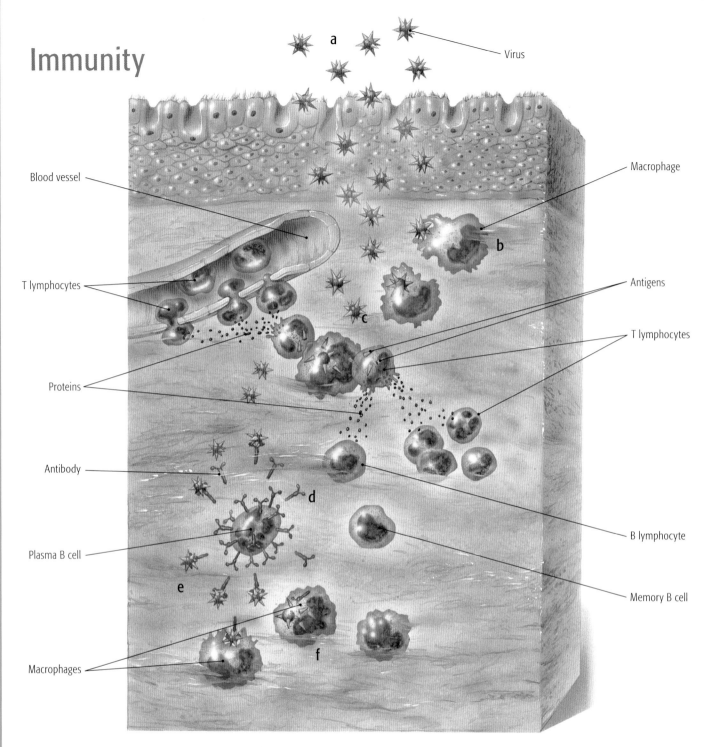

a

Virus

Macrophage

Blood vessel

T lymphocytes

b

Antigens

c

T lymphocytes

Proteins

Antibody

d

Plasma B cell

B lymphocyte

e

Memory B cell

Macrophages

f

HUMORAL IMMUNE RESPONSE

B lymphocytes (white blood cells) produce antibodies to help identify and eliminate invading antigens (carried by bacteria or viruses). They are helped in the body's defenses by circulating T lymphocytes and macrophages (scavenging white blood cells).

a   Virus particles invade tissue through surface cells and multiply.

b   Virus particles are consumed by macrophages.

c   Macrophages break down the virus and present antigens to circulating T lymphocytes, which release proteins that attract more T and B lymphocytes.

d   B lymphocytes divide into memory B cells (which remember the virus for future attacks) and plasma B cells (which make virus-specific antibodies).

e   Circulating antibodies attach to the virus particles.

f   Macrophages primed to recognize the antibody consume the virus and break it down, saving the body from infection.

ALLERGIC REACTION

The body's exposure to allergens leads to the release of histamine, which causes symptoms such as sneezing and rash.

a On first exposure to allergens, plasma B cells produce antibodies.

b Antibodies attach to mast cells in the body's tissues.

c Subsequent exposure sees allergens captured by antibodies.

d Mast cells respond by releasing histamine.

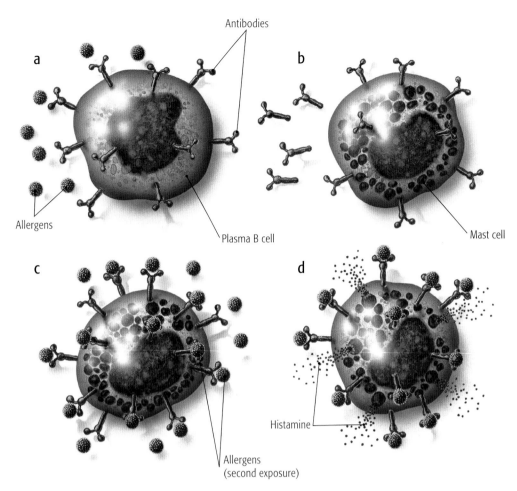

Antibodies

a

b

Allergens

Plasma B cell

Mast cell

c

d

Histamine

Allergens
(second exposure)

CELL-MEDIATED IMMUNE RESPONSE

T lymphocytes (a type of white blood cell) are responsible for the delayed action of the cell-mediated immune response.

a Circulating macrophages ingest the invading virus.

b Macrophages process the virus and present antigens to T cells.

c T cells produce clones that each play a special role in the immune response: memory T cells remember the invading antigen for future attacks; helper T cells recruit B and T cells to the site of the antigen attack; suppressor T cells inhibit the action of B and T cells; and killer T cells attach to invading antigens and destroy them.

Virus entering macrophage

Antigens

b

a

Macrophage

T cell

Killer T cell

Memory T cell

Helper T cell

Suppressor T cell

Tissues

LOOSE CONNECTIVE TISSUE

Connective tissue is the framework that supports, connects, and fills out body structures.

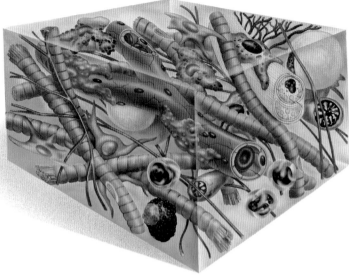

BONE TISSUE

Spongy or cancellous bone consists of a lattice-work system of bony spikes called trabeculae, arranged in different directions.

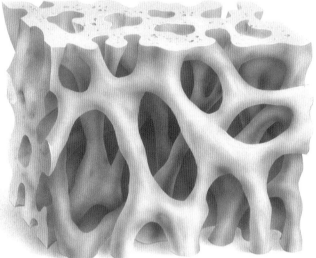

ADIPOSE TISSUE

Adipose tissue is a specialized connective tissue that stores fat.

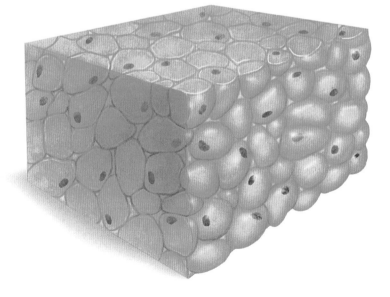

EPITHELIAL TISSUE

Formed from cells that are packed closely together, epithelial tissue is found in the outermost layer of the skin and in some internal organs.

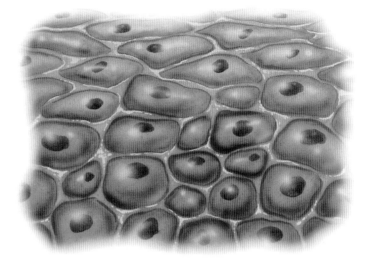

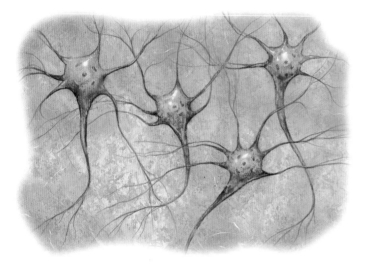

NEURAL TISSUE

The nervous system is made up of neural tissue, which transmits messages to and from the brain.

LYMPHATIC TISSUE

Found at the entrances to the respiratory system and in the digestive and urogenital tracts, lymphatic tissue acts as a first line of defense against infection.

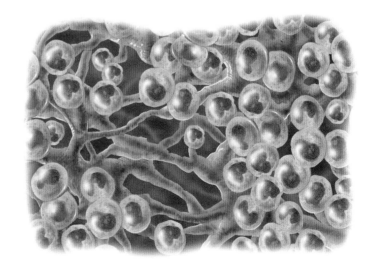

Tissues

MUSCLE TISSUE: SKELETAL MUSCLE

Featuring long, cylindrical muscle fibers, skeletal muscle is usually attached to bones via tendons.

MUSCLE TISSUE: SMOOTH MUSCLE

Smooth muscle is found in the walls of blood vessels, in airways, and inside the eye.

MUSCLE TISSUE: CARDIAC MUSCLE

Found only in the heart, cardiac muscle cannot regenerate after being destroyed.

TENDON TISSUE (RELAXED)

Tendons are constructed primarily of collagen fibers arranged in a regular formation, which provide the strength to attach muscles to bones.

CARTILAGE TISSUE: HYALINE CARTILAGE

Found in many places in the body, hyaline cartilage forms the skeleton in the embryo, the end of the nose and ribs, and the rings around the windpipe.

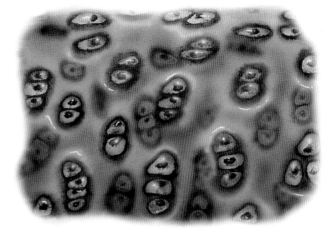

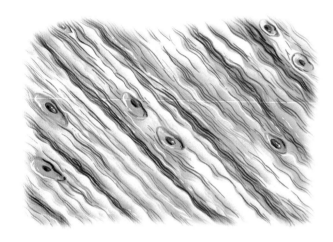

CARTILAGE TISSUE: FIBROCARTILAGE

Resilient and able to withstand compression, fibrocartilage is located between the bones of the spinal column, hip, and pelvis.

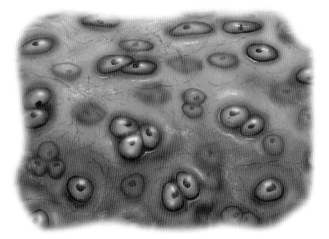

CARTILAGE TISSUE: ELASTIC CARTILAGE

Elastic cartilage is strong but supple, and makes up the epiglottis and the springy part of the outer ear.

LIGAMENT TISSUE (TIGHT)

Ligaments are tough, white, fibrous, slightly elastic tissues that mainly support and strengthen joints.

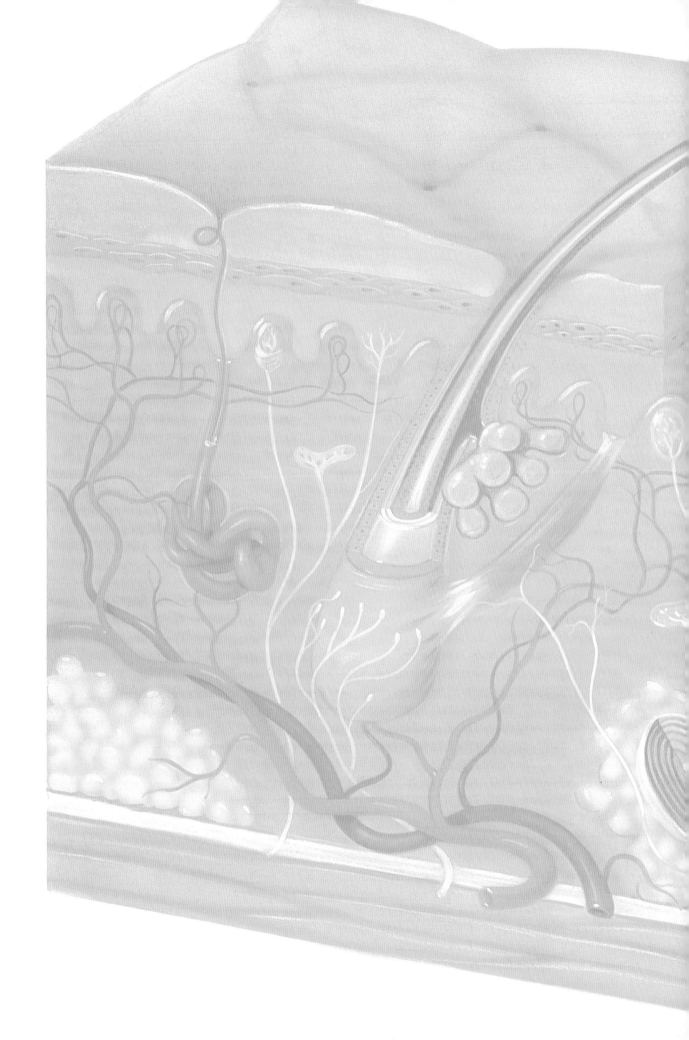

The Skin, Nails, and Hair

The Skin

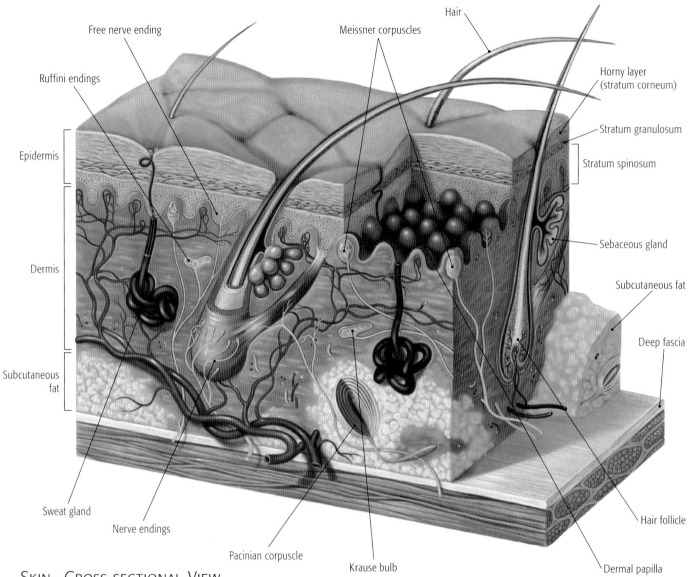

Free nerve ending

Ruffini endings

Meissner corpuscles

Hair

Horny layer (stratum corneum)

Epidermis

Stratum granulosum

Stratum spinosum

Dermis

Sebaceous gland

Subcutaneous fat

Deep fascia

Subcutaneous fat

Sweat gland

Nerve endings

Pacinian corpuscle

Krause bulb

Dermal papilla

Hair follicle

SKIN—CROSS-SECTIONAL VIEW

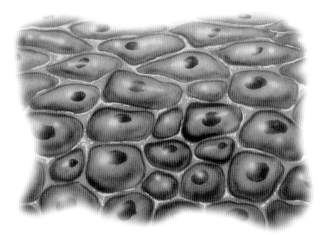

STRATIFIED SQUAMOUS SKIN CELLS

Near the surface of the skin (the horny layer), cells are flattened. The arrangement of cell layers provides a protective shield and prevents dehydration.

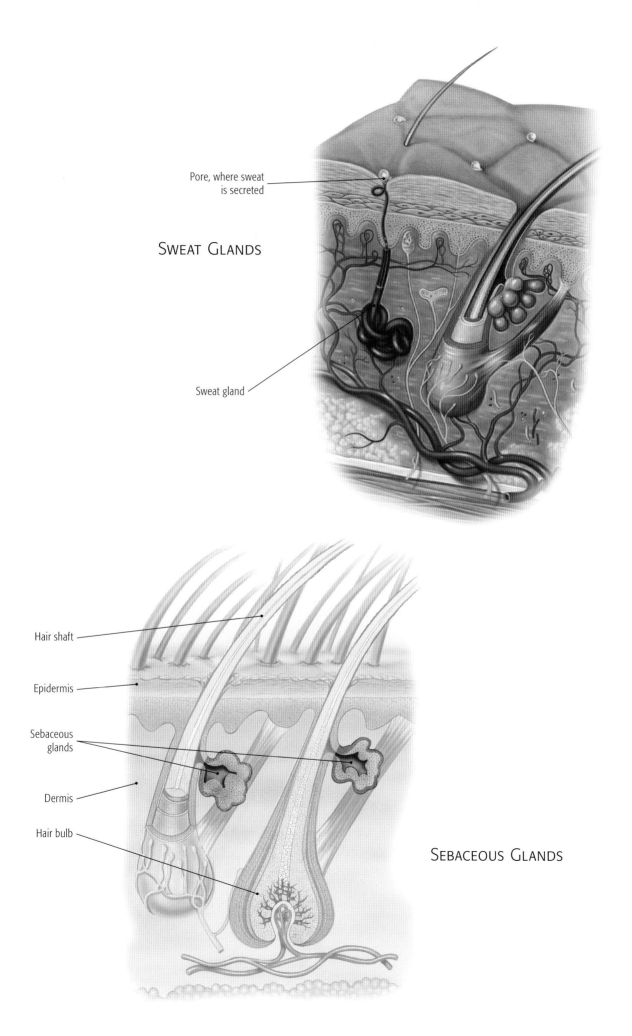

Pore, where sweat
is secreted

SWEAT GLANDS

Sweat gland

Hair shaft

Epidermis

Sebaceous
glands

Dermis

Hair bulb

SEBACEOUS GLANDS

Skin and Temperature

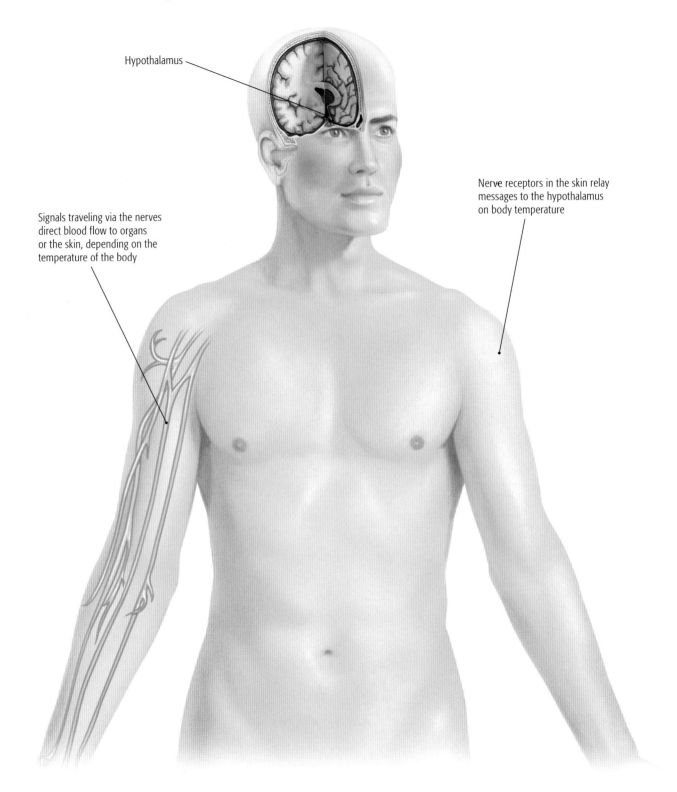

Hypothalamus

Nerve receptors in the skin relay messages to the hypothalamus on body temperature

Signals traveling via the nerves direct blood flow to organs or the skin, depending on the temperature of the body

TEMPERATURE REGULATION

The body has a built-in mechanism regulated by the hypothalamus for maintaining a stable temperature. Nerve endings in the skin relay temperature changes to the hypothalamus. If the body is cold, the hypothalamus increases heat production in the body by increasing the metabolic rate. If the body is hot, the hypothalamus sends blood to the skin, where heat can be lost through radiation, conduction, convection, and evaporation.

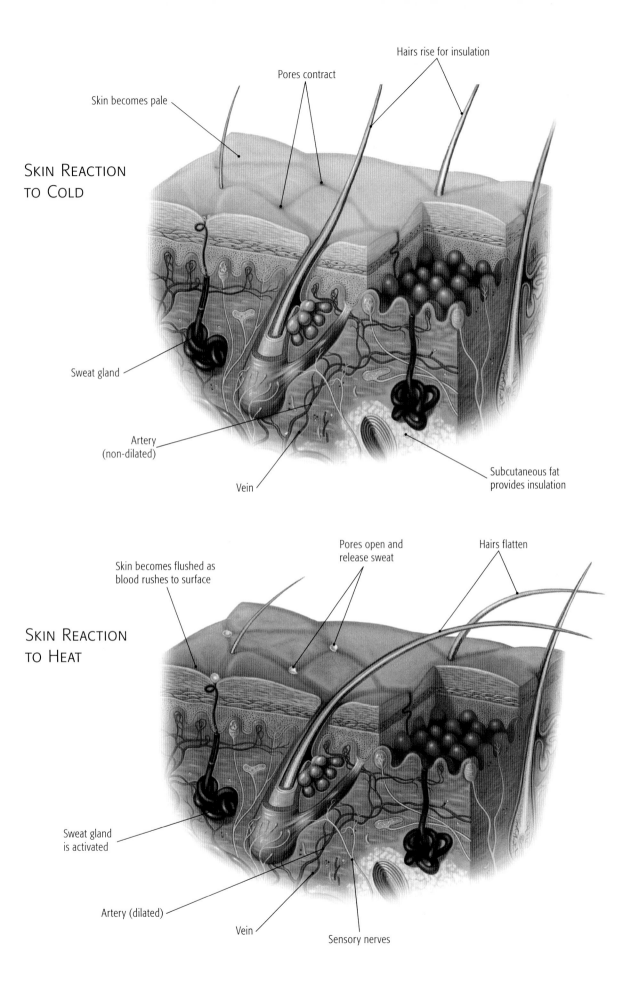

SKIN REACTION TO COLD

Skin becomes pale

Pores contract

Hairs rise for insulation

Sweat gland

Artery (non-dilated)

Vein

Subcutaneous fat provides insulation

SKIN REACTION TO HEAT

Skin becomes flushed as blood rushes to surface

Pores open and release sweat

Hairs flatten

Sweat gland is activated

Artery (dilated)

Vein

Sensory nerves

The Hair and Nails

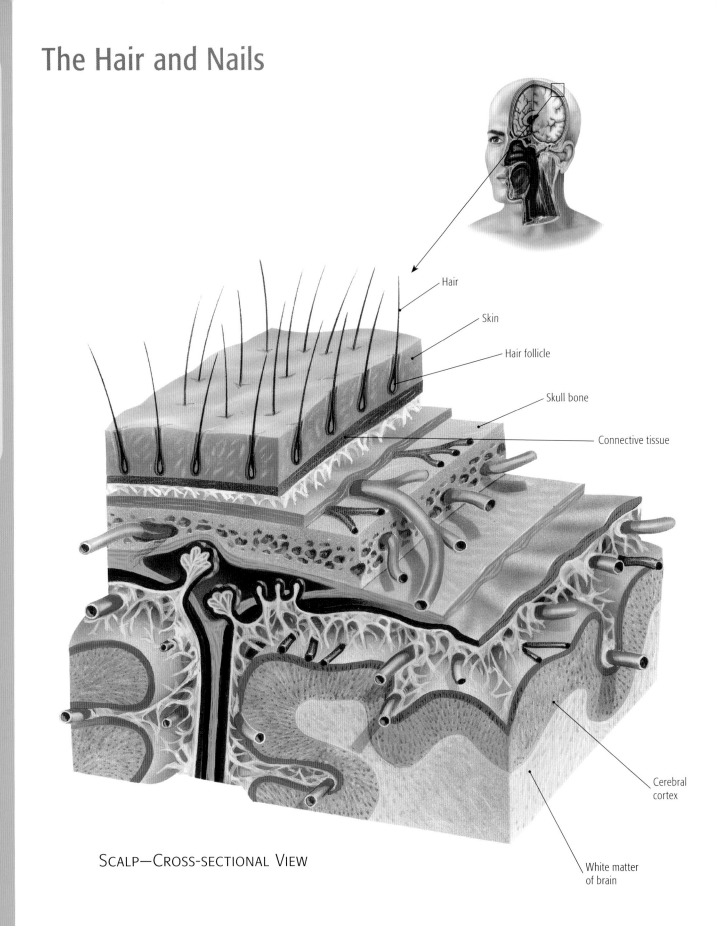

Hair

Skin

Hair follicle

Skull bone

Connective tissue

Cerebral cortex

White matter of brain

SCALP—CROSS-SECTIONAL VIEW

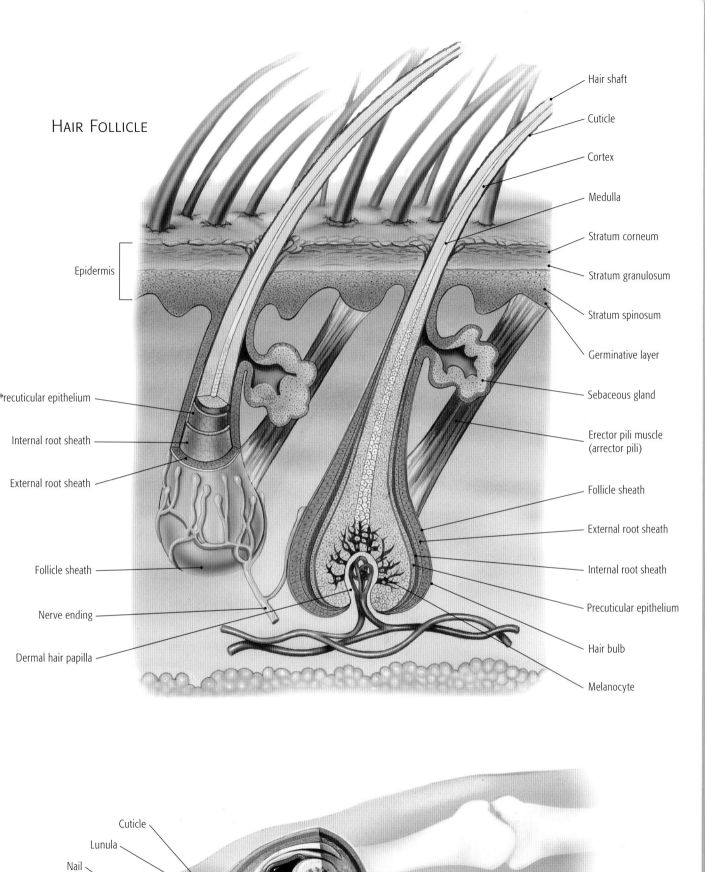

Hair Follicle

Hair shaft
Cuticle
Cortex
Medulla
Stratum corneum
Stratum granulosum
Stratum spinosum
Germinative layer
Sebaceous gland
Erector pili muscle (arrector pili)
Follicle sheath
External root sheath
Internal root sheath
Precuticular epithelium
Hair bulb
Melanocyte

Epidermis

Precuticular epithelium
Internal root sheath
External root sheath
Follicle sheath
Nerve ending
Dermal hair papilla

Nail

Cuticle
Lunula
Nail
Root of nail

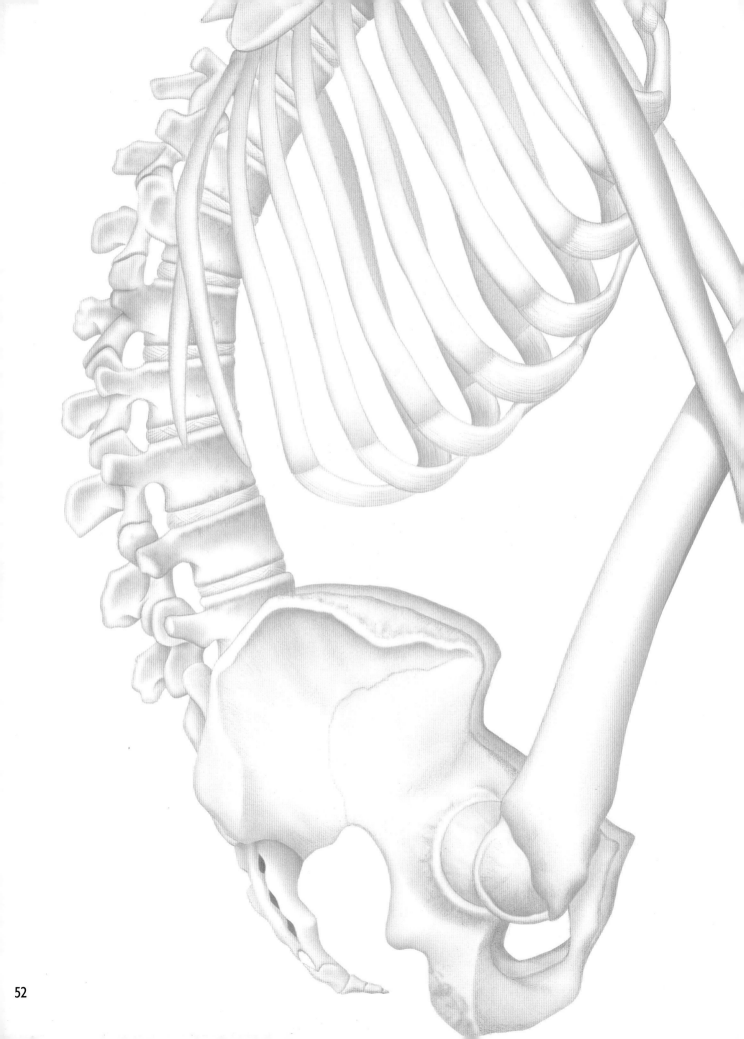

The Skeletal System

Bones of the Body

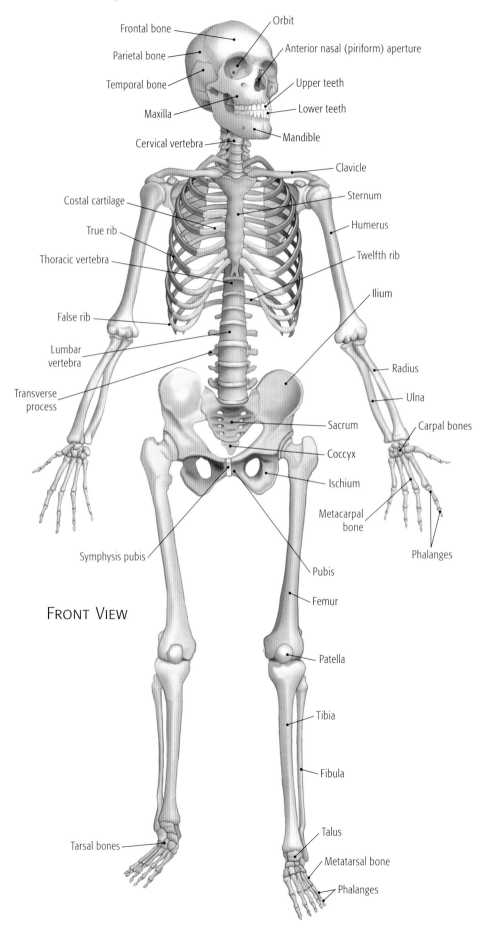

Frontal bone

Parietal bone

Temporal bone

Maxilla

Cervical vertebra

Orbit

Anterior nasal (piriform) aperture

Upper teeth

Lower teeth

Mandible

Costal cartilage

True rib

Thoracic vertebra

False rib

Lumbar vertebra

Transverse process

Clavicle

Sternum

Humerus

Twelfth rib

Ilium

Radius

Ulna

Carpal bones

Sacrum

Coccyx

Ischium

Metacarpal bone

Phalanges

Symphysis pubis

Pubis

Femur

Patella

Tibia

Fibula

Talus

Tarsal bones

Metatarsal bone

Phalanges

FRONT VIEW

54

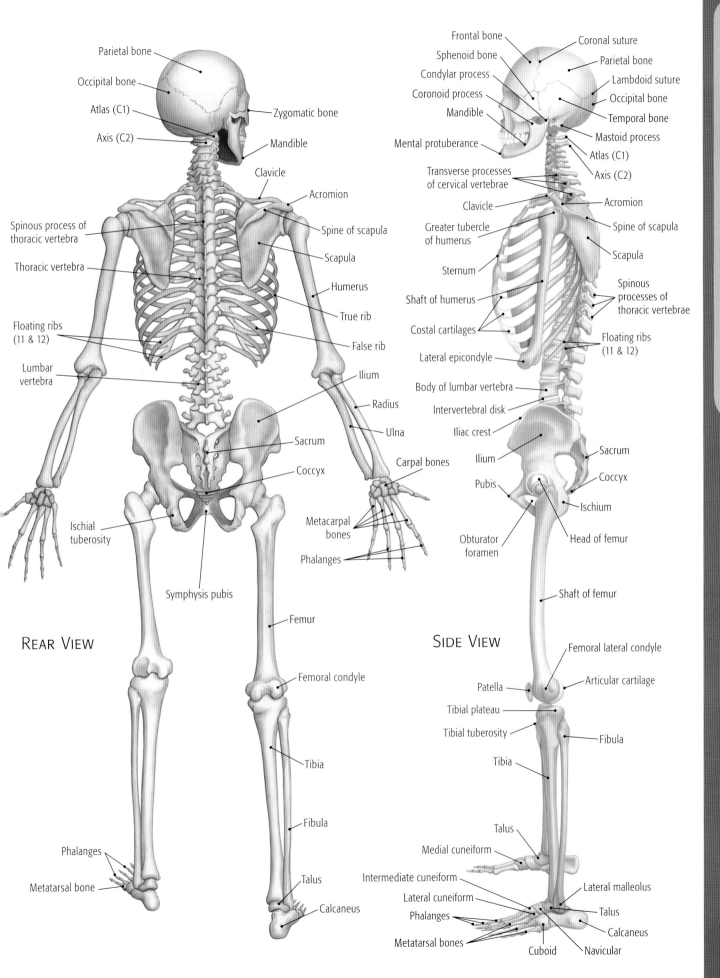

Parietal bone

Occipital bone

Atlas (C1)

Axis (C2)

Zygomatic bone

Mandible

Clavicle

Acromion

Spine of scapula

Spinous process of
thoracic vertebra

Scapula

Thoracic vertebra

Humerus

True rib

Floating ribs
(11 & 12)

False rib

Lumbar
vertebra

Ilium

Radius

Ulna

Sacrum

Coccyx

Carpal bones

Ischial
tuberosity

Metacarpal
bones

Phalanges

Symphysis pubis

Femur

REAR VIEW

Femoral condyle

Tibia

Fibula

Phalanges

Talus

Metatarsal bone

Calcaneus

Frontal bone

Coronal suture

Sphenoid bone

Parietal bone

Condylar process

Lambdoid suture

Coronoid process

Occipital bone

Mandible

Temporal bone

Mental protuberance

Mastoid process

Atlas (C1)

Transverse processes
of cervical vertebrae

Axis (C2)

Acromion

Clavicle

Spine of scapula

Greater tubercle
of humerus

Scapula

Sternum

Spinous
processes of
thoracic vertebrae

Shaft of humerus

Costal cartilages

Lateral epicondyle

Floating ribs
(11 & 12)

Body of lumbar vertebra

Intervertebral disk

Iliac crest

Sacrum

Ilium

Coccyx

Pubis

Ischium

Obturator
foramen

Head of femur

Shaft of femur

SIDE VIEW

Femoral lateral condyle

Articular cartilage

Patella

Tibial plateau

Tibial tuberosity

Fibula

Tibia

Talus

Medial cuneiform

Intermediate cuneiform

Lateral malleolus

Lateral cuneiform

Talus

Phalanges

Calcaneus

Metatarsal bones

Navicular

Cuboid

Bone

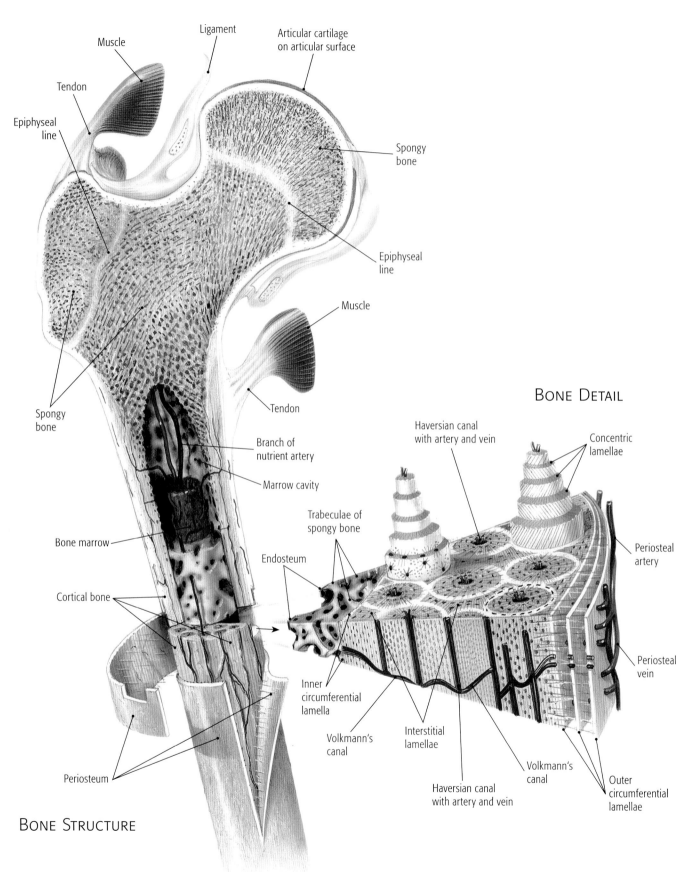

Muscle

Ligament

Articular cartilage
on articular surface

Tendon

Epiphyseal
line

Spongy
bone

Epiphyseal
line

Muscle

Tendon

Spongy
bone

Branch of
nutrient artery

Marrow cavity

Bone marrow

Cortical bone

Periosteum

BONE STRUCTURE

BONE DETAIL

Haversian canal
with artery and vein

Concentric
lamellae

Periosteal
artery

Trabeculae of
spongy bone

Endosteum

Periosteal
vein

Inner
circumferential
lamella

Volkmann's
canal

Interstitial
lamellae

Volkmann's
canal

Outer
circumferential
lamellae

Haversian canal
with artery and vein

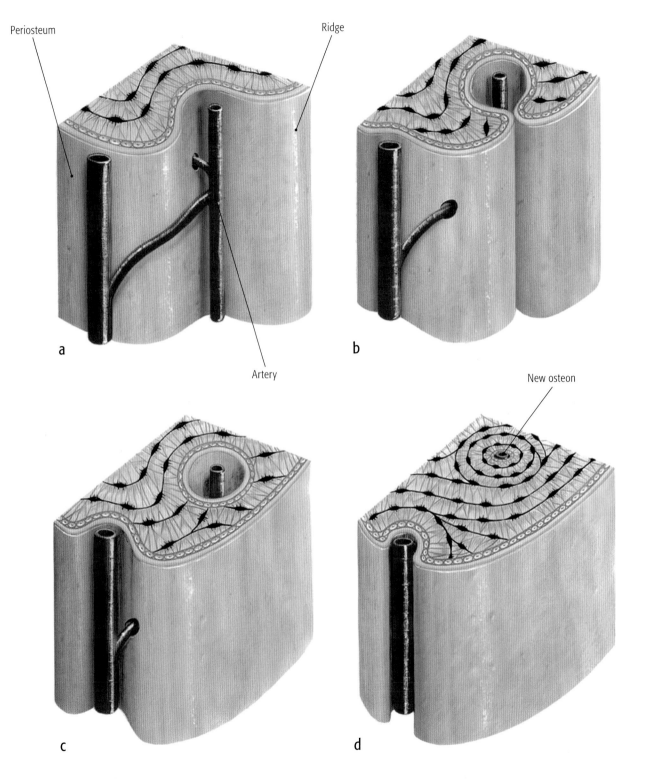

Periosteum

Ridge

Artery

a

b

New osteon

c

d

BONE FORMATION

Bone grows in width as new bone is laid down in ridges (**a**) either side of a blood vessel. The ridges grow together around the vessel (**b**). More bone is laid down, diminishing the space around the vessel (**c**) and eventually forming an osteon. The process continues with parallel blood vessels (**d**).

Bones of the Skull

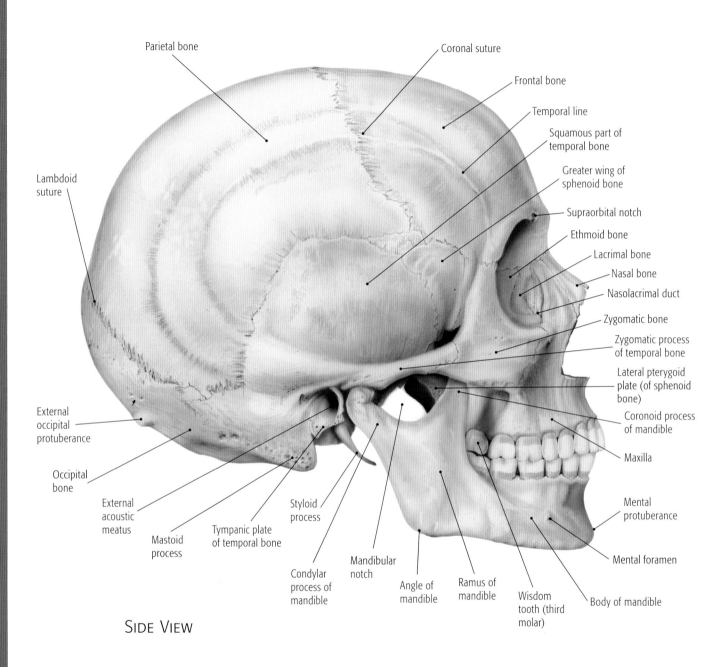

Parietal bone

Coronal suture

Frontal bone

Temporal line

Squamous part of
temporal bone

Greater wing of
sphenoid bone

Supraorbital notch

Ethmoid bone

Lacrimal bone

Nasal bone

Nasolacrimal duct

Zygomatic bone

Zygomatic process
of temporal bone

Lateral pterygoid
plate (of sphenoid
bone)

Coronoid process
of mandible

Maxilla

Mental
protuberance

Mental foramen

Body of mandible

Wisdom
tooth (third
molar)

Ramus of
mandible

Angle of
mandible

Mandibular
notch

Condylar
process of
mandible

Styloid
process

Tympanic plate
of temporal bone

Mastoid
process

External
acoustic
meatus

Occipital
bone

External
occipital
protuberance

Lambdoid
suture

SIDE VIEW

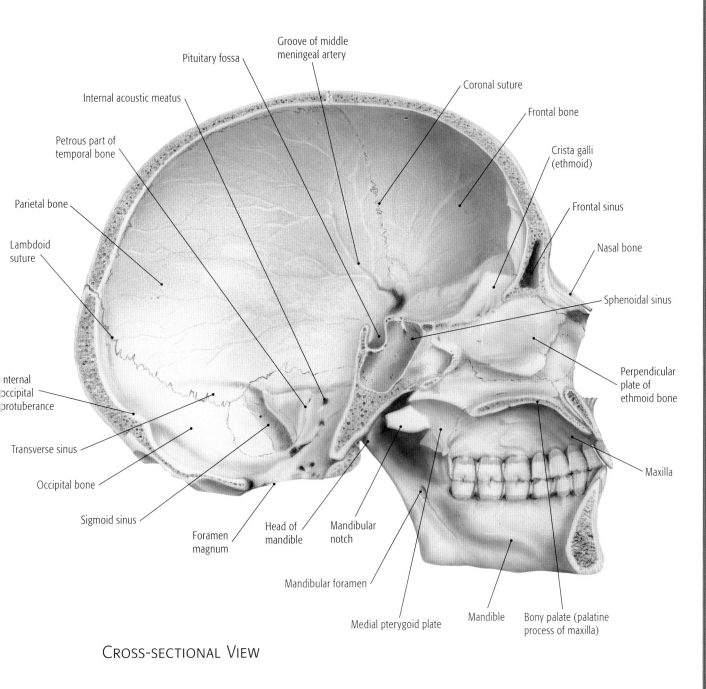

Groove of middle
meningeal artery

Pituitary fossa

Internal acoustic meatus

Coronal suture

Frontal bone

Petrous part of
temporal bone

Crista galli
(ethmoid)

Parietal bone

Frontal sinus

Lambdoid
suture

Nasal bone

nternal
ccipital
rotuberance

Sphenoidal sinus

Transverse sinus

Perpendicular
plate of
ethmoid bone

Occipital bone

Sigmoid sinus

Maxilla

Foramen
magnum

Head of
mandible

Mandibular
notch

Mandibular foramen

Medial pterygoid plate

Mandible

Bony palate (palatine
process of maxilla)

CROSS-SECTIONAL VIEW

Bones of the Skull

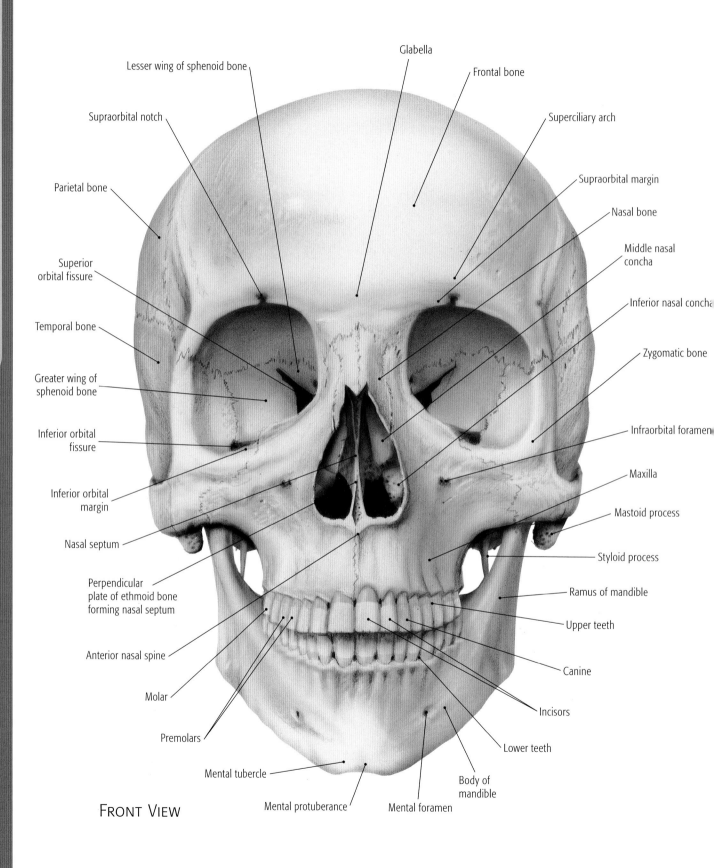

Lesser wing of sphenoid bone

Glabella

Frontal bone

Supraorbital notch

Superciliary arch

Parietal bone

Supraorbital margin

Nasal bone

Middle nasal concha

Superior orbital fissure

Inferior nasal concha

Temporal bone

Zygomatic bone

Greater wing of sphenoid bone

Inferior orbital fissure

Infraorbital foramen

Inferior orbital margin

Maxilla

Nasal septum

Mastoid process

Styloid process

Perpendicular plate of ethmoid bone forming nasal septum

Ramus of mandible

Upper teeth

Anterior nasal spine

Canine

Molar

Incisors

Premolars

Lower teeth

Mental tubercle

Body of mandible

FRONT VIEW

Mental protuberance

Mental foramen

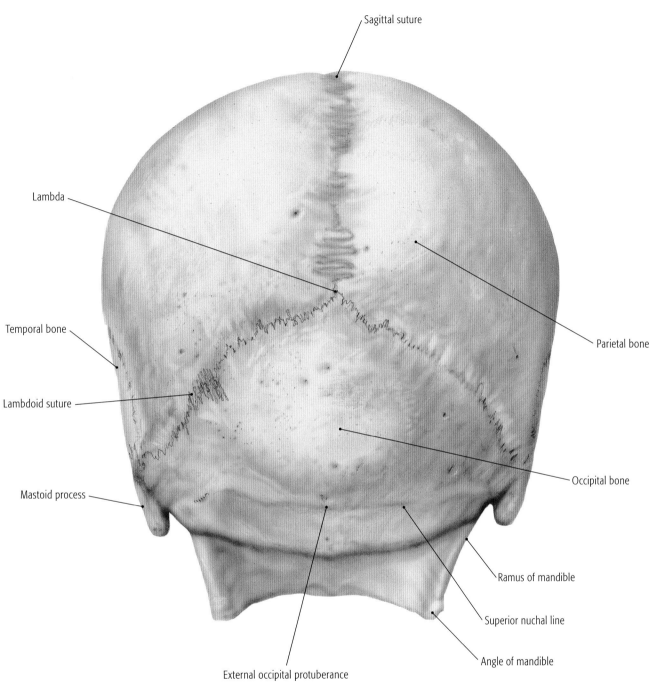

Sagittal suture

Lambda

Temporal bone

Lambdoid suture

Mastoid process

Parietal bone

Occipital bone

Ramus of mandible

Superior nuchal line

Angle of mandible

External occipital protuberance

REAR VIEW

Bones of the Skull

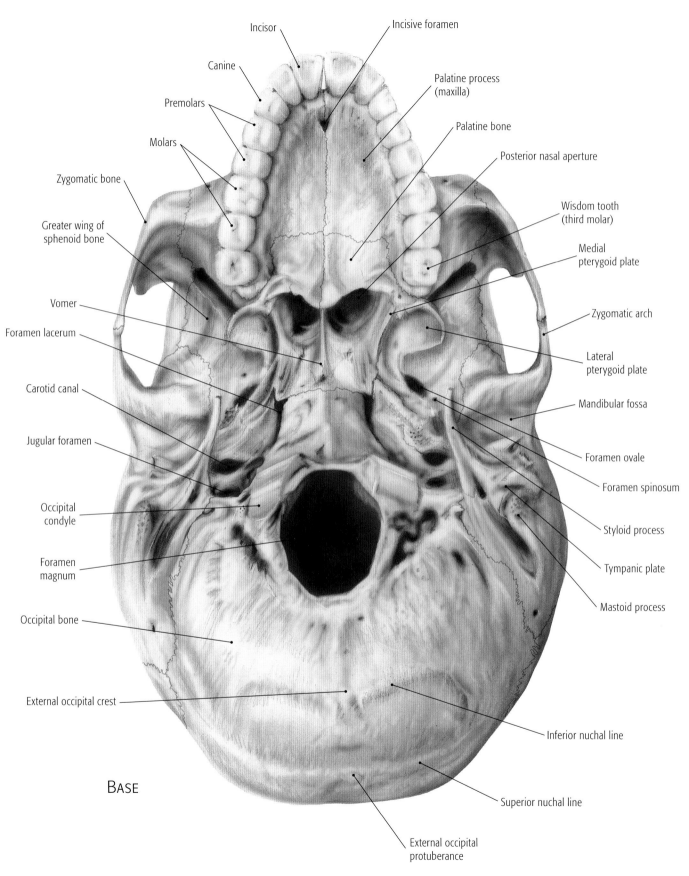

Incisor

Incisive foramen

Canine

Palatine process
(maxilla)

Premolars

Palatine bone

Molars

Posterior nasal aperture

Zygomatic bone

Wisdom tooth
(third molar)

Greater wing of
sphenoid bone

Medial
pterygoid plate

Vomer

Zygomatic arch

Foramen lacerum

Lateral
pterygoid plate

Carotid canal

Mandibular fossa

Jugular foramen

Foramen ovale

Occipital
condyle

Foramen spinosum

Foramen
magnum

Styloid process

Occipital bone

Tympanic plate

External occipital crest

Mastoid process

Inferior nuchal line

BASE

Superior nuchal line

External occipital
protuberance

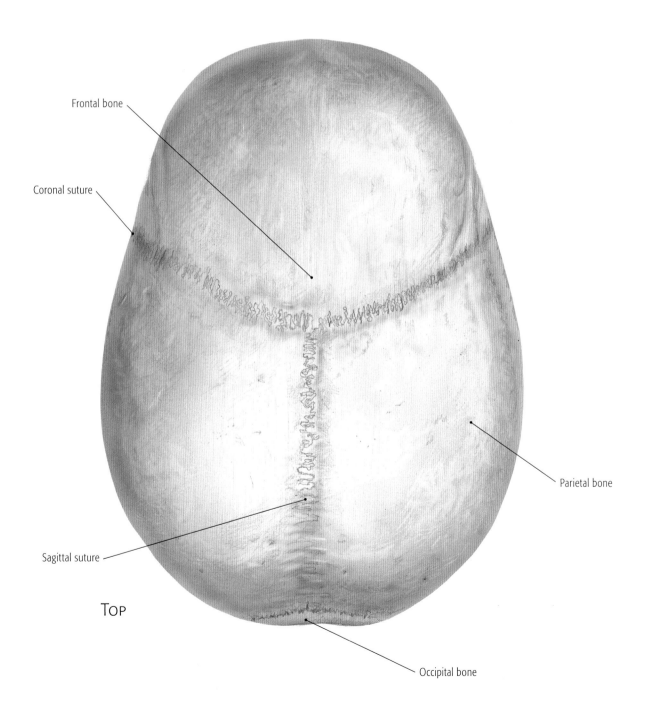

Frontal bone

Coronal suture

Parietal bone

Sagittal suture

TOP

Occipital bone

Bones of the Head and Face

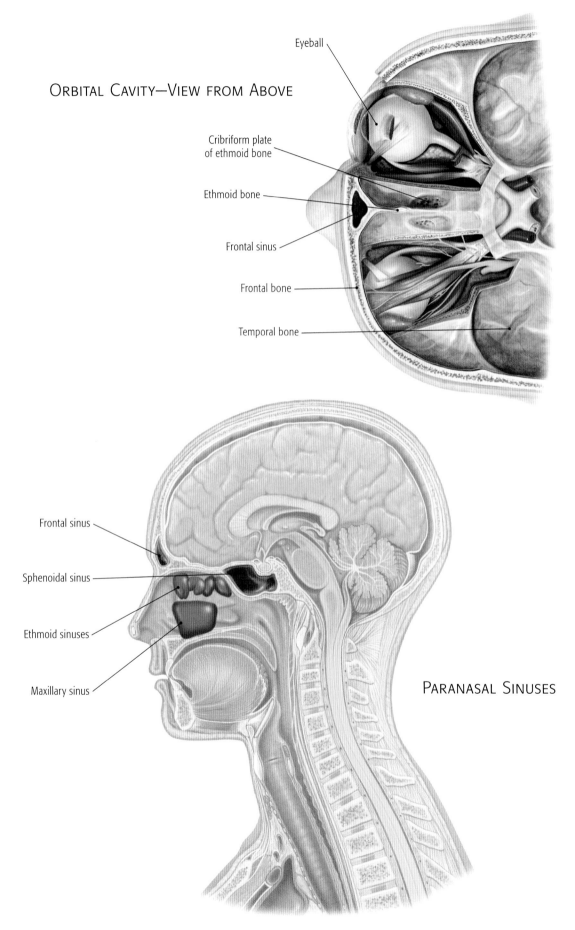

ORBITAL CAVITY—VIEW FROM ABOVE

Eyeball

Cribriform plate
of ethmoid bone

Ethmoid bone

Frontal sinus

Frontal bone

Temporal bone

Frontal sinus

Sphenoidal sinus

Ethmoid sinuses

Maxillary sinus

PARANASAL SINUSES

64

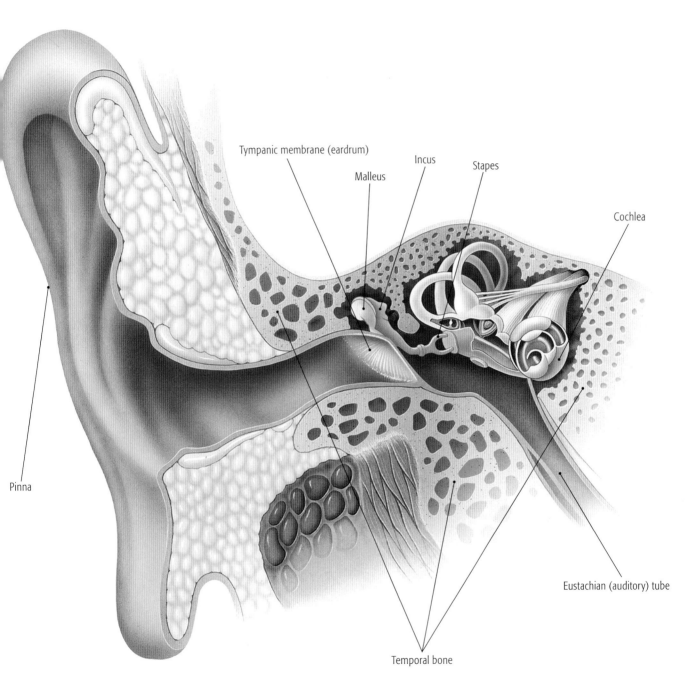

Tympanic membrane (eardrum)

Malleus

Incus

Stapes

Cochlea

Pinna

Eustachian (auditory) tube

Temporal bone

BONES OF THE EAR

Spine

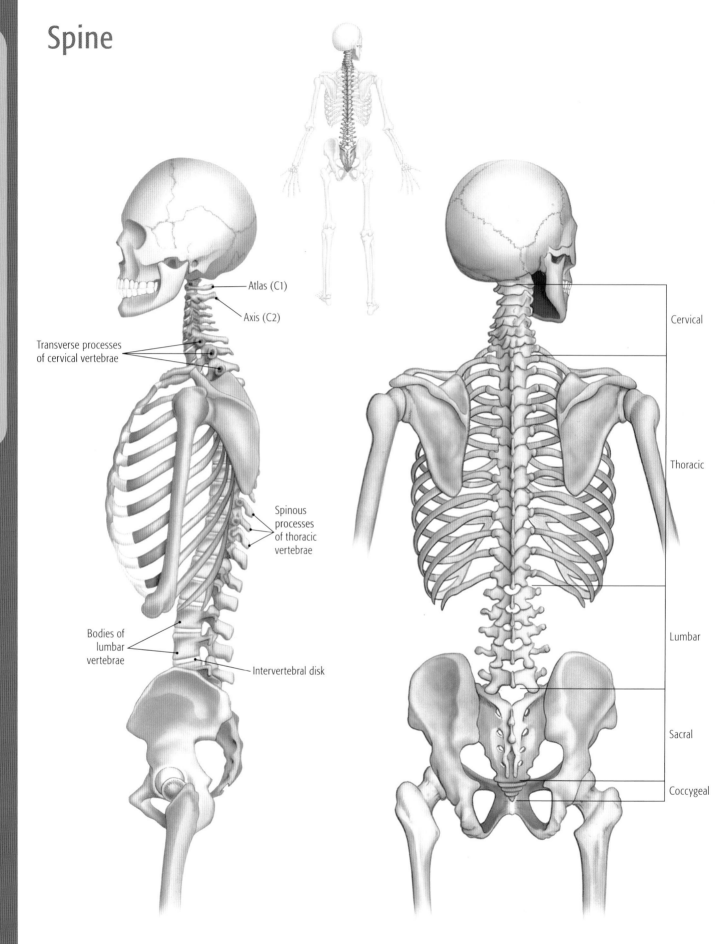

Atlas (C1)

Axis (C2)

Transverse processes
of cervical vertebrae

Spinous
processes
of thoracic
vertebrae

Bodies of
lumbar
vertebrae

Intervertebral disk

Cervical

Thoracic

Lumbar

Sacral

Coccygeal

SPINE IN SITU—SIDE VIEW

SPINE IN SITU—REAR VIEW

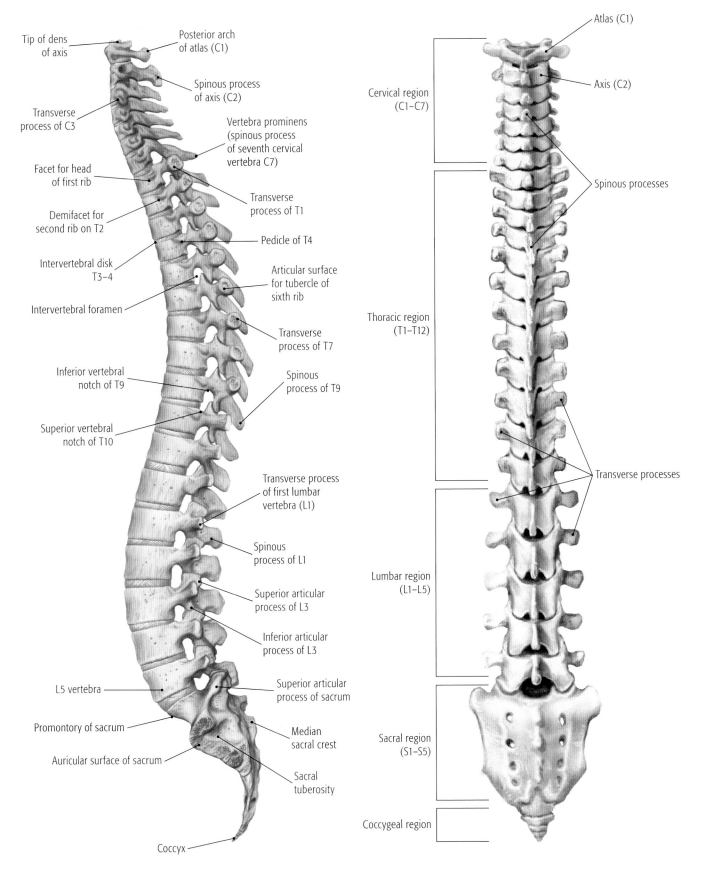

Tip of dens of axis

Posterior arch of atlas (C1)

Spinous process of axis (C2)

Transverse process of C3

Vertebra prominens (spinous process of seventh cervical vertebra C7)

Facet for head of first rib

Transverse process of T1

Demifacet for second rib on T2

Pedicle of T4

Intervertebral disk T3–4

Articular surface for tubercle of sixth rib

Intervertebral foramen

Transverse process of T7

Inferior vertebral notch of T9

Spinous process of T9

Superior vertebral notch of T10

Transverse process of first lumbar vertebra (L1)

Spinous process of L1

Superior articular process of L3

Inferior articular process of L3

L5 vertebra

Superior articular process of sacrum

Promontory of sacrum

Median sacral crest

Auricular surface of sacrum

Sacral tuberosity

Coccyx

Atlas (C1)

Axis (C2)

Cervical region (C1–C7)

Spinous processes

Thoracic region (T1–T12)

Transverse processes

Lumbar region (L1–L5)

Sacral region (S1–S5)

Coccygeal region

SPINE—SIDE VIEW

SPINE—REAR VIEW

Vertebrae

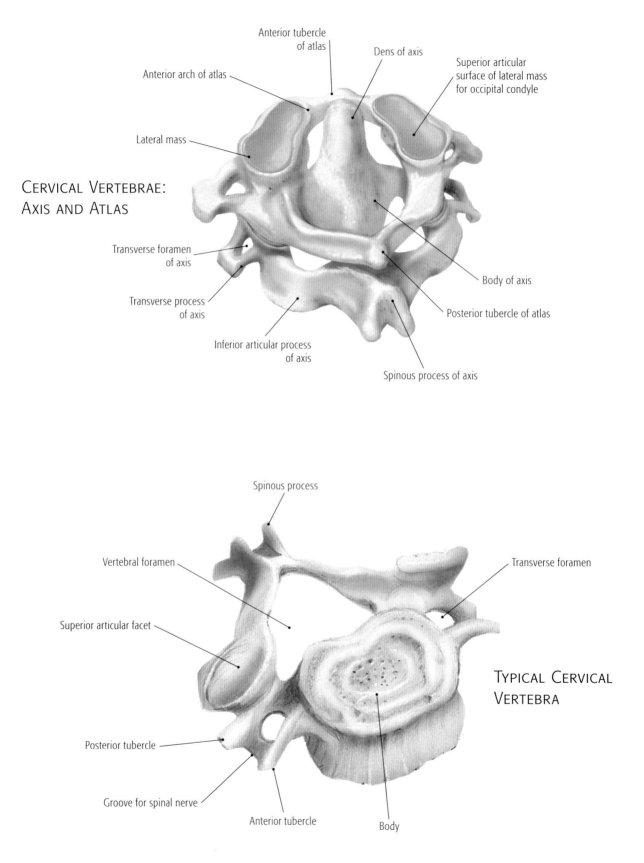

Anterior tubercle
of atlas

Dens of axis

Superior articular
surface of lateral mass
for occipital condyle

Anterior arch of atlas

Lateral mass

CERVICAL VERTEBRAE:
AXIS AND ATLAS

Transverse foramen
of axis

Body of axis

Transverse process
of axis

Posterior tubercle of atlas

Inferior articular process
of axis

Spinous process of axis

Spinous process

Vertebral foramen

Transverse foramen

Superior articular facet

TYPICAL CERVICAL
VERTEBRA

Posterior tubercle

Groove for spinal nerve

Anterior tubercle

Body

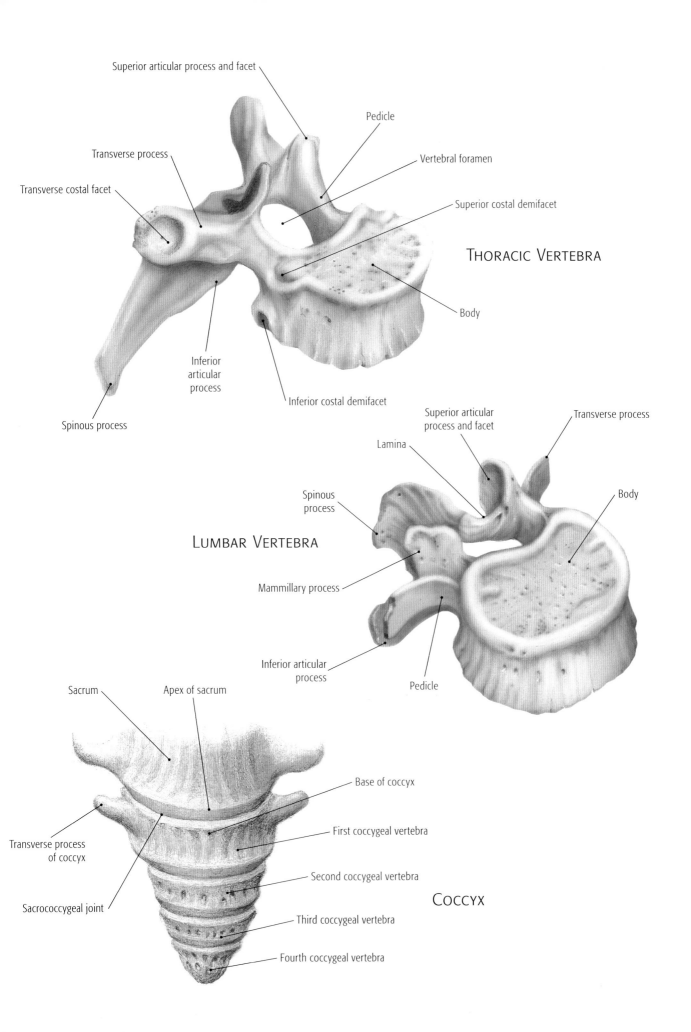

Superior articular process and facet

Pedicle

Transverse process

Vertebral foramen

Transverse costal facet

Superior costal demifacet

THORACIC VERTEBRA

Body

Inferior articular process

Inferior costal demifacet

Spinous process

Superior articular process and facet

Transverse process

Lamina

Body

Spinous process

LUMBAR VERTEBRA

Mammillary process

Inferior articular process

Pedicle

Sacrum

Apex of sacrum

Base of coccyx

First coccygeal vertebra

Transverse process of coccyx

Second coccygeal vertebra

COCCYX

Sacrococcygeal joint

Third coccygeal vertebra

Fourth coccygeal vertebra

Rib Cage and Clavicles

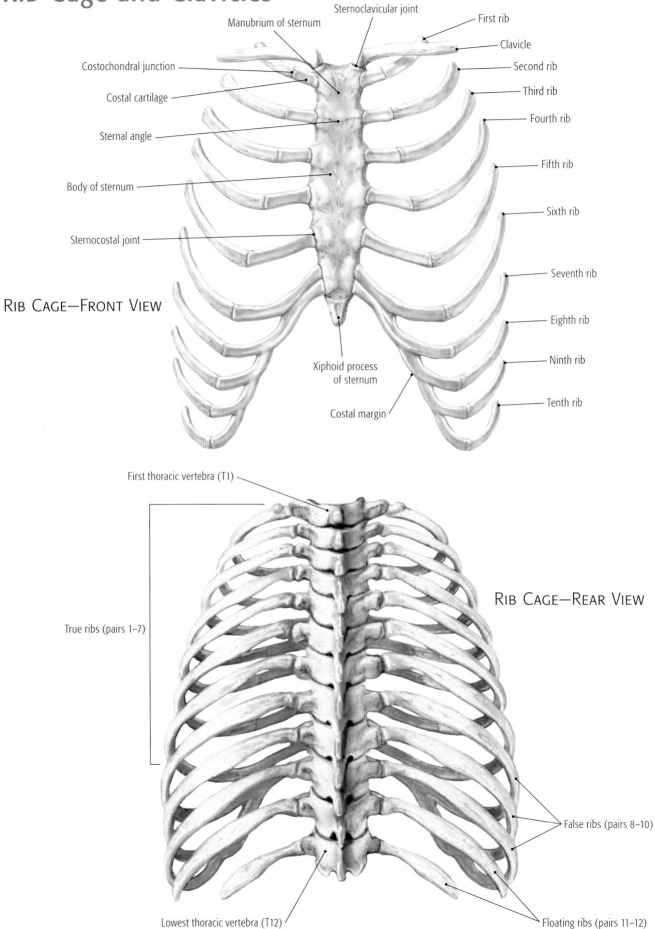

Sternoclavicular joint

Manubrium of sternum

First rib

Clavicle

Costochondral junction

Second rib

Costal cartilage

Third rib

Sternal angle

Fourth rib

Fifth rib

Body of sternum

Sixth rib

Sternocostal joint

Seventh rib

RIB CAGE—FRONT VIEW

Eighth rib

Ninth rib

Xiphoid process
of sternum

Tenth rib

Costal margin

First thoracic vertebra (T1)

RIB CAGE—REAR VIEW

True ribs (pairs 1–7)

False ribs (pairs 8–10)

Lowest thoracic vertebra (T12)

Floating ribs (pairs 11–12)

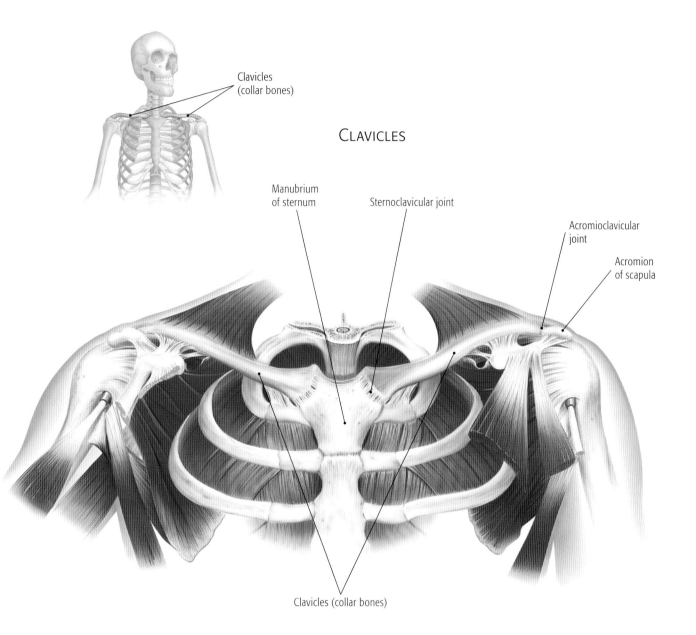

Clavicles
(collar bones)

Clavicles

Manubrium
of sternum

Sternoclavicular joint

Acromioclavicular
joint

Acromion
of scapula

Clavicles (collar bones)

Bones of the Arm

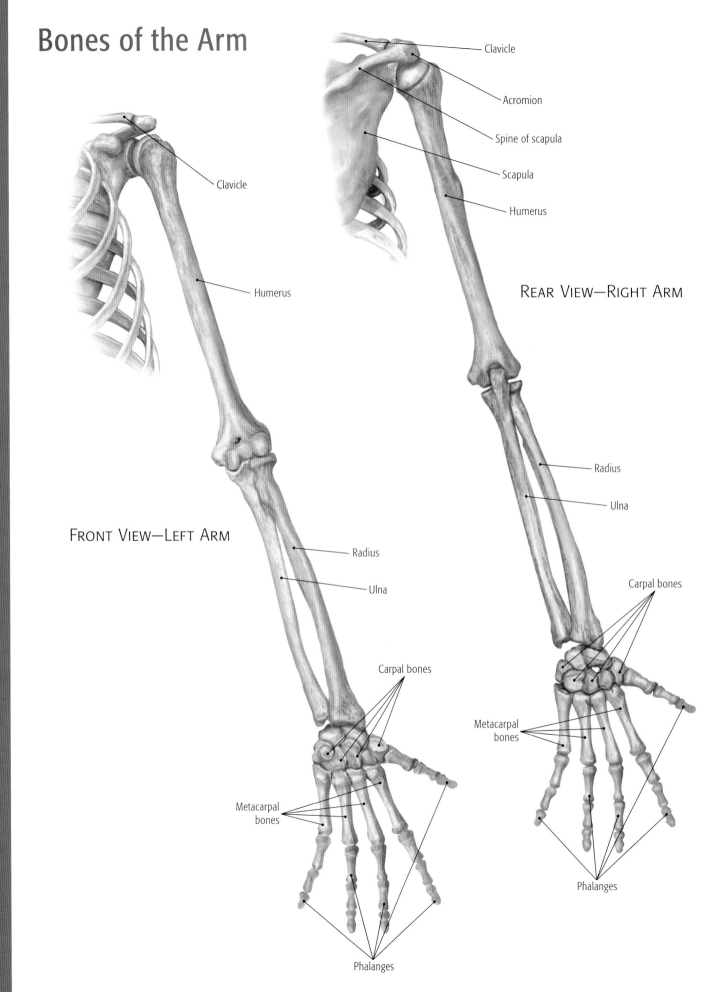

Clavicle

Acromion

Spine of scapula

Scapula

Humerus

REAR VIEW—RIGHT ARM

Clavicle

Humerus

Radius

Ulna

FRONT VIEW—LEFT ARM

Radius

Ulna

Carpal bones

Metacarpal bones

Carpal bones

Metacarpal bones

Phalanges

Phalanges

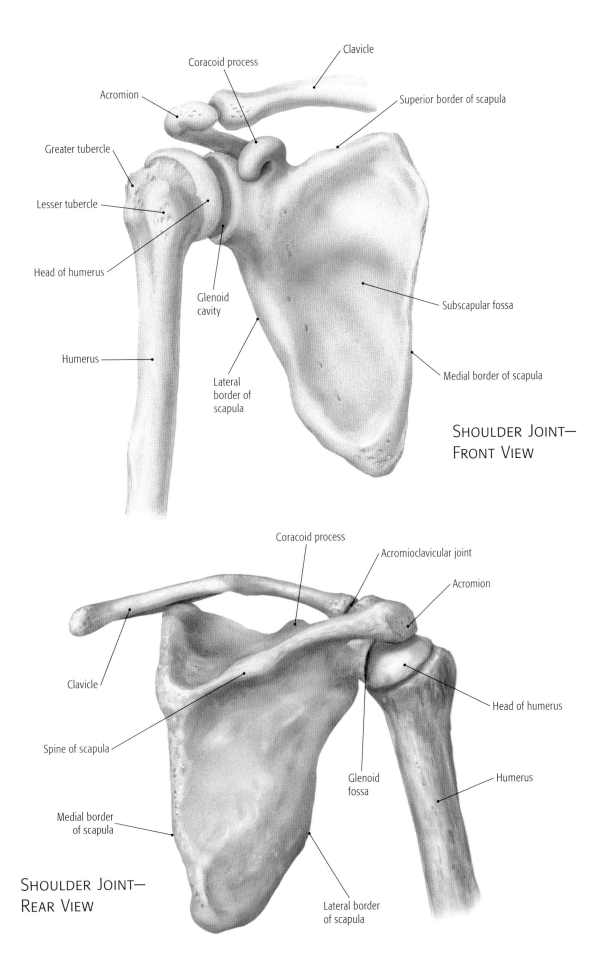

Coracoid process

Clavicle

Acromion

Superior border of scapula

Greater tubercle

Lesser tubercle

Head of humerus

Glenoid cavity

Subscapular fossa

Humerus

Lateral border of scapula

Medial border of scapula

SHOULDER JOINT—
FRONT VIEW

Coracoid process

Acromioclavicular joint

Acromion

Clavicle

Spine of scapula

Head of humerus

Medial border of scapula

Glenoid fossa

Humerus

SHOULDER JOINT—
REAR VIEW

Lateral border of scapula

Bones of the Upper Arm

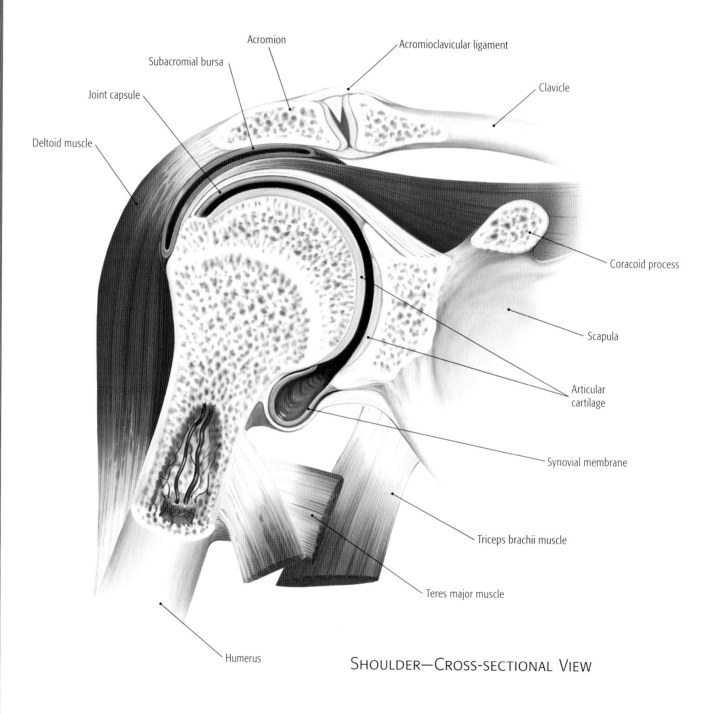

Acromion

Acromioclavicular ligament

Subacromial bursa

Clavicle

Joint capsule

Deltoid muscle

Coracoid process

Scapula

Articular cartilage

Synovial membrane

Triceps brachii muscle

Teres major muscle

Humerus

SHOULDER—CROSS-SECTIONAL VIEW

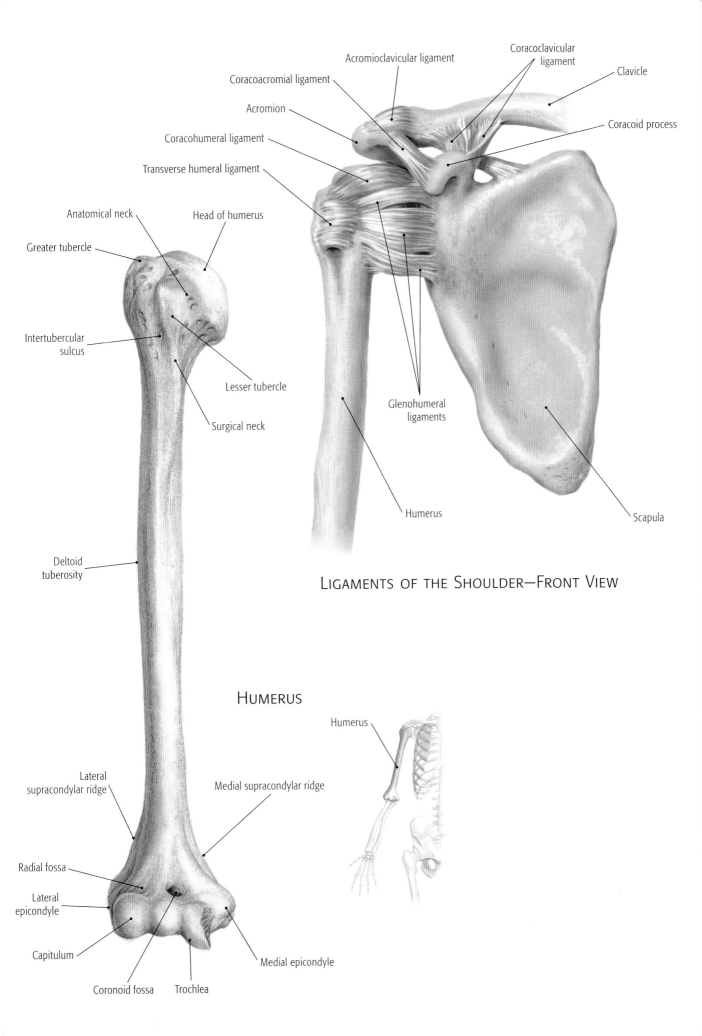

Acromioclavicular ligament

Coracoclavicular ligament

Clavicle

Coracoacromial ligament

Acromion

Coracoid process

Coracohumeral ligament

Transverse humeral ligament

Anatomical neck

Head of humerus

Greater tubercle

Intertubercular sulcus

Lesser tubercle

Surgical neck

Glenohumeral ligaments

Humerus

Scapula

LIGAMENTS OF THE SHOULDER—FRONT VIEW

Deltoid tuberosity

HUMERUS

Humerus

Lateral supracondylar ridge

Medial supracondylar ridge

Radial fossa

Lateral epicondyle

Capitulum

Coronoid fossa

Trochlea

Medial epicondyle

Bones of the Lower Arm

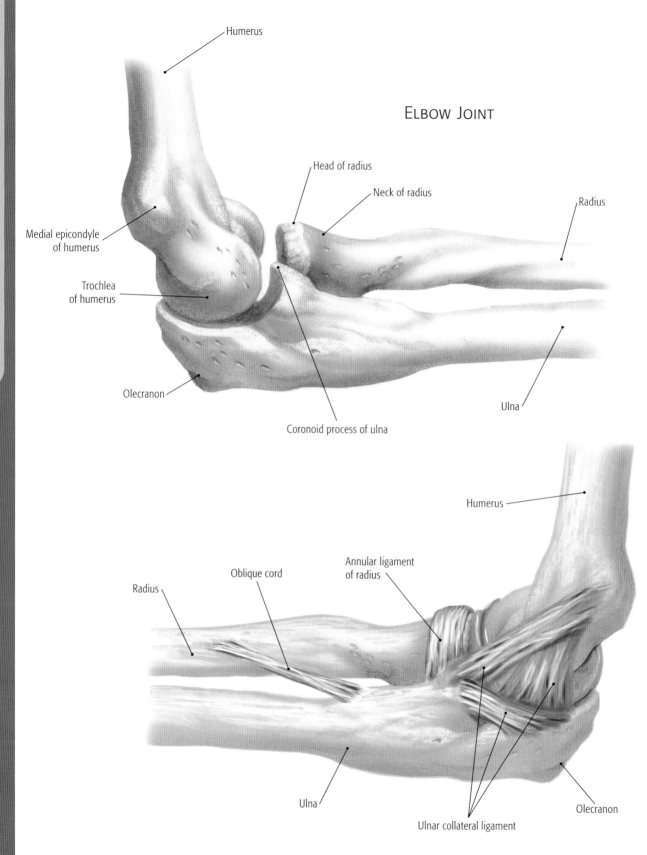

ELBOW JOINT

Humerus

Head of radius

Neck of radius

Radius

Medial epicondyle
of humerus

Trochlea
of humerus

Olecranon

Coronoid process of ulna

Ulna

Humerus

Oblique cord

Annular ligament
of radius

Radius

Ulna

Ulnar collateral ligament

Olecranon

LIGAMENTS OF THE ELBOW

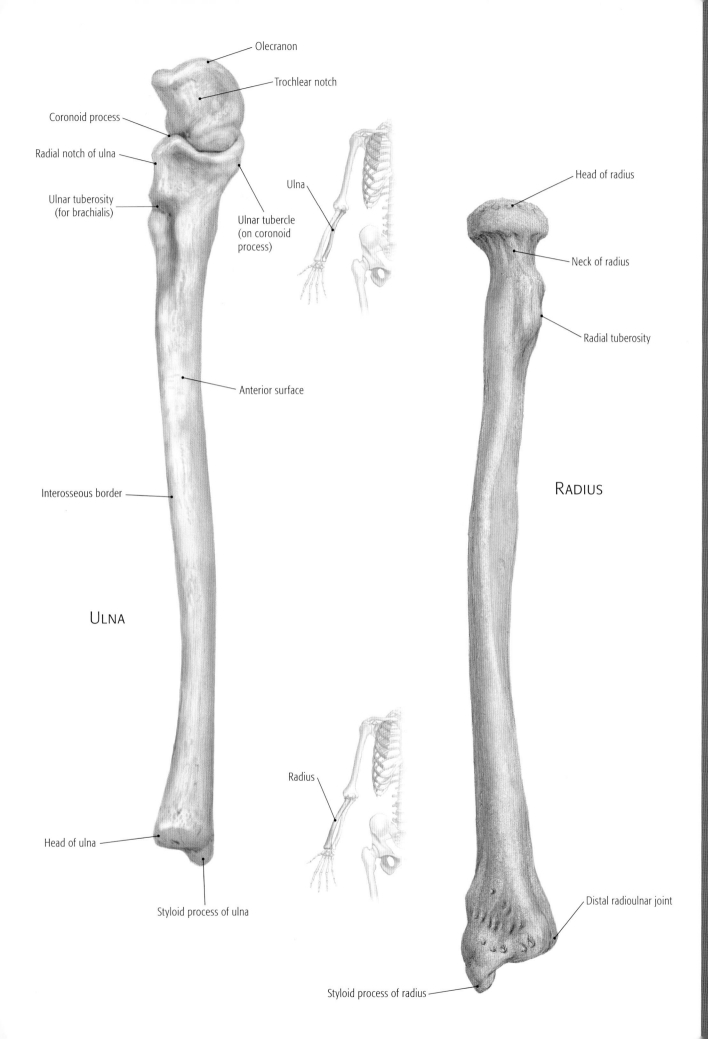

Olecranon

Trochlear notch

Coronoid process

Radial notch of ulna

Ulnar tuberosity
(for brachialis)

Ulnar tubercle
(on coronoid
process)

Ulna

Head of radius

Neck of radius

Radial tuberosity

Anterior surface

Interosseous border

RADIUS

ULNA

Radius

Head of ulna

Styloid process of ulna

Distal radioulnar joint

Styloid process of radius

Bones of the Wrist and Hand

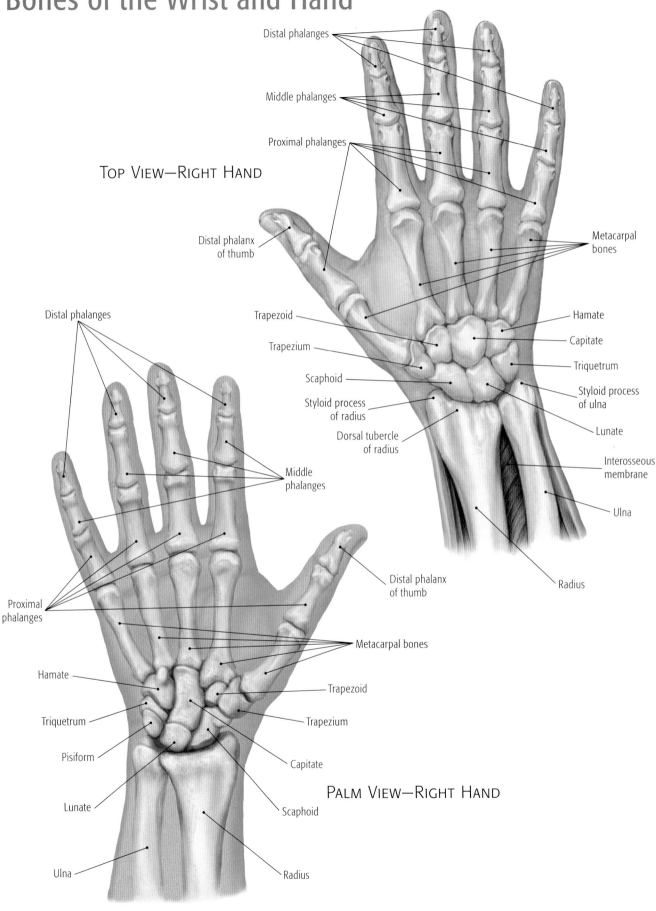

TOP VIEW—RIGHT HAND

Distal phalanges

Middle phalanges

Proximal phalanges

Distal phalanx of thumb

Metacarpal bones

Trapezoid

Trapezium

Scaphoid

Styloid process of radius

Dorsal tubercle of radius

Hamate

Capitate

Triquetrum

Styloid process of ulna

Lunate

Interosseous membrane

Ulna

Radius

Distal phalanges

Middle phalanges

Proximal phalanges

Distal phalanx of thumb

Metacarpal bones

Hamate

Triquetrum

Pisiform

Lunate

Ulna

Trapezoid

Trapezium

Capitate

Scaphoid

Radius

PALM VIEW—RIGHT HAND

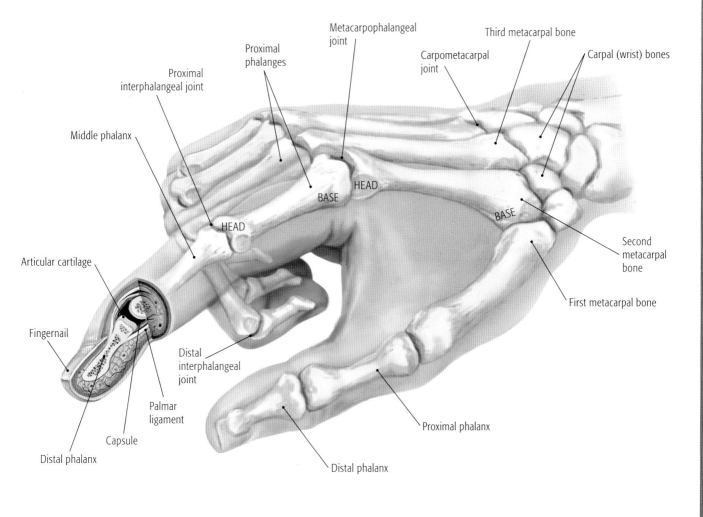

Metacarpophalangeal joint

Proximal phalanges

Third metacarpal bone

Carpometacarpal joint

Carpal (wrist) bones

Proximal interphalangeal joint

Middle phalanx

HEAD

BASE

HEAD

BASE

Articular cartilage

Second metacarpal bone

Fingernail

First metacarpal bone

Distal interphalangeal joint

Palmar ligament

Proximal phalanx

Distal phalanx

Capsule

Distal phalanx

Distal phalanx

FINGER

Bones of the Pelvis

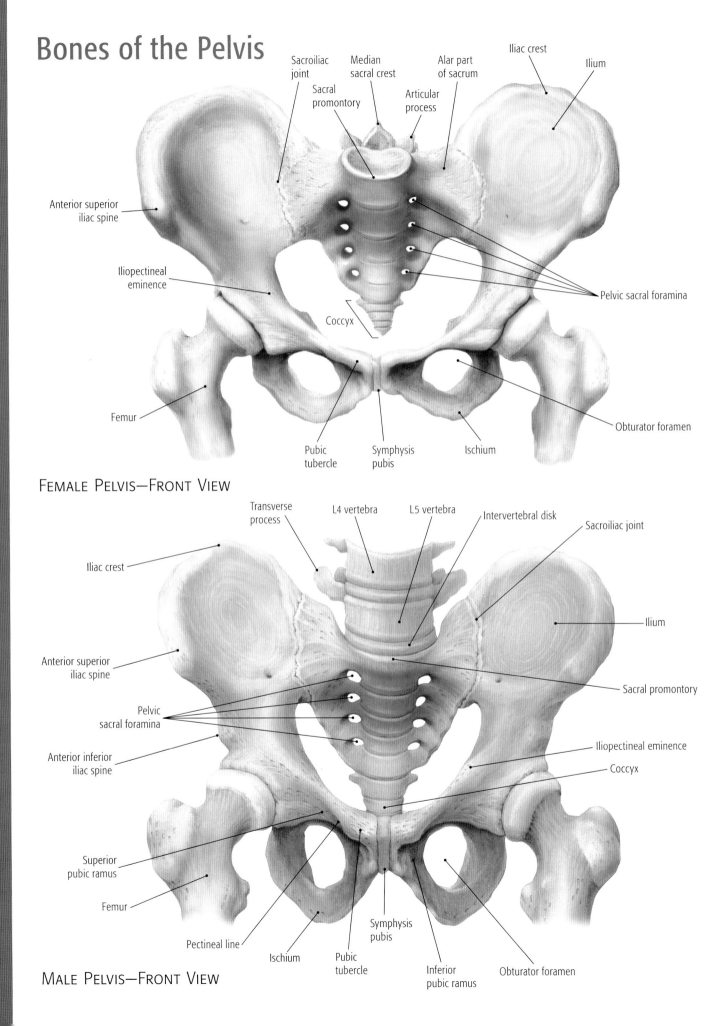

Sacroiliac joint

Sacral promontory

Median sacral crest

Alar part of sacrum

Articular process

Iliac crest

Ilium

Anterior superior iliac spine

Iliopectineal eminence

Pelvic sacral foramina

Coccyx

Femur

Obturator foramen

Pubic tubercle

Symphysis pubis

Ischium

FEMALE PELVIS—FRONT VIEW

Transverse process

L4 vertebra

L5 vertebra

Intervertebral disk

Sacroiliac joint

Iliac crest

Ilium

Anterior superior iliac spine

Sacral promontory

Pelvic sacral foramina

Iliopectineal eminence

Coccyx

Anterior inferior iliac spine

Superior pubic ramus

Femur

Pectineal line

Ischium

Pubic tubercle

Symphysis pubis

Inferior pubic ramus

Obturator foramen

MALE PELVIS—FRONT VIEW

L5 vertebra

Intervertebral disk

Sacral promontory

Sacroiliac joint

Pelvic sacral foramina

Coccyx

SACRUM

Lumbar vertebrae

Ilium

Sacrum

Coccyx

Ischium

Femur

Symphysis pubis

Pubis

HIP BONE AND JOINT

Bones of the Leg

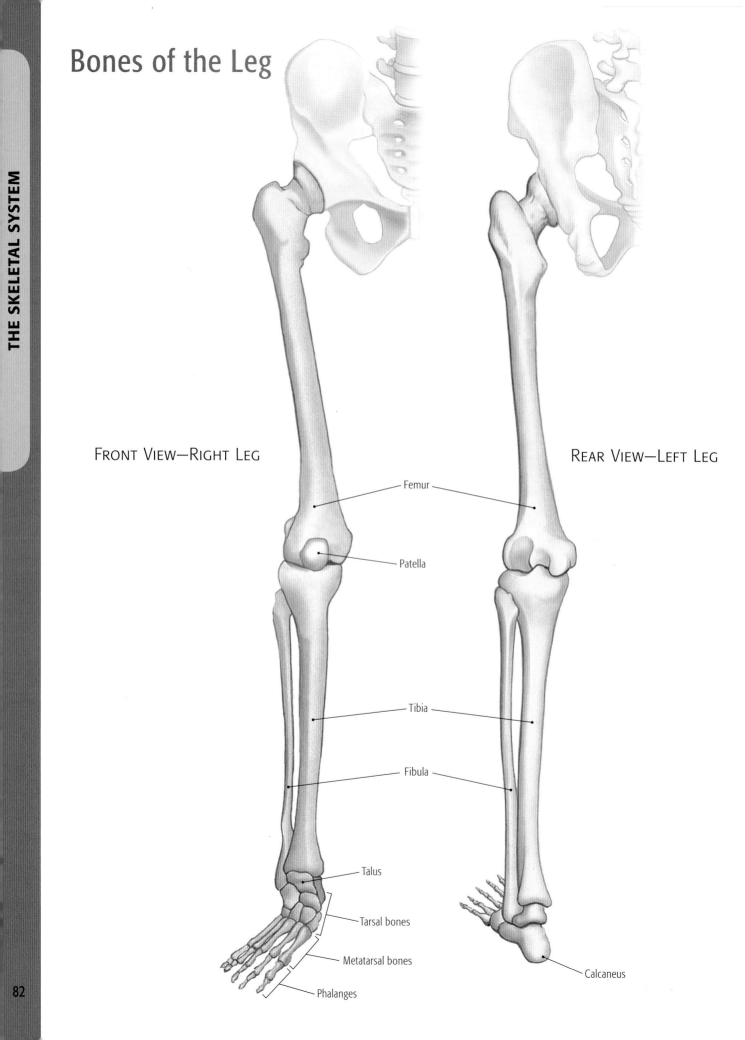

FRONT VIEW—RIGHT LEG

REAR VIEW—LEFT LEG

Femur

Patella

Tibia

Fibula

Talus

Tarsal bones

Metatarsal bones

Phalanges

Calcaneus

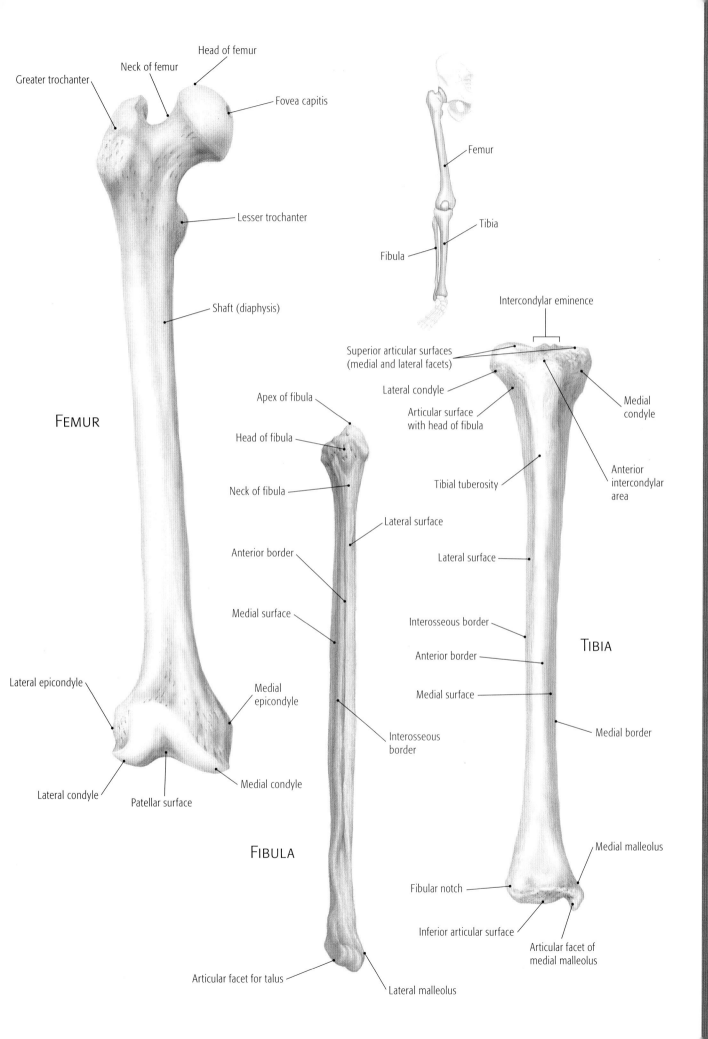

Greater trochanter

Neck of femur

Head of femur

Fovea capitis

Lesser trochanter

Shaft (diaphysis)

FEMUR

Lateral epicondyle

Medial epicondyle

Medial condyle

Lateral condyle

Patellar surface

Femur

Tibia

Fibula

Apex of fibula

Head of fibula

Neck of fibula

Anterior border

Medial surface

Interosseous border

FIBULA

Articular facet for talus

Lateral malleolus

Intercondylar eminence

Superior articular surfaces
(medial and lateral facets)

Lateral condyle

Articular surface
with head of fibula

Tibial tuberosity

Medial
condyle

Anterior
intercondylar
area

Lateral surface

Lateral surface

Interosseous border

Anterior border

Medial surface

Medial border

TIBIA

Medial malleolus

Fibular notch

Inferior articular surface

Articular facet of
medial malleolus

83

Bones of the Knee

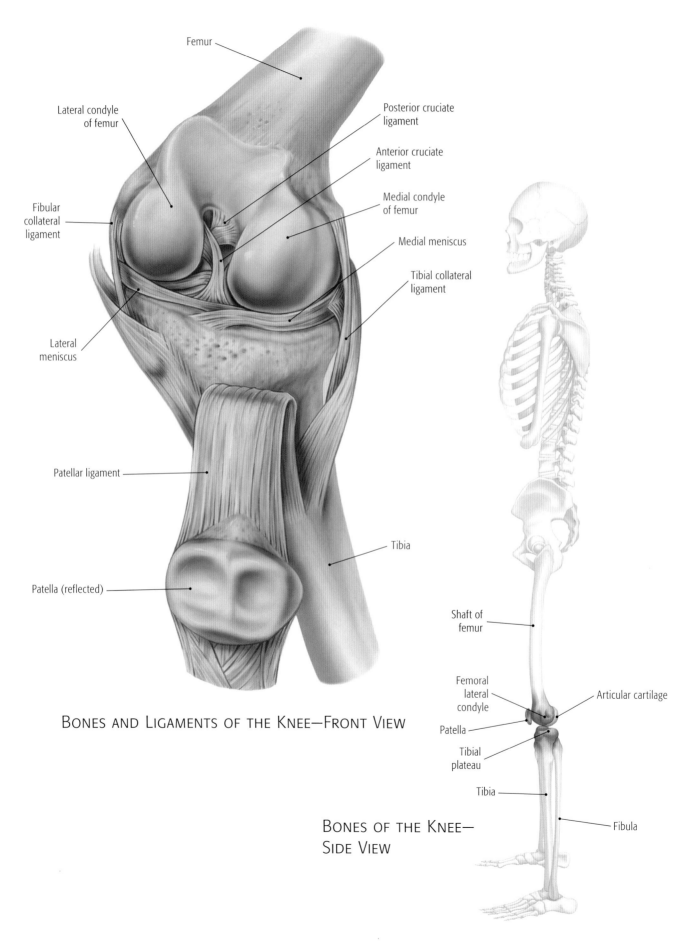

Femur

Lateral condyle
of femur

Posterior cruciate
ligament

Anterior cruciate
ligament

Fibular
collateral
ligament

Medial condyle
of femur

Medial meniscus

Tibial collateral
ligament

Lateral
meniscus

Patellar ligament

Tibia

Patella (reflected)

BONES AND LIGAMENTS OF THE KNEE—FRONT VIEW

Shaft of
femur

Femoral
lateral
condyle

Articular cartilage

Patella

Tibial
plateau

Tibia

Fibula

BONES OF THE KNEE—
SIDE VIEW

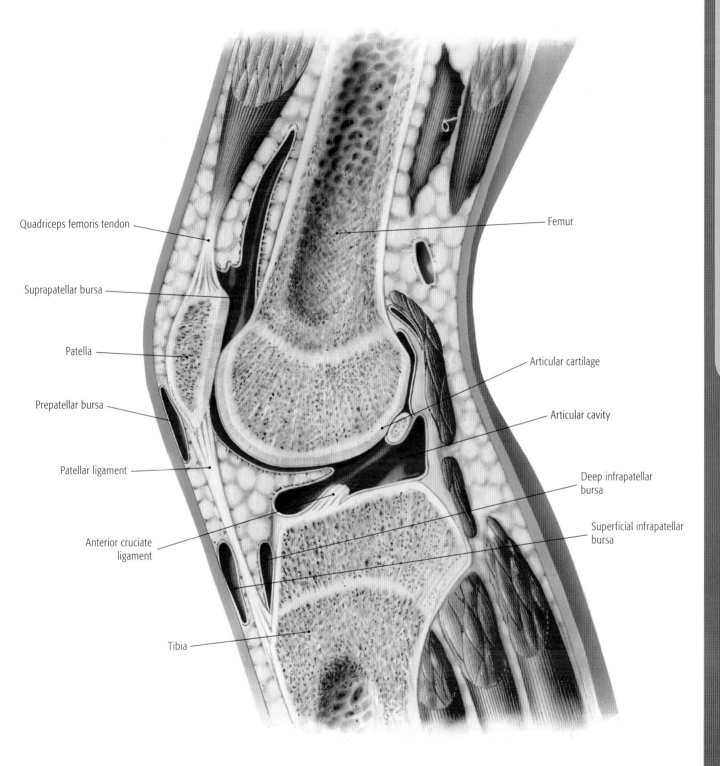

Quadriceps femoris tendon

Suprapatellar bursa

Patella

Prepatellar bursa

Patellar ligament

Anterior cruciate ligament

Tibia

Femur

Articular cartilage

Articular cavity

Deep infrapatellar bursa

Superficial infrapatellar bursa

KNEE JOINT—CROSS-SECTIONAL VIEW

Bones of the Ankle and Foot

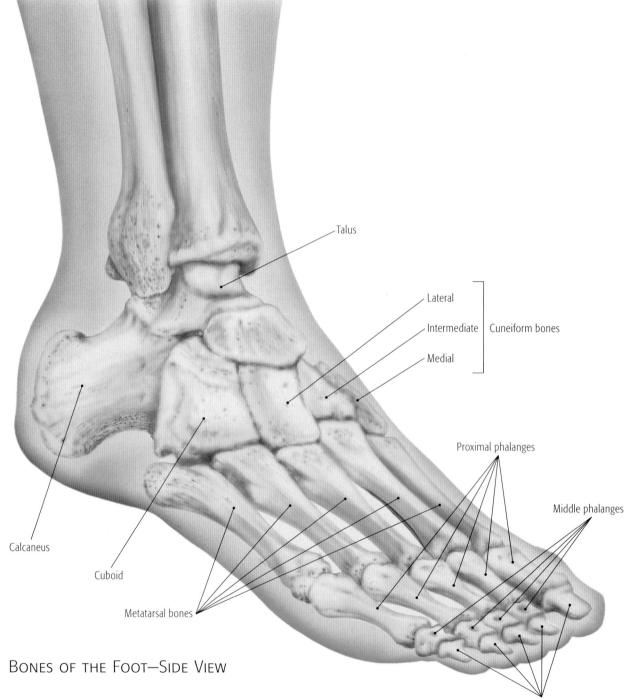

Talus

Lateral ⎤
Intermediate ⎬ Cuneiform bones
Medial ⎦

Proximal phalanges

Middle phalanges

Calcaneus

Cuboid

Metatarsal bones

Distal phalanges

BONES OF THE FOOT—SIDE VIEW

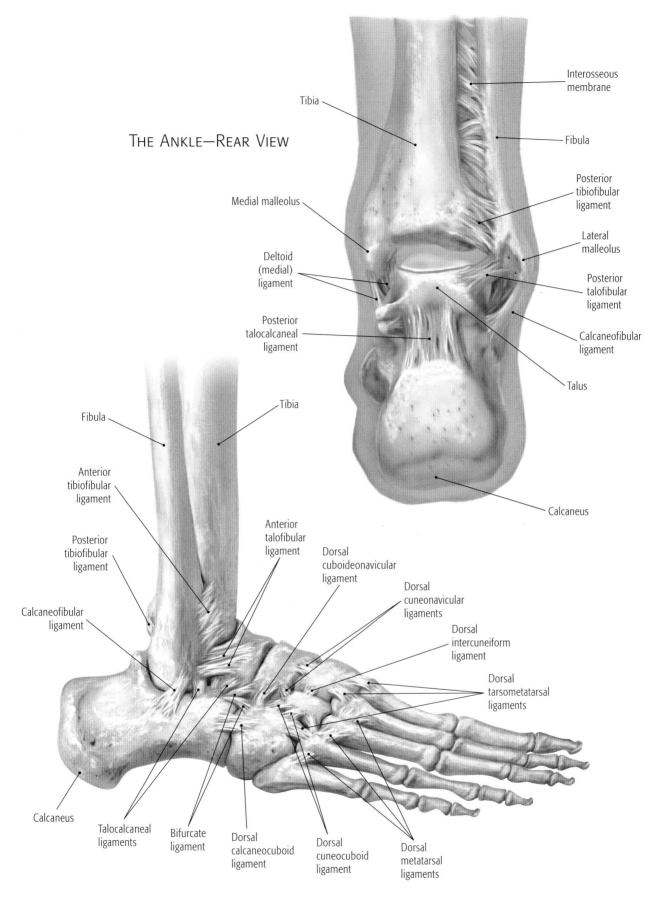

THE ANKLE—REAR VIEW

Interosseous membrane

Tibia

Fibula

Posterior tibiofibular ligament

Medial malleolus

Lateral malleolus

Deltoid (medial) ligament

Posterior talofibular ligament

Posterior talocalcaneal ligament

Calcaneofibular ligament

Talus

Calcaneus

Fibula

Tibia

Anterior tibiofibular ligament

Posterior tibiofibular ligament

Anterior talofibular ligament

Dorsal cuboideonavicular ligament

Dorsal cuneonavicular ligaments

Dorsal intercuneiform ligament

Calcaneofibular ligament

Dorsal tarsometatarsal ligaments

Calcaneus

Talocalcaneal ligaments

Bifurcate ligament

Dorsal calcaneocuboid ligament

Dorsal cuneocuboid ligament

Dorsal metatarsal ligaments

LIGAMENTS OF THE ANKLE AND FOOT—SIDE VIEW

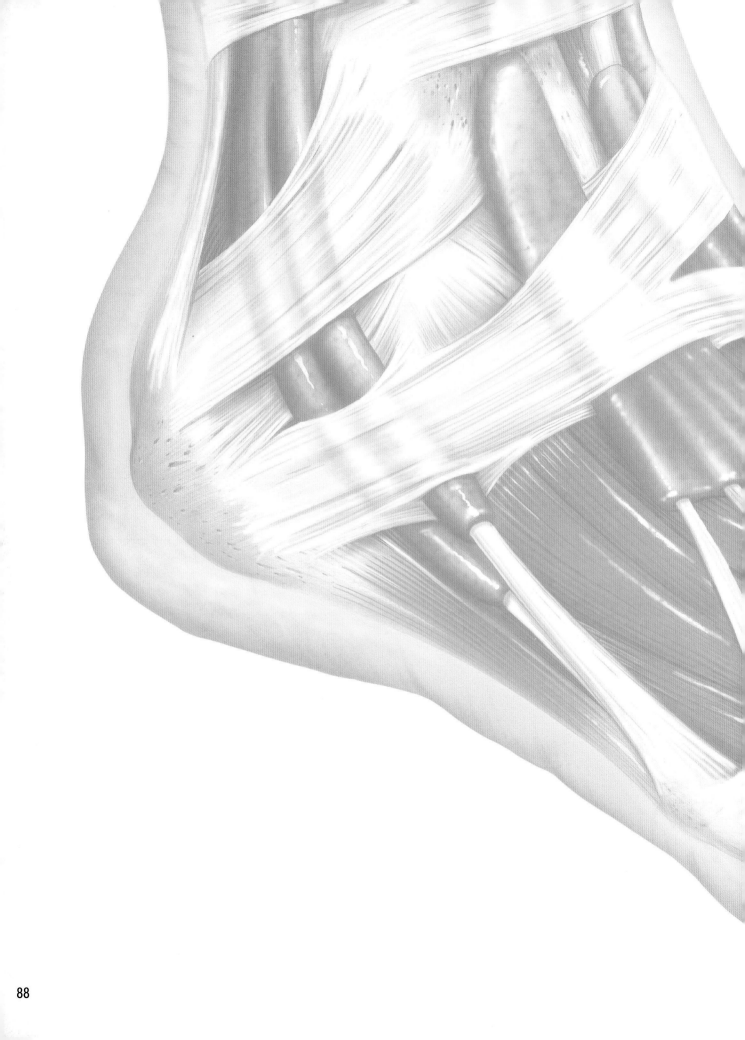

Body Movement

Movements of the Body

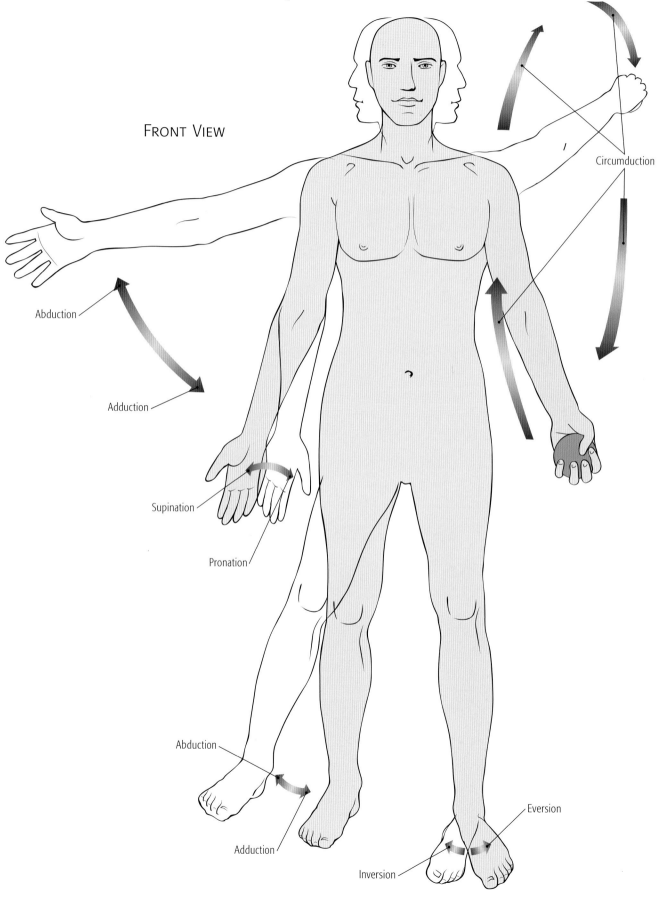

FRONT VIEW

Abduction

Adduction

Supination

Pronation

Abduction

Adduction

Circumduction

Eversion

Inversion

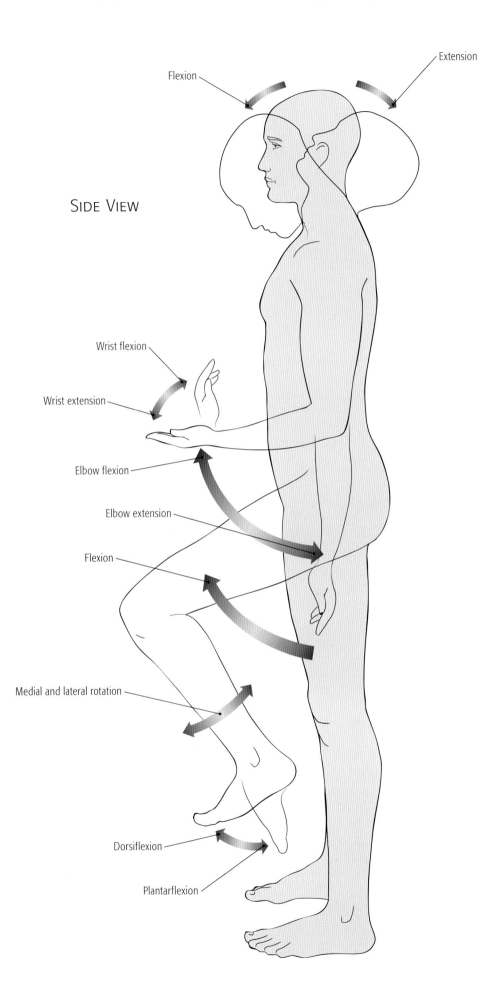

Flexion

Extension

SIDE VIEW

Wrist flexion

Wrist extension

Elbow flexion

Elbow extension

Flexion

Medial and lateral rotation

Dorsiflexion

Plantarflexion

Types of Joints

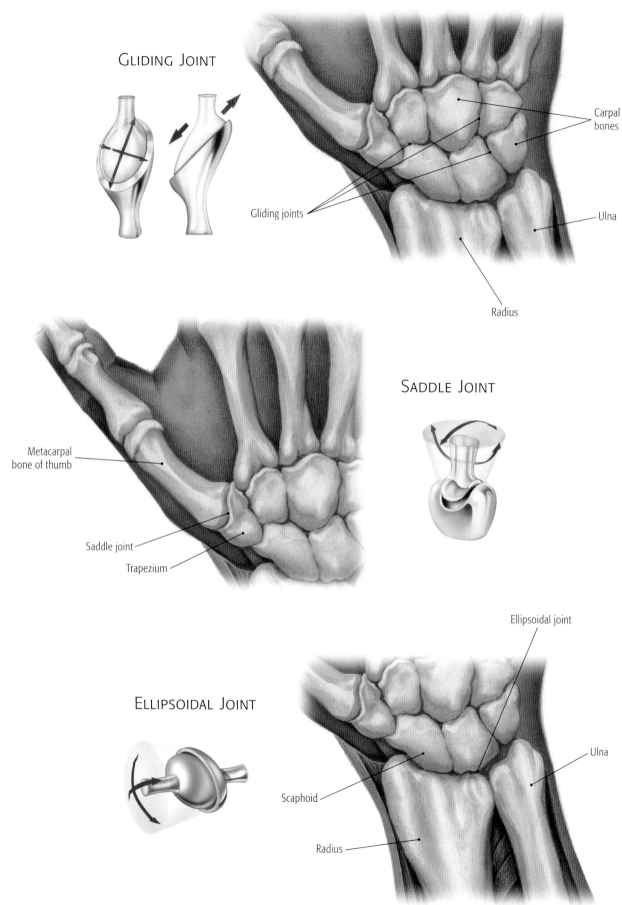

GLIDING JOINT

Carpal bones

Gliding joints

Ulna

Radius

Metacarpal bone of thumb

SADDLE JOINT

Saddle joint

Trapezium

Ellipsoidal joint

ELLIPSOIDAL JOINT

Ulna

Scaphoid

Radius

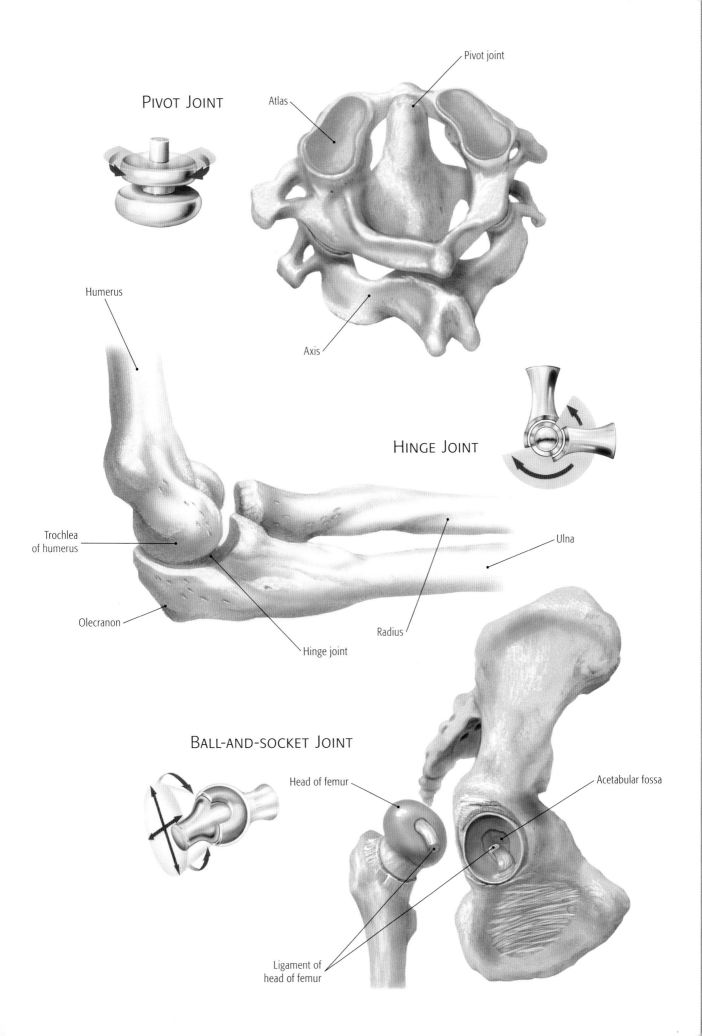

PIVOT JOINT

Pivot joint

Atlas

Axis

Humerus

HINGE JOINT

Trochlea
of humerus

Ulna

Olecranon

Radius

Hinge joint

BALL-AND-SOCKET JOINT

Head of femur

Acetabular fossa

Ligament of
head of femur

Joints

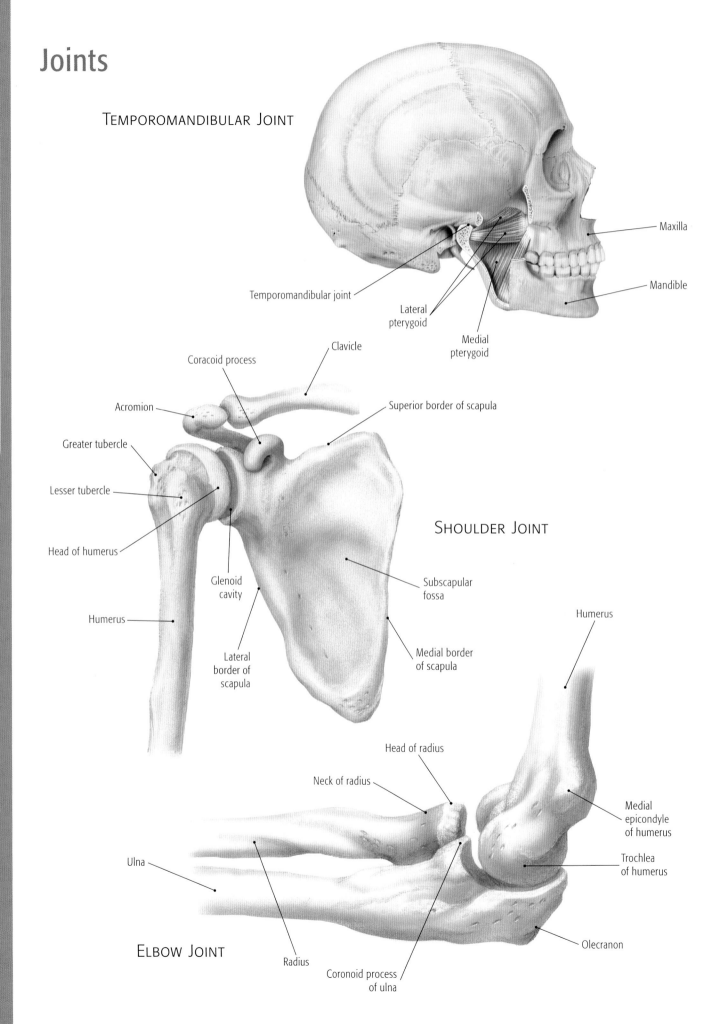

TEMPOROMANDIBULAR JOINT

Maxilla

Mandible

Temporomandibular joint

Lateral pterygoid

Medial pterygoid

Coracoid process

Clavicle

Acromion

Superior border of scapula

Greater tubercle

SHOULDER JOINT

Lesser tubercle

Head of humerus

Subscapular fossa

Humerus

Glenoid cavity

Lateral border of scapula

Medial border of scapula

Humerus

Head of radius

Neck of radius

Medial epicondyle of humerus

Ulna

Trochlea of humerus

Radius

Olecranon

ELBOW JOINT

Coronoid process of ulna

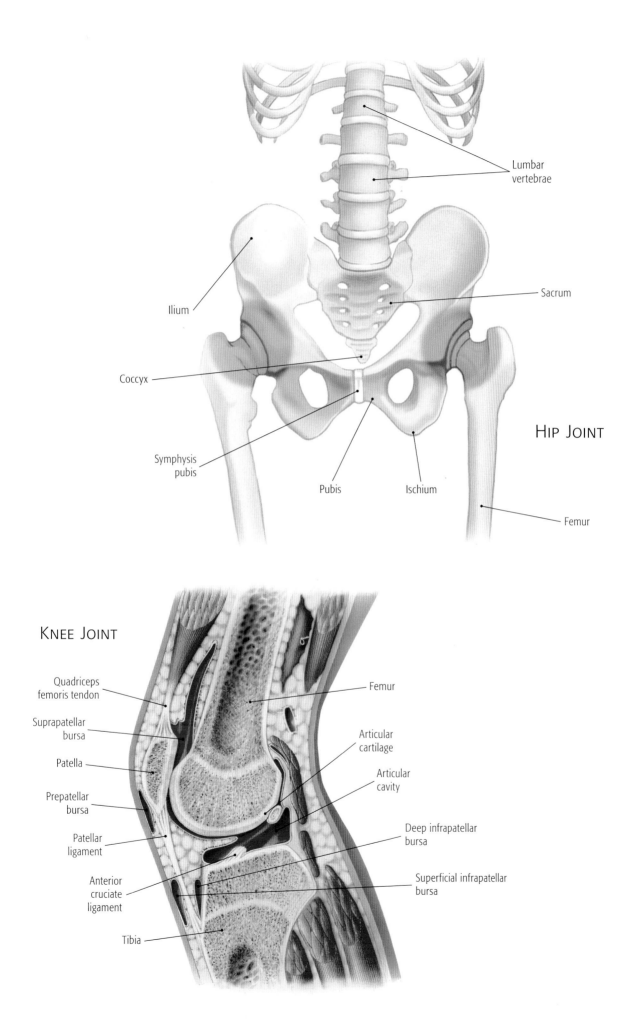

Lumbar
vertebrae

Ilium

Sacrum

Coccyx

HIP JOINT

Symphysis
pubis

Pubis

Ischium

Femur

KNEE JOINT

Quadriceps
femoris tendon

Femur

Suprapatellar
bursa

Articular
cartilage

Patella

Articular
cavity

Prepatellar
bursa

Patellar
ligament

Deep infrapatellar
bursa

Anterior
cruciate
ligament

Superficial infrapatellar
bursa

Tibia

The Muscular System

Muscles of the Body

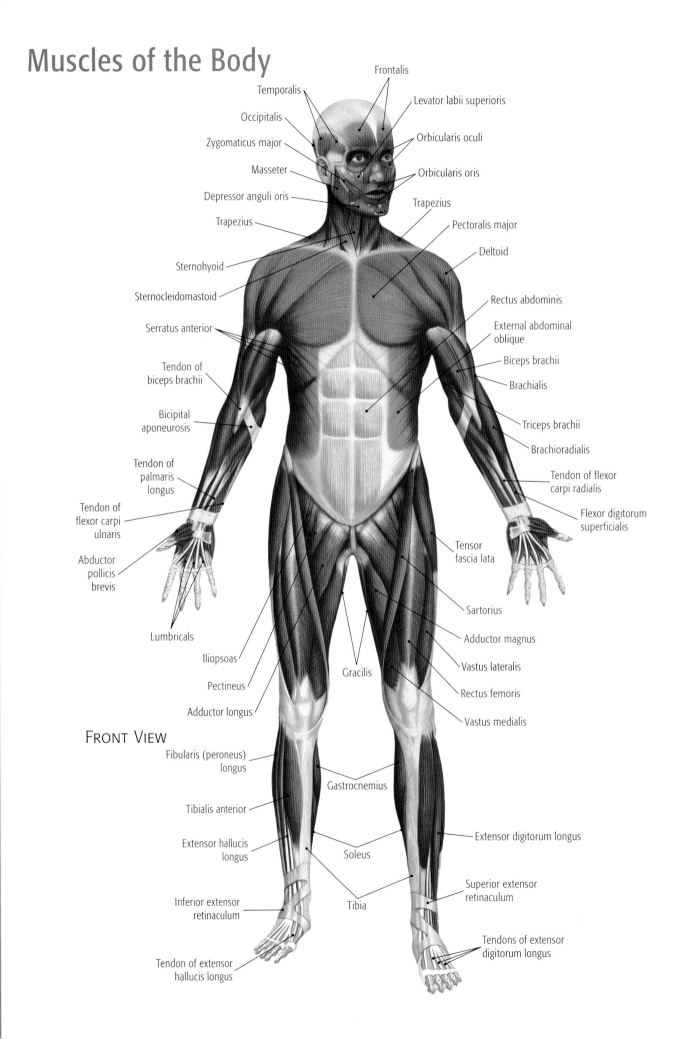

Frontalis

Temporalis

Levator labii superioris

Occipitalis

Zygomaticus major

Orbicularis oculi

Masseter

Orbicularis oris

Depressor anguli oris

Trapezius

Trapezius

Pectoralis major

Sternohyoid

Deltoid

Sternocleidomastoid

Rectus abdominis

Serratus anterior

External abdominal oblique

Tendon of biceps brachii

Biceps brachii

Brachialis

Bicipital aponeurosis

Triceps brachii

Brachioradialis

Tendon of palmaris longus

Tendon of flexor carpi radialis

Tendon of flexor carpi ulnaris

Flexor digitorum superficialis

Abductor pollicis brevis

Tensor fascia lata

Lumbricals

Sartorius

Iliopsoas

Adductor magnus

Pectineus

Vastus lateralis

Adductor longus

Gracilis

Rectus femoris

Vastus medialis

FRONT VIEW

Fibularis (peroneus) longus

Gastrocnemius

Tibialis anterior

Extensor digitorum longus

Extensor hallucis longus

Soleus

Superior extensor retinaculum

Inferior extensor retinaculum

Tibia

Tendon of extensor hallucis longus

Tendons of extensor digitorum longus

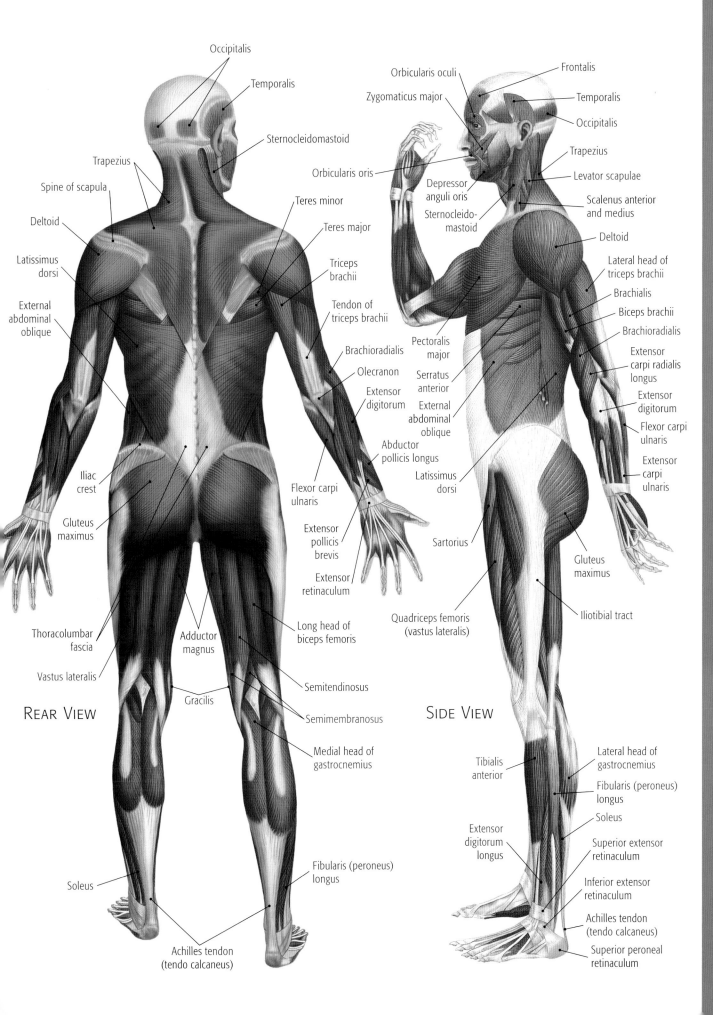

Occipitalis

Temporalis

Sternocleidomastoid

Trapezius

Spine of scapula

Deltoid

Latissimus dorsi

External abdominal oblique

Teres minor

Teres major

Triceps brachii

Tendon of triceps brachii

Brachioradialis

Olecranon

Extensor digitorum

Iliac crest

Gluteus maximus

Flexor carpi ulnaris

Extensor pollicis brevis

Extensor retinaculum

Thoracolumbar fascia

Vastus lateralis

Adductor magnus

Gracilis

Long head of biceps femoris

Semitendinosus

Semimembranosus

Medial head of gastrocnemius

Soleus

Fibularis (peroneus) longus

Achilles tendon (tendo calcaneus)

REAR VIEW

Orbicularis oculi

Zygomaticus major

Orbicularis oris

Depressor anguli oris

Sternocleido-mastoid

Frontalis

Temporalis

Occipitalis

Trapezius

Levator scapulae

Scalenus anterior and medius

Deltoid

Lateral head of triceps brachii

Brachialis

Biceps brachii

Brachioradialis

Extensor carpi radialis longus

Extensor digitorum

Flexor carpi ulnaris

Extensor carpi ulnaris

Pectoralis major

Serratus anterior

External abdominal oblique

Latissimus dorsi

Sartorius

Gluteus maximus

Quadriceps femoris (vastus lateralis)

Iliotibial tract

Tibialis anterior

Extensor digitorum longus

Lateral head of gastrocnemius

Fibularis (peroneus) longus

Soleus

Superior extensor retinaculum

Inferior extensor retinaculum

Achilles tendon (tendo calcaneus)

Superior peroneal retinaculum

SIDE VIEW

Muscle Types

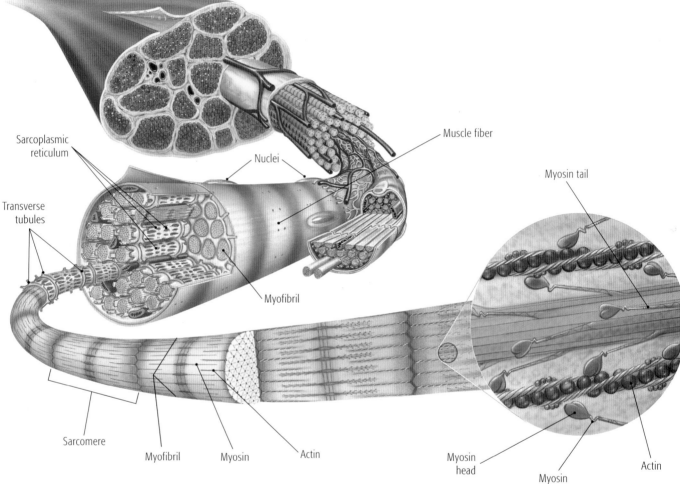

Sarcoplasmic reticulum

Transverse tubules

Nuclei

Muscle fiber

Myofibril

Myosin tail

Sarcomere

Myofibril

Myosin

Actin

Myosin head

Myosin crossbridge

Actin

MUSCLE FIBER—MICROSTRUCTURE

Muscle fibers are elongated cells containing fine threads made of myofibrils. Myofibrils consist of contractile protein myofilaments, arranged in regular arrays. Contraction of the muscle is produced by the interaction of myosin heads with actin.

MUSCLE SHAPES

Muscles are classified based on their general shape—some muscles have mainly parallel fibers, and others have oblique fibers. The shape and arrangement of muscle fibers reflects the function of the muscle (for example, muscle fibers that support organs are criss-crossed).

Unipennate   Bipennate   Multipennate

Spiral   Spiral   Radial   Circular   Multicaudal

Quadrilateral   Strap   Strap   Cruciate   Triangular
                              (with tendinous intersections)

Fusiform   Bicipital   Tricipital   Quadricipital   Digastric

Muscle Action

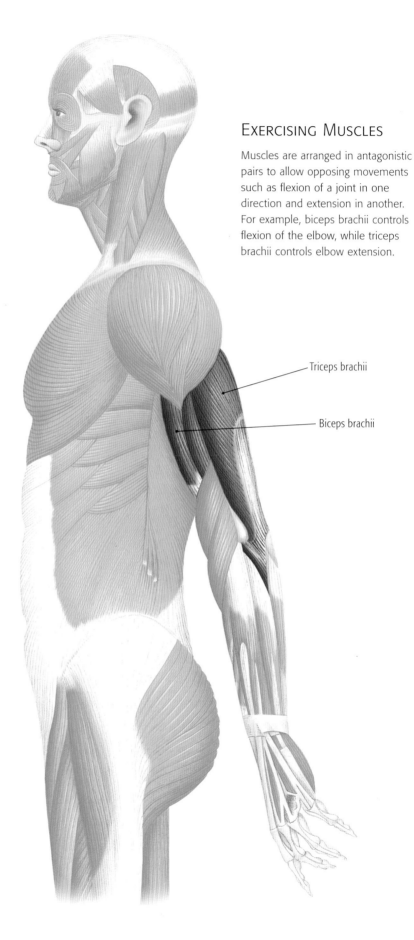

EXERCISING MUSCLES

Muscles are arranged in antagonistic pairs to allow opposing movements such as flexion of a joint in one direction and extension in another. For example, biceps brachii controls flexion of the elbow, while triceps brachii controls elbow extension.

Triceps brachii

Biceps brachii

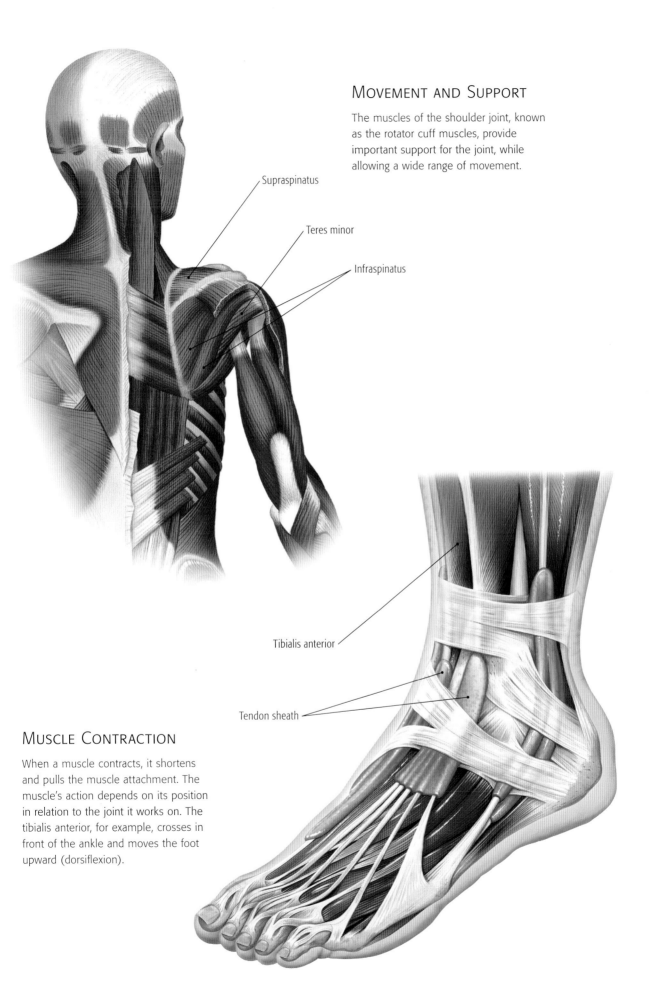

MOVEMENT AND SUPPORT

The muscles of the shoulder joint, known as the rotator cuff muscles, provide important support for the joint, while allowing a wide range of movement.

Supraspinatus

Teres minor

Infraspinatus

Tibialis anterior

Tendon sheath

MUSCLE CONTRACTION

When a muscle contracts, it shortens and pulls the muscle attachment. The muscle's action depends on its position in relation to the joint it works on. The tibialis anterior, for example, crosses in front of the ankle and moves the foot upward (dorsiflexion).

Muscles of the Head

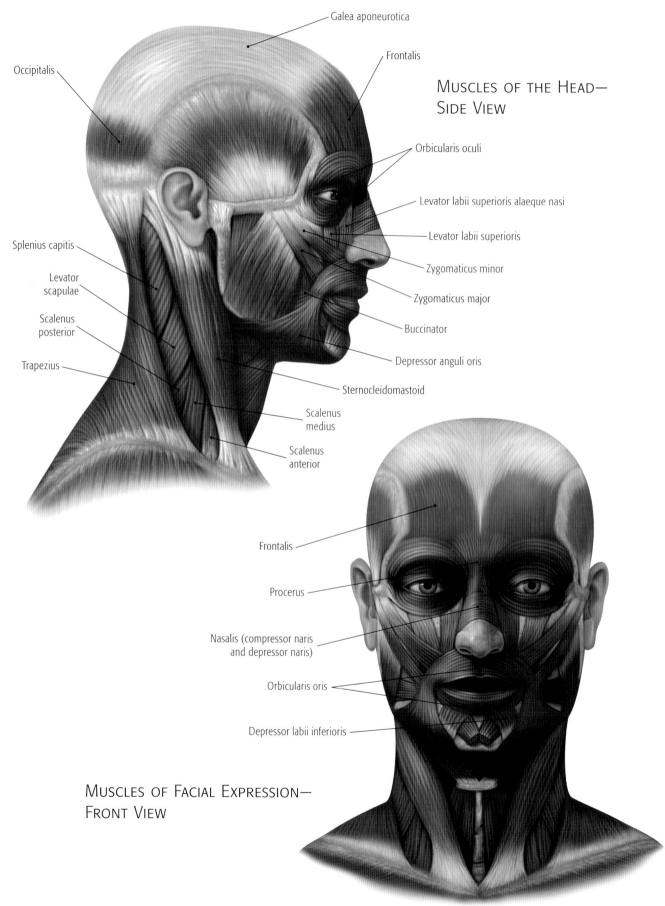

Galea aponeurotica

Frontalis

Occipitalis

MUSCLES OF THE HEAD—
SIDE VIEW

Orbicularis oculi

Levator labii superioris alaeque nasi

Levator labii superioris

Splenius capitis

Zygomaticus minor

Levator
scapulae

Zygomaticus major

Scalenus
posterior

Buccinator

Trapezius

Depressor anguli oris

Sternocleidomastoid

Scalenus
medius

Scalenus
anterior

Frontalis

Procerus

Nasalis (compressor naris
and depressor naris)

Orbicularis oris

Depressor labii inferioris

MUSCLES OF FACIAL EXPRESSION—
FRONT VIEW

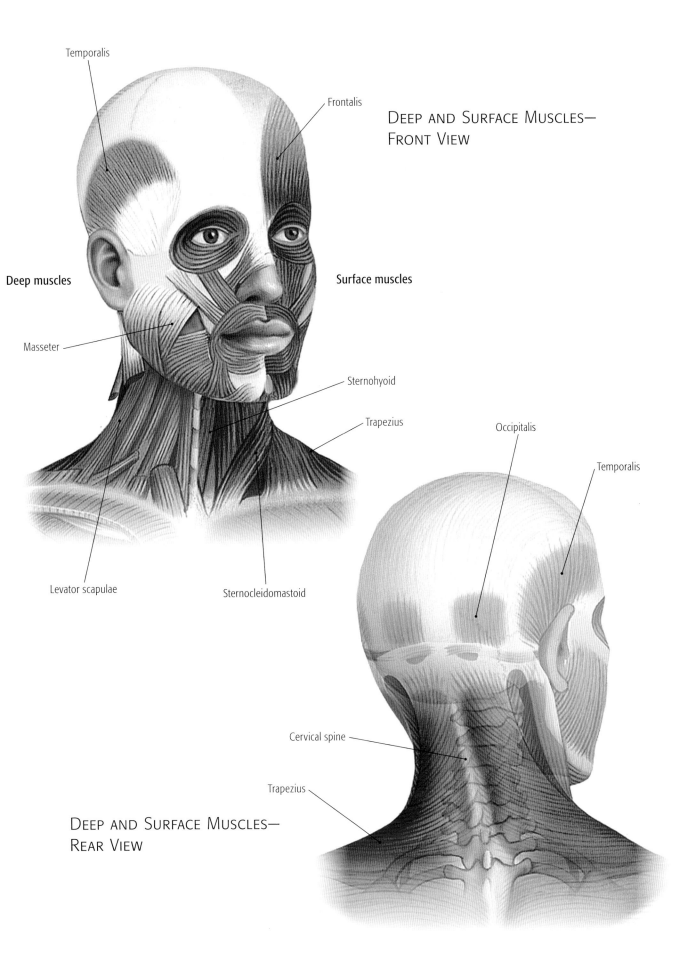

Temporalis

Frontalis

DEEP AND SURFACE MUSCLES—
FRONT VIEW

Deep muscles

Surface muscles

Masseter

Sternohyoid

Trapezius

Occipitalis

Temporalis

Levator scapulae

Sternocleidomastoid

Cervical spine

Trapezius

DEEP AND SURFACE MUSCLES—
REAR VIEW

Muscles of the Eye and Neck

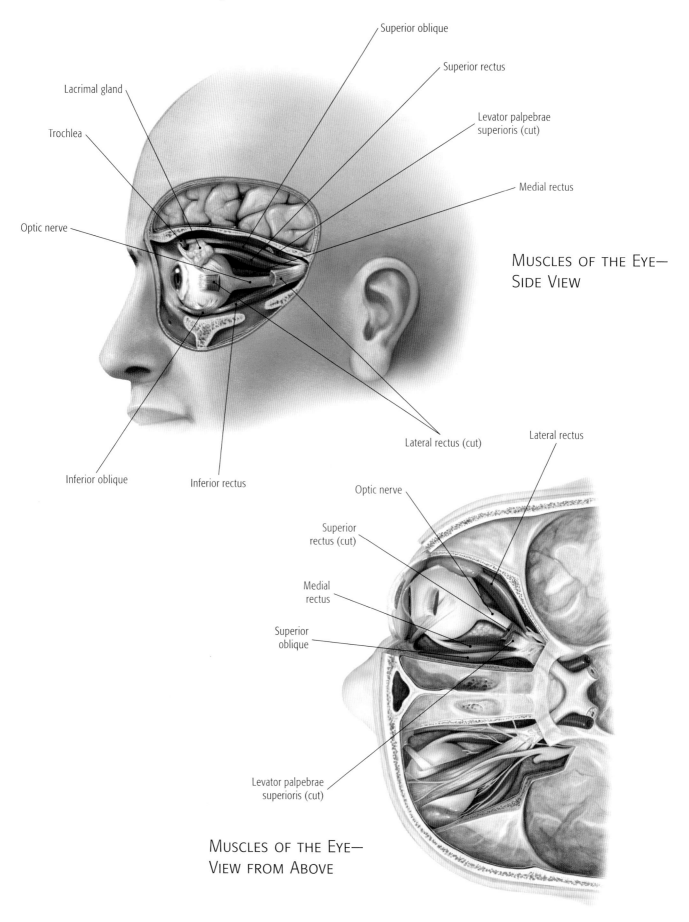

Superior oblique

Superior rectus

Levator palpebrae superioris (cut)

Medial rectus

Lacrimal gland

Trochlea

Optic nerve

MUSCLES OF THE EYE—
SIDE VIEW

Inferior oblique

Inferior rectus

Lateral rectus (cut)

Lateral rectus

Optic nerve

Superior
rectus (cut)

Medial
rectus

Superior
oblique

Levator palpebrae
superioris (cut)

MUSCLES OF THE EYE—
VIEW FROM ABOVE

Muscles of the Neck—Cross-sectional View

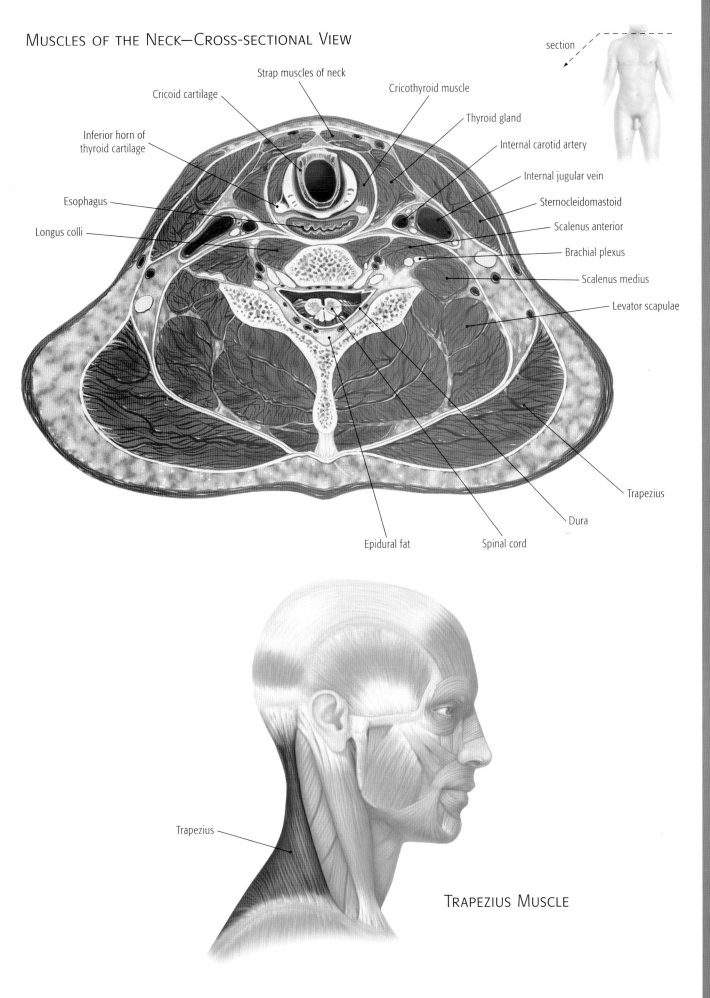

section

Strap muscles of neck

Cricoid cartilage

Cricothyroid muscle

Thyroid gland

Inferior horn of thyroid cartilage

Internal carotid artery

Internal jugular vein

Esophagus

Sternocleidomastoid

Longus colli

Scalenus anterior

Brachial plexus

Scalenus medius

Levator scapulae

Trapezius

Dura

Epidural fat

Spinal cord

Trapezius

Trapezius Muscle

Muscles of the Jaw and Throat

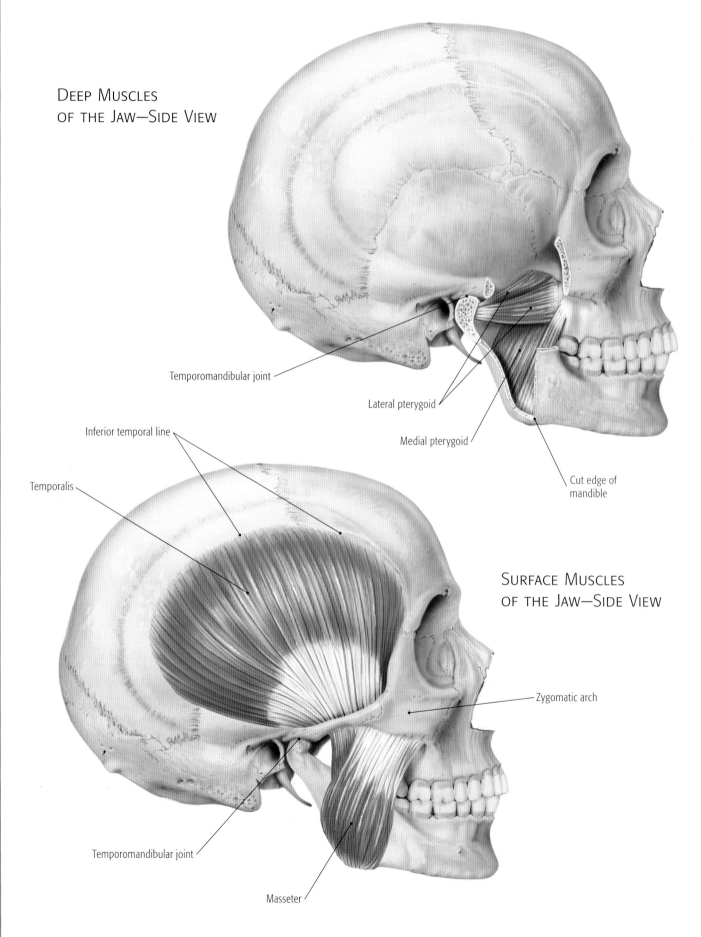

DEEP MUSCLES
OF THE JAW—SIDE VIEW

Temporomandibular joint

Lateral pterygoid

Medial pterygoid

Cut edge of
mandible

Inferior temporal line

Temporalis

SURFACE MUSCLES
OF THE JAW—SIDE VIEW

Zygomatic arch

Temporomandibular joint

Masseter

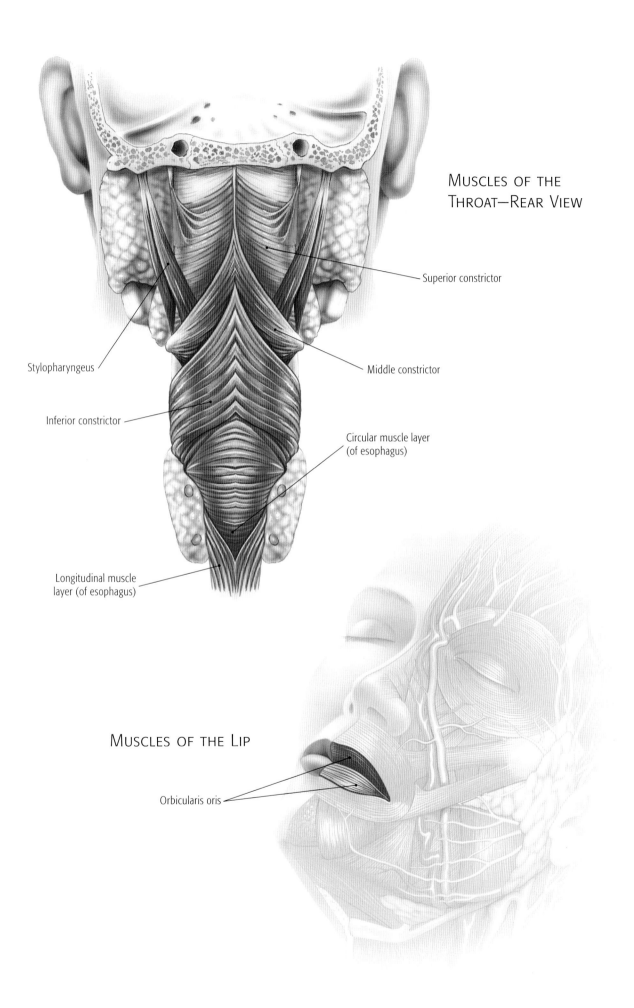

MUSCLES OF THE
THROAT—REAR VIEW

Superior constrictor

Stylopharyngeus

Middle constrictor

Inferior constrictor

Circular muscle layer
(of esophagus)

Longitudinal muscle
layer (of esophagus)

MUSCLES OF THE LIP

Orbicularis oris

Muscles of the Back and Abdomen

Surface muscles

Deep muscles

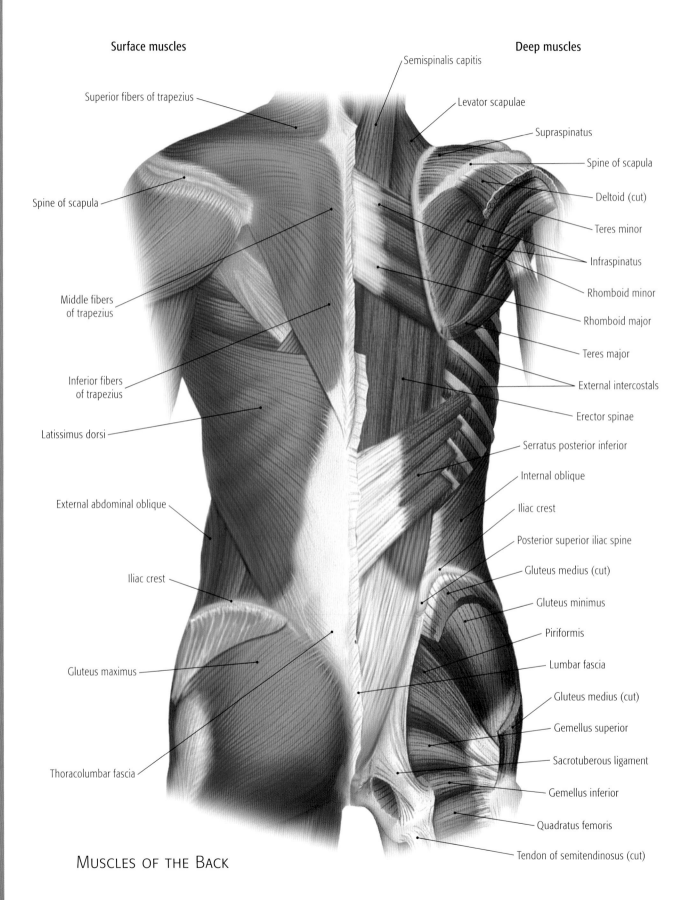

Semispinalis capitis

Superior fibers of trapezius

Levator scapulae

Supraspinatus

Spine of scapula

Spine of scapula

Deltoid (cut)

Teres minor

Infraspinatus

Middle fibers
of trapezius

Rhomboid minor

Rhomboid major

Teres major

Inferior fibers
of trapezius

External intercostals

Erector spinae

Latissimus dorsi

Serratus posterior inferior

Internal oblique

Iliac crest

External abdominal oblique

Posterior superior iliac spine

Gluteus medius (cut)

Iliac crest

Gluteus minimus

Piriformis

Lumbar fascia

Gluteus maximus

Gluteus medius (cut)

Gemellus superior

Sacrotuberous ligament

Gemellus inferior

Thoracolumbar fascia

Quadratus femoris

Tendon of semitendinosus (cut)

MUSCLES OF THE BACK

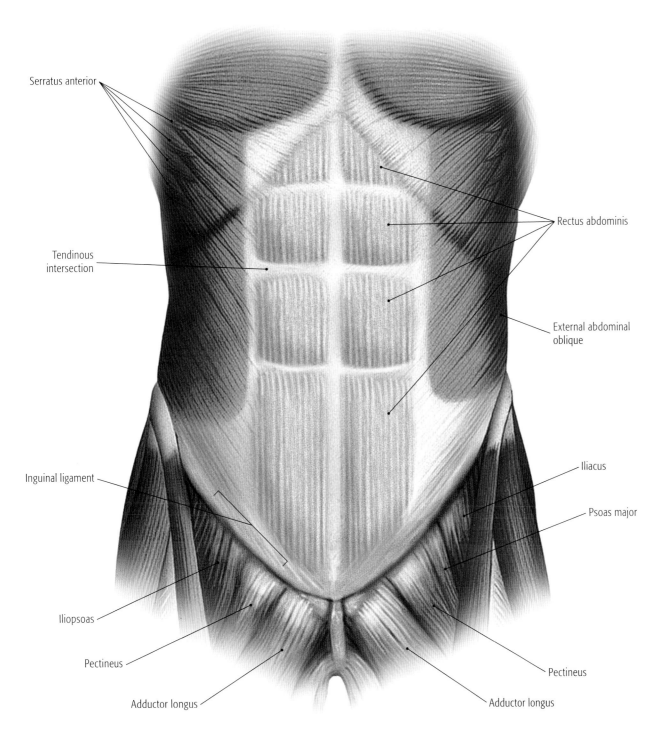

Serratus anterior

Tendinous intersection

Inguinal ligament

Iliopsoas

Pectineus

Adductor longus

Rectus abdominis

External abdominal oblique

Iliacus

Psoas major

Pectineus

Adductor longus

MUSCLES OF THE ABDOMEN

Muscles of Breathing and the Pelvis

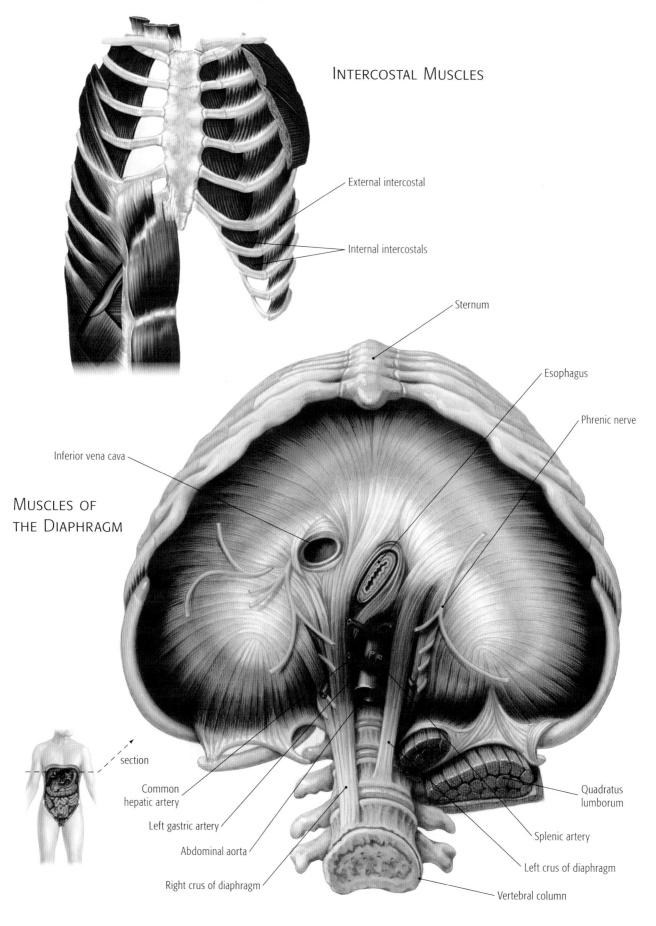

INTERCOSTAL MUSCLES

External intercostal

Internal intercostals

Sternum

Esophagus

Phrenic nerve

Inferior vena cava

MUSCLES OF
THE DIAPHRAGM

section

Common
hepatic artery

Left gastric artery

Abdominal aorta

Right crus of diaphragm

Quadratus
lumborum

Splenic artery

Left crus of diaphragm

Vertebral column

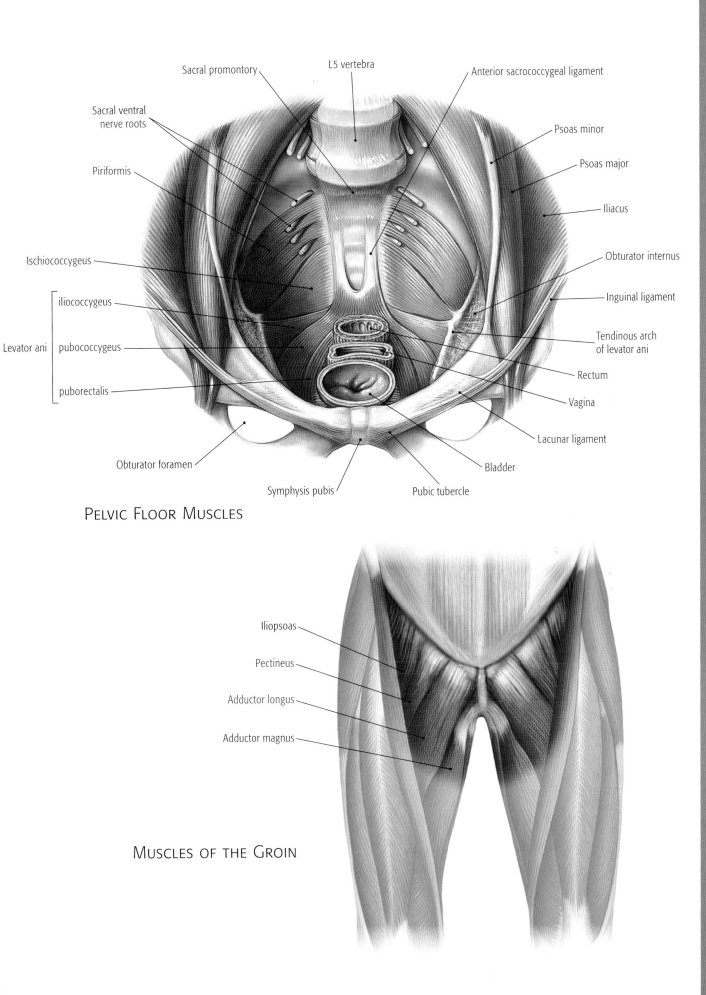

Sacral promontory

L5 vertebra

Anterior sacrococcygeal ligament

Sacral ventral
nerve roots

Psoas minor

Psoas major

Piriformis

Iliacus

Ischiococcygeus

Obturator internus

Levator ani

iliococcygeus

Inguinal ligament

pubococcygeus

Tendinous arch
of levator ani

puborectalis

Rectum

Vagina

Lacunar ligament

Obturator foramen

Bladder

Symphysis pubis

Pubic tubercle

Pelvic Floor Muscles

Iliopsoas

Pectineus

Adductor longus

Adductor magnus

Muscles of the Groin

113

Muscles of the Arm

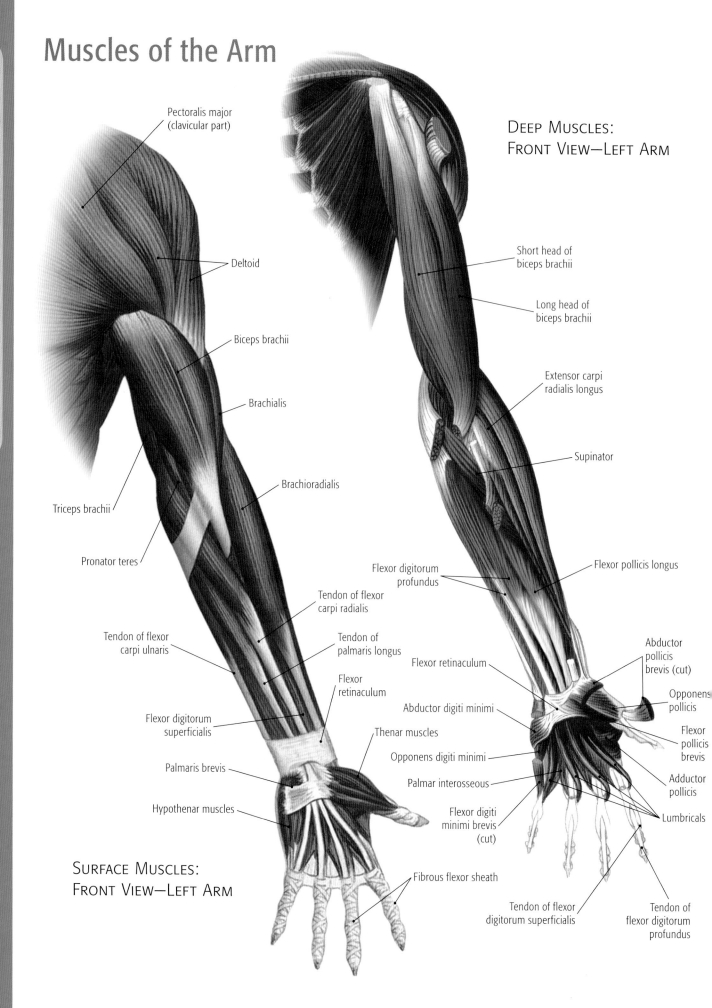

Pectoralis major
(clavicular part)

Deltoid

Biceps brachii

Brachialis

Brachioradialis

Triceps brachii

Pronator teres

Tendon of flexor
carpi radialis

Tendon of flexor
carpi ulnaris

Tendon of
palmaris longus

Flexor
retinaculum

Flexor digitorum
superficialis

Palmaris brevis

Hypothenar muscles

SURFACE MUSCLES:
FRONT VIEW—LEFT ARM

DEEP MUSCLES:
FRONT VIEW—LEFT ARM

Short head of
biceps brachii

Long head of
biceps brachii

Extensor carpi
radialis longus

Supinator

Flexor digitorum
profundus

Flexor pollicis longus

Flexor retinaculum

Abductor digiti minimi

Thenar muscles

Opponens digiti minimi

Palmar interosseous

Flexor digiti
minimi brevis
(cut)

Fibrous flexor sheath

Abductor
pollicis
brevis (cut)

Opponens
pollicis

Flexor
pollicis
brevis

Adductor
pollicis

Lumbricals

Tendon of flexor
digitorum superficialis

Tendon of
flexor digitorum
profundus

114

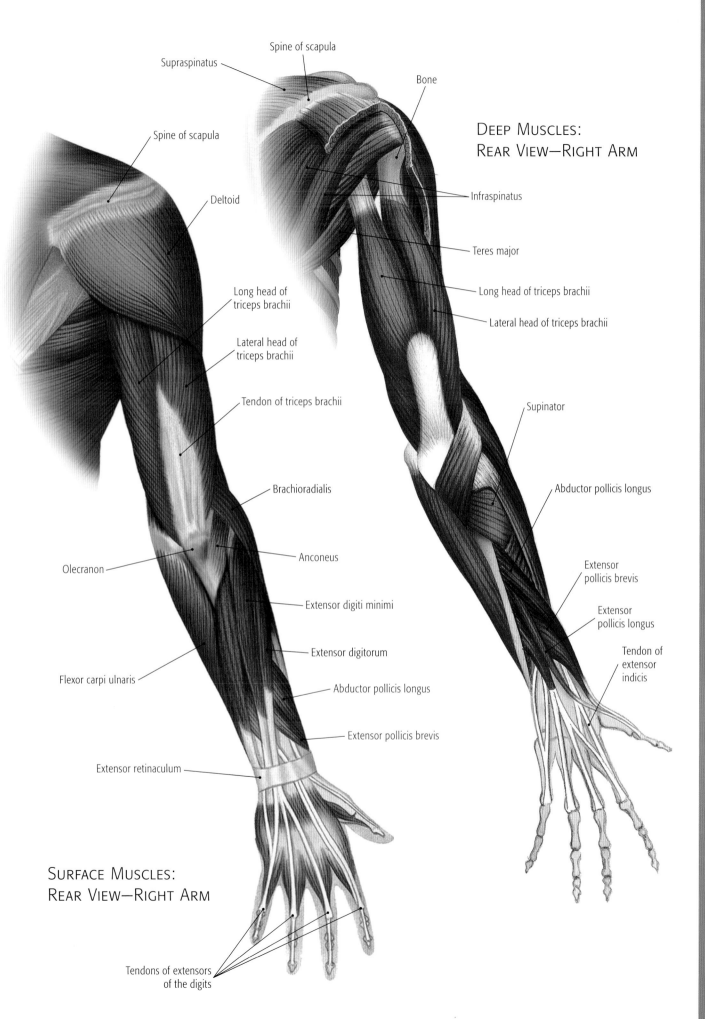

Spine of scapula

Supraspinatus

Bone

Spine of scapula

Deltoid

DEEP MUSCLES:
REAR VIEW—RIGHT ARM

Infraspinatus

Teres major

Long head of
triceps brachii

Long head of triceps brachii

Lateral head of
triceps brachii

Lateral head of triceps brachii

Tendon of triceps brachii

Supinator

Brachioradialis

Anconeus

Abductor pollicis longus

Olecranon

Extensor
pollicis brevis

Extensor digiti minimi

Extensor
pollicis longus

Extensor digitorum

Tendon of
extensor
indicis

Flexor carpi ulnaris

Abductor pollicis longus

Extensor pollicis brevis

Extensor retinaculum

SURFACE MUSCLES:
REAR VIEW—RIGHT ARM

Tendons of extensors
of the digits

Muscles of the Arm

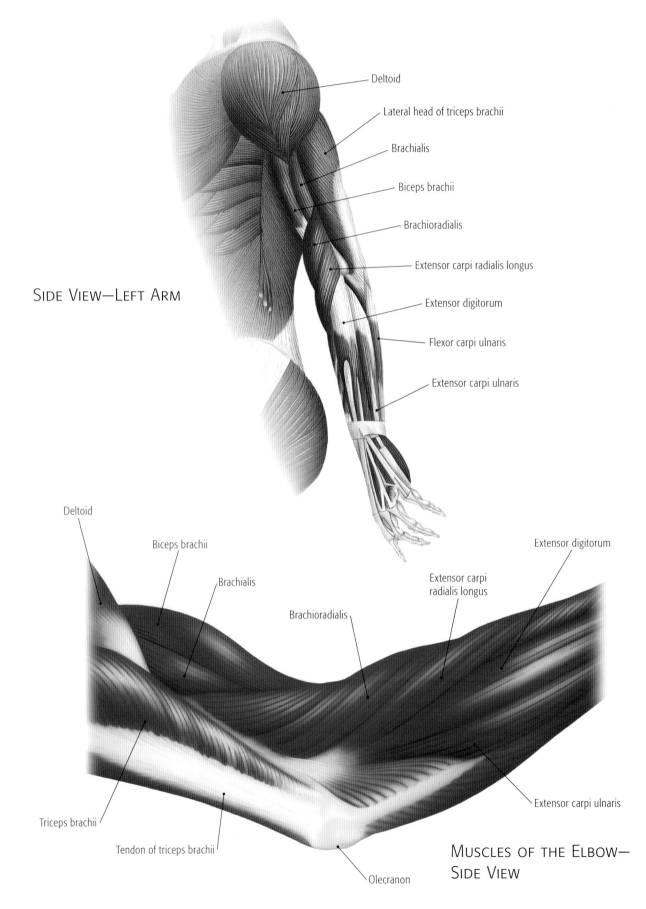

Deltoid

Lateral head of triceps brachii

Brachialis

Biceps brachii

Brachioradialis

Extensor carpi radialis longus

Extensor digitorum

Flexor carpi ulnaris

Extensor carpi ulnaris

SIDE VIEW—LEFT ARM

Deltoid

Biceps brachii

Brachialis

Brachioradialis

Extensor carpi
radialis longus

Extensor digitorum

Extensor carpi ulnaris

Triceps brachii

Tendon of triceps brachii

Olecranon

MUSCLES OF THE ELBOW—
SIDE VIEW

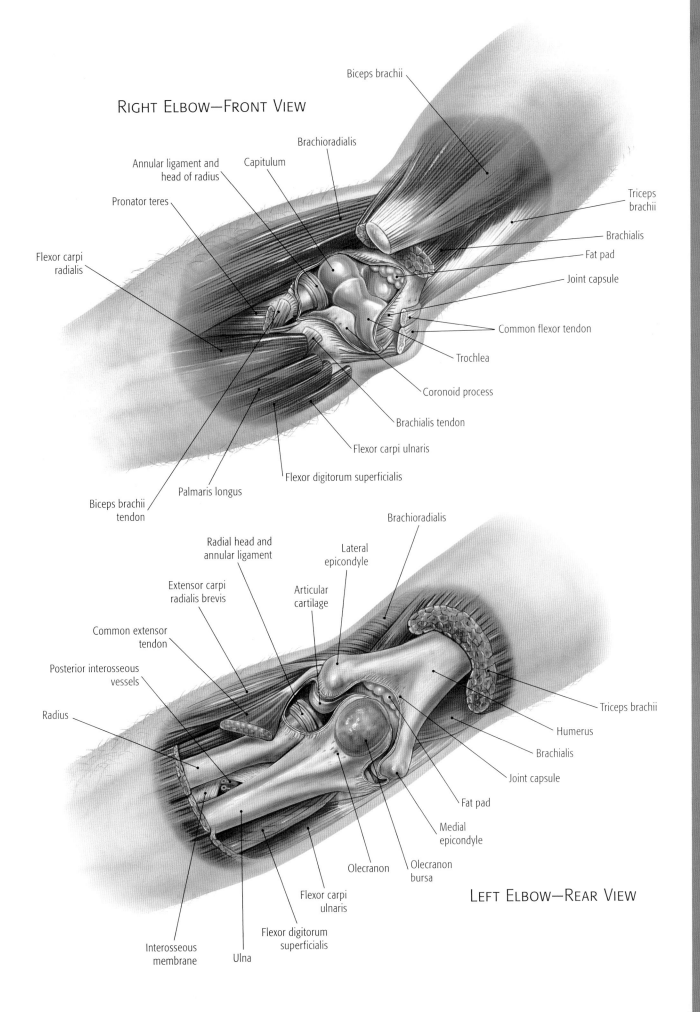

RIGHT ELBOW—FRONT VIEW

Biceps brachii

Brachioradialis

Annular ligament and head of radius

Capitulum

Pronator teres

Flexor carpi radialis

Triceps brachii

Brachialis

Fat pad

Joint capsule

Common flexor tendon

Trochlea

Coronoid process

Brachialis tendon

Flexor carpi ulnaris

Flexor digitorum superficialis

Biceps brachii tendon

Palmaris longus

Radial head and annular ligament

Extensor carpi radialis brevis

Common extensor tendon

Posterior interosseous vessels

Radius

Lateral epicondyle

Brachioradialis

Articular cartilage

Triceps brachii

Humerus

Brachialis

Joint capsule

Fat pad

Medial epicondyle

Olecranon bursa

Olecranon

Flexor carpi ulnaris

Flexor digitorum superficialis

LEFT ELBOW—REAR VIEW

Interosseous membrane

Ulna

Muscles of the Arm and Hand

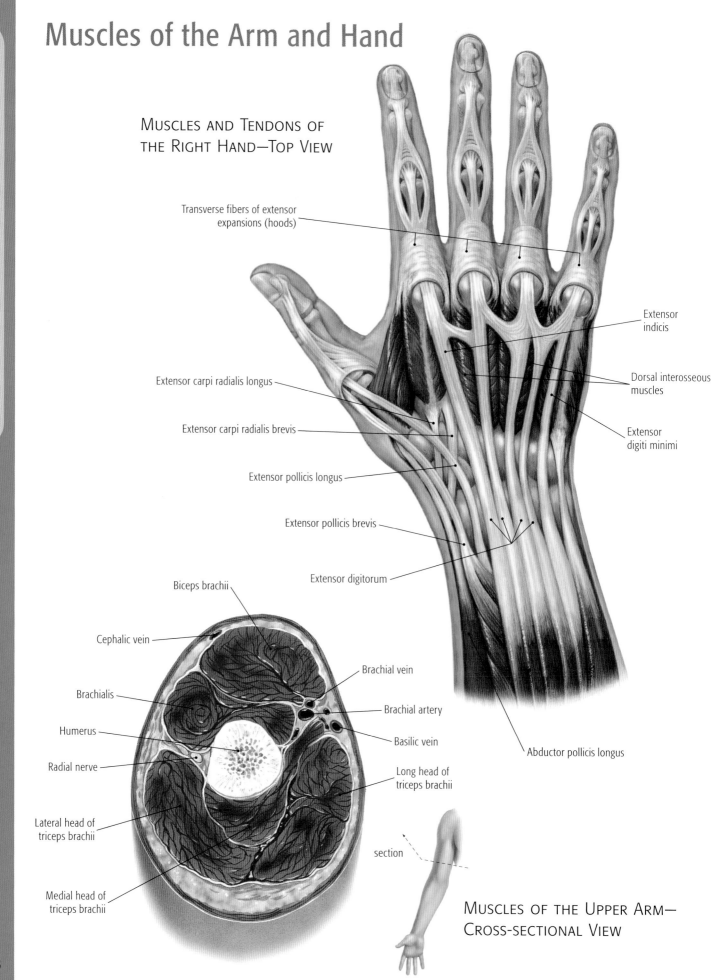

MUSCLES AND TENDONS OF
THE RIGHT HAND—TOP VIEW

Transverse fibers of extensor
expansions (hoods)

Extensor
indicis

Dorsal interosseous
muscles

Extensor carpi radialis longus

Extensor
digiti minimi

Extensor carpi radialis brevis

Extensor pollicis longus

Extensor pollicis brevis

Extensor digitorum

Biceps brachii

Cephalic vein

Brachial vein

Brachialis

Brachial artery

Humerus

Basilic vein

Radial nerve

Long head of
triceps brachii

Lateral head of
triceps brachii

Medial head of
triceps brachii

Abductor pollicis longus

section

MUSCLES OF THE UPPER ARM—
CROSS-SECTIONAL VIEW

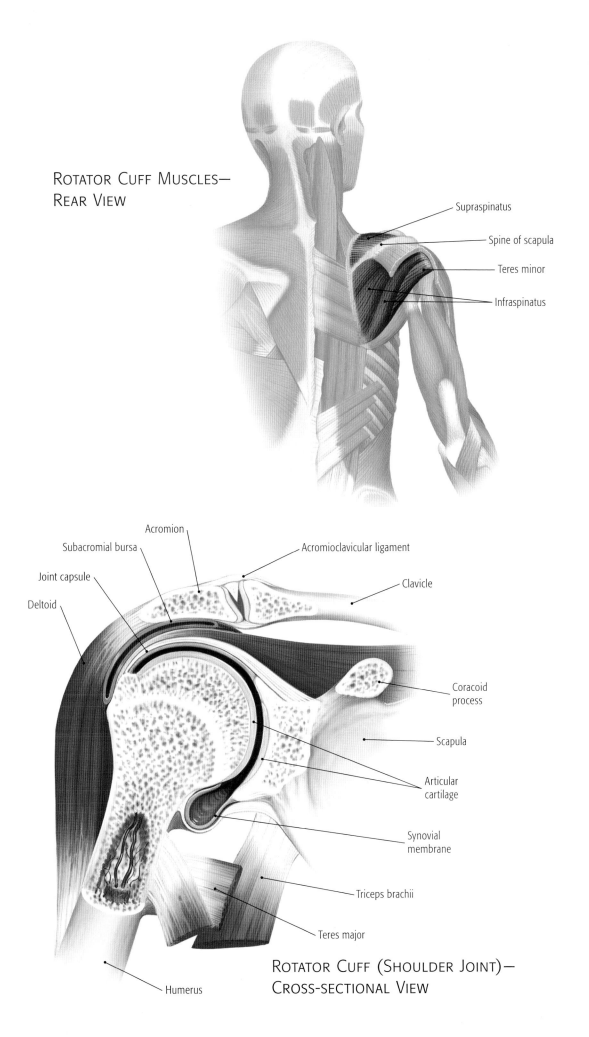

ROTATOR CUFF MUSCLES—
REAR VIEW

Supraspinatus

Spine of scapula

Teres minor

Infraspinatus

Acromion

Subacromial bursa

Acromioclavicular ligament

Joint capsule

Clavicle

Deltoid

Coracoid
process

Scapula

Articular
cartilage

Synovial
membrane

Triceps brachii

Teres major

Humerus

ROTATOR CUFF (SHOULDER JOINT)—
CROSS-SECTIONAL VIEW

Muscles of the Leg

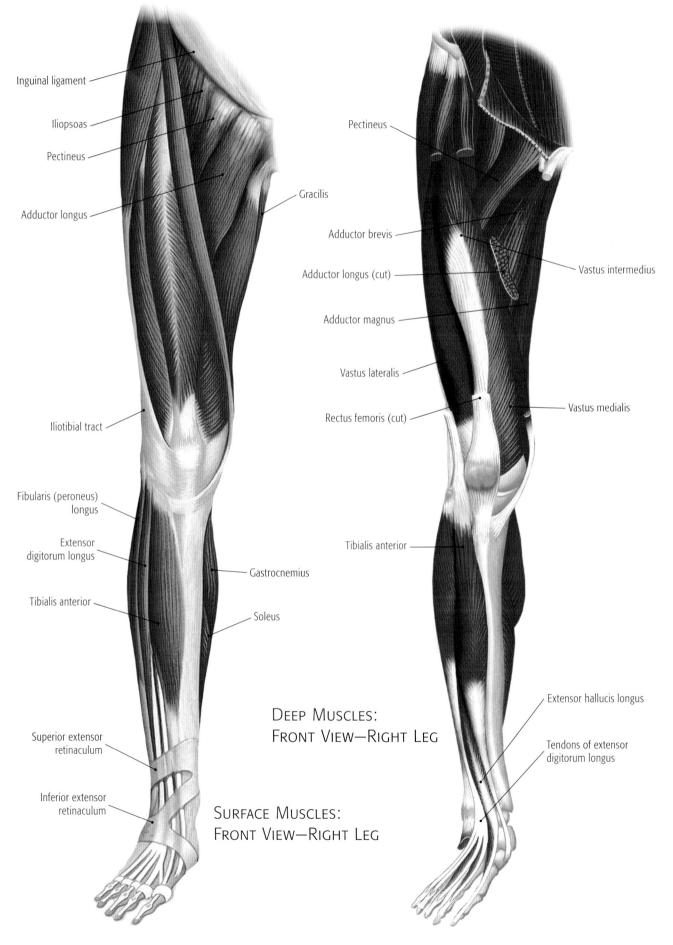

Inguinal ligament

Iliopsoas

Pectineus

Adductor longus

Gracilis

Iliotibial tract

Fibularis (peroneus)
longus

Extensor
digitorum longus

Tibialis anterior

Gastrocnemius

Soleus

Superior extensor
retinaculum

Inferior extensor
retinaculum

Pectineus

Adductor brevis

Adductor longus (cut)

Adductor magnus

Vastus lateralis

Rectus femoris (cut)

Vastus intermedius

Vastus medialis

Tibialis anterior

Extensor hallucis longus

Tendons of extensor
digitorum longus

DEEP MUSCLES:
FRONT VIEW—RIGHT LEG

SURFACE MUSCLES:
FRONT VIEW—RIGHT LEG

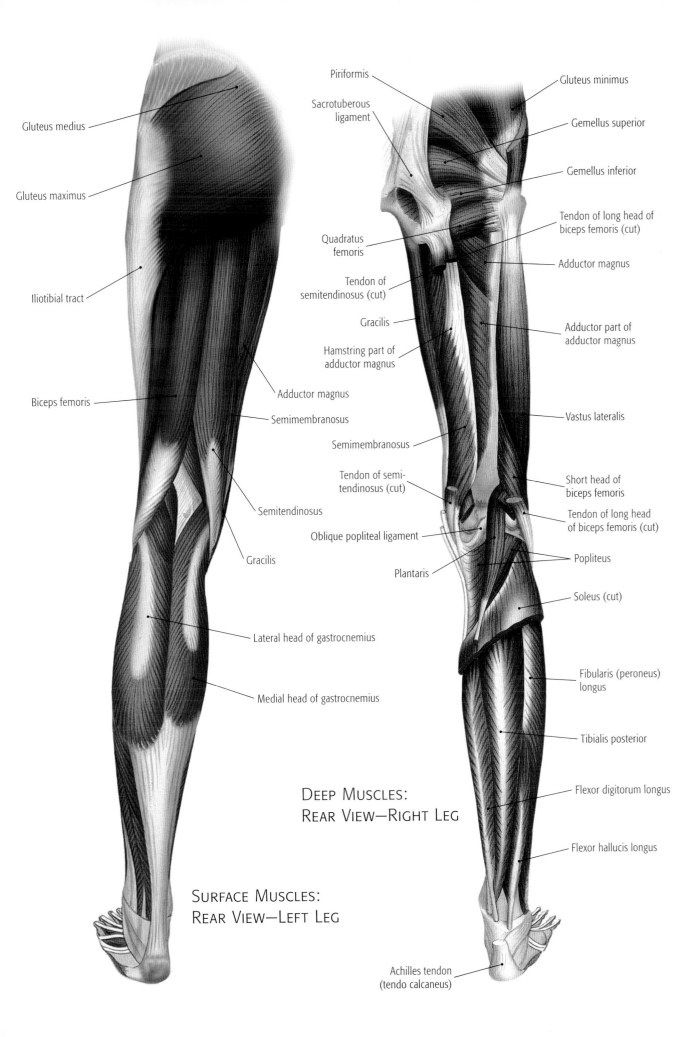

Gluteus medius

Gluteus maximus

Iliotibial tract

Biceps femoris

Piriformis

Sacrotuberous ligament

Quadratus femoris

Tendon of semitendinosus (cut)

Gracilis

Hamstring part of adductor magnus

Adductor magnus

Semimembranosus

Semimembranosus

Tendon of semi-tendinosus (cut)

Oblique popliteal ligament

Plantaris

Semitendinosus

Gracilis

Lateral head of gastrocnemius

Medial head of gastrocnemius

Gluteus minimus

Gemellus superior

Gemellus inferior

Tendon of long head of biceps femoris (cut)

Adductor magnus

Adductor part of adductor magnus

Vastus lateralis

Short head of biceps femoris

Tendon of long head of biceps femoris (cut)

Popliteus

Soleus (cut)

Fibularis (peroneus) longus

Tibialis posterior

Flexor digitorum longus

Flexor hallucis longus

DEEP MUSCLES:
REAR VIEW—RIGHT LEG

SURFACE MUSCLES:
REAR VIEW—LEFT LEG

Achilles tendon (tendo calcaneus)

121

Muscles of the Leg and Foot

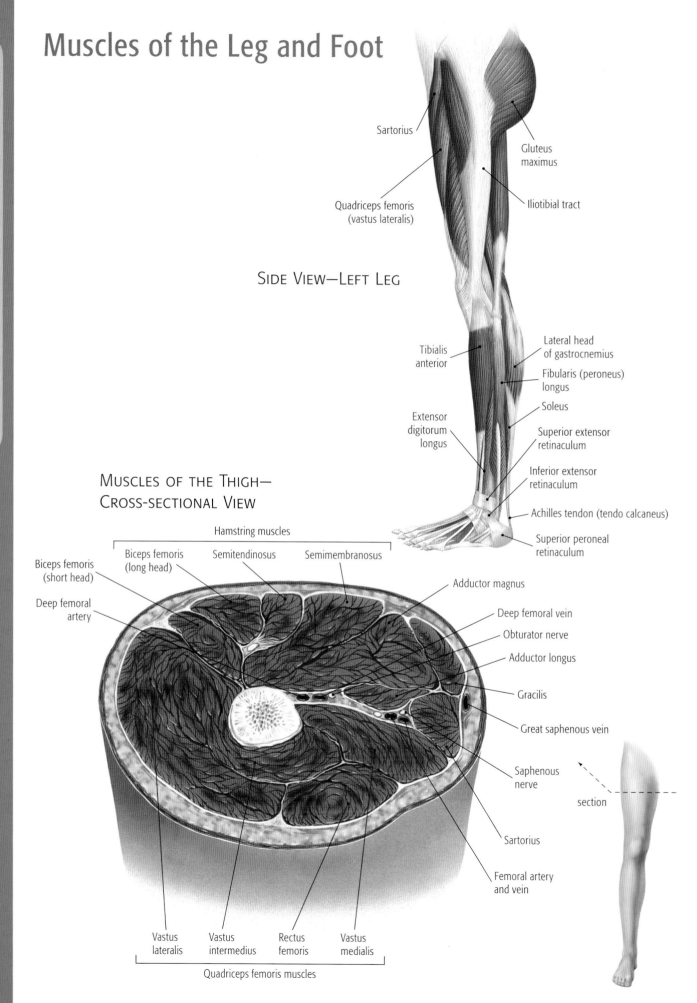

Sartorius

Gluteus maximus

Quadriceps femoris (vastus lateralis)

Iliotibial tract

SIDE VIEW—LEFT LEG

Tibialis anterior

Lateral head of gastrocnemius

Fibularis (peroneus) longus

Extensor digitorum longus

Soleus

Superior extensor retinaculum

MUSCLES OF THE THIGH— CROSS-SECTIONAL VIEW

Inferior extensor retinaculum

Achilles tendon (tendo calcaneus)

Superior peroneal retinaculum

Hamstring muscles

Biceps femoris (long head)

Semitendinosus

Semimembranosus

Biceps femoris (short head)

Adductor magnus

Deep femoral artery

Deep femoral vein

Obturator nerve

Adductor longus

Gracilis

Great saphenous vein

Saphenous nerve

section

Sartorius

Femoral artery and vein

Vastus lateralis

Vastus intermedius

Rectus femoris

Vastus medialis

Quadriceps femoris muscles

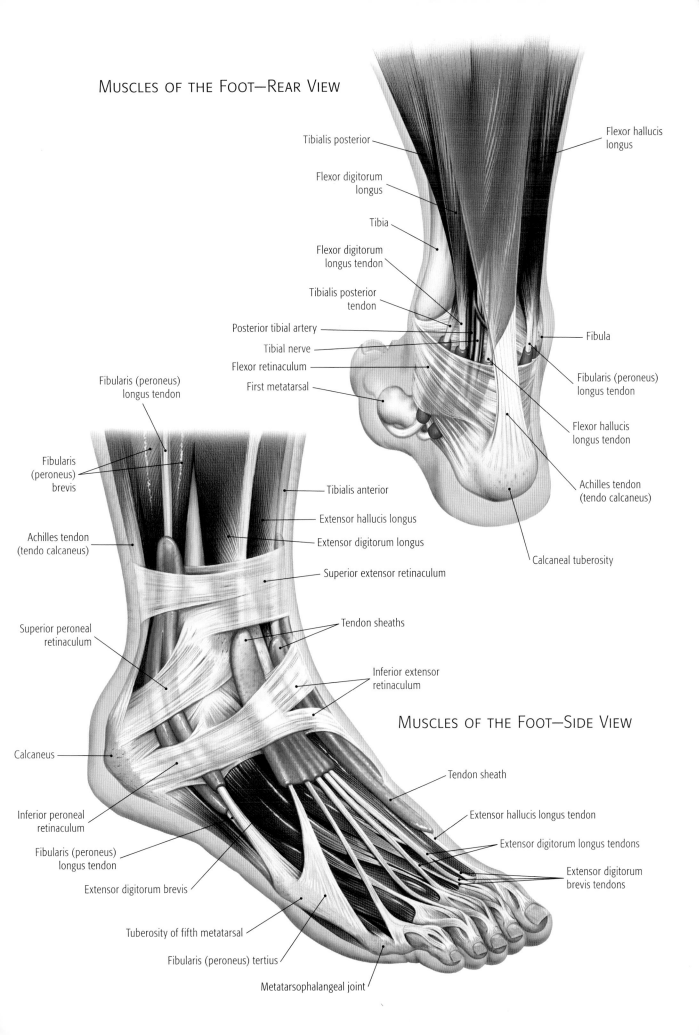

MUSCLES OF THE FOOT—REAR VIEW

Tibialis posterior

Flexor digitorum longus

Tibia

Flexor digitorum longus tendon

Tibialis posterior tendon

Posterior tibial artery

Tibial nerve

Flexor retinaculum

First metatarsal

Flexor hallucis longus

Fibula

Fibularis (peroneus) longus tendon

Flexor hallucis longus tendon

Achilles tendon (tendo calcaneus)

Calcaneal tuberosity

Fibularis (peroneus) longus tendon

Fibularis (peroneus) brevis

Achilles tendon (tendo calcaneus)

Superior peroneal retinaculum

Calcaneus

Inferior peroneal retinaculum

Fibularis (peroneus) longus tendon

Extensor digitorum brevis

Tuberosity of fifth metatarsal

Fibularis (peroneus) tertius

Metatarsophalangeal joint

Tibialis anterior

Extensor hallucis longus

Extensor digitorum longus

Superior extensor retinaculum

Tendon sheaths

Inferior extensor retinaculum

MUSCLES OF THE FOOT—SIDE VIEW

Tendon sheath

Extensor hallucis longus tendon

Extensor digitorum longus tendons

Extensor digitorum brevis tendons

Muscles of the Foot

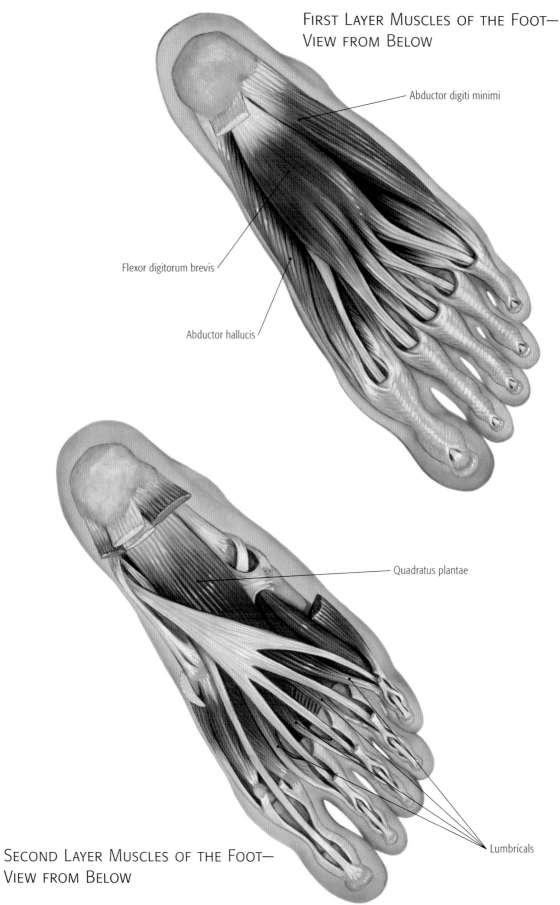

Abductor digiti minimi

Flexor digitorum brevis

Abductor hallucis

Quadratus plantae

Lumbricals

SECOND LAYER MUSCLES OF THE FOOT—
VIEW FROM BELOW

124

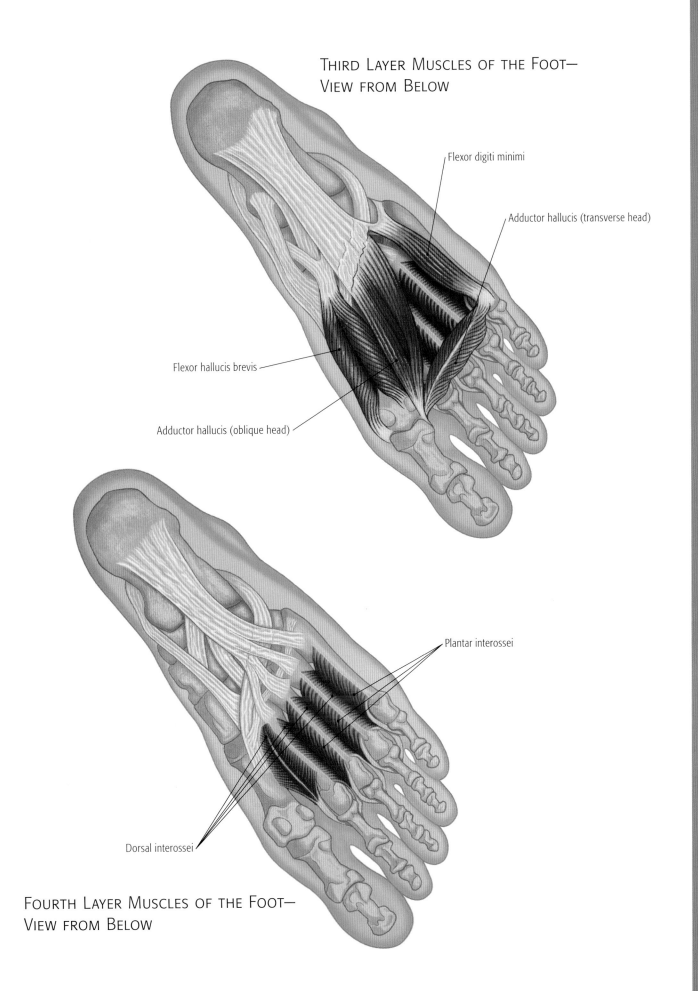

THIRD LAYER MUSCLES OF THE FOOT—
VIEW FROM BELOW

Flexor digiti minimi

Adductor hallucis (transverse head)

Flexor hallucis brevis

Adductor hallucis (oblique head)

Plantar interossei

Dorsal interossei

FOURTH LAYER MUSCLES OF THE FOOT—
VIEW FROM BELOW

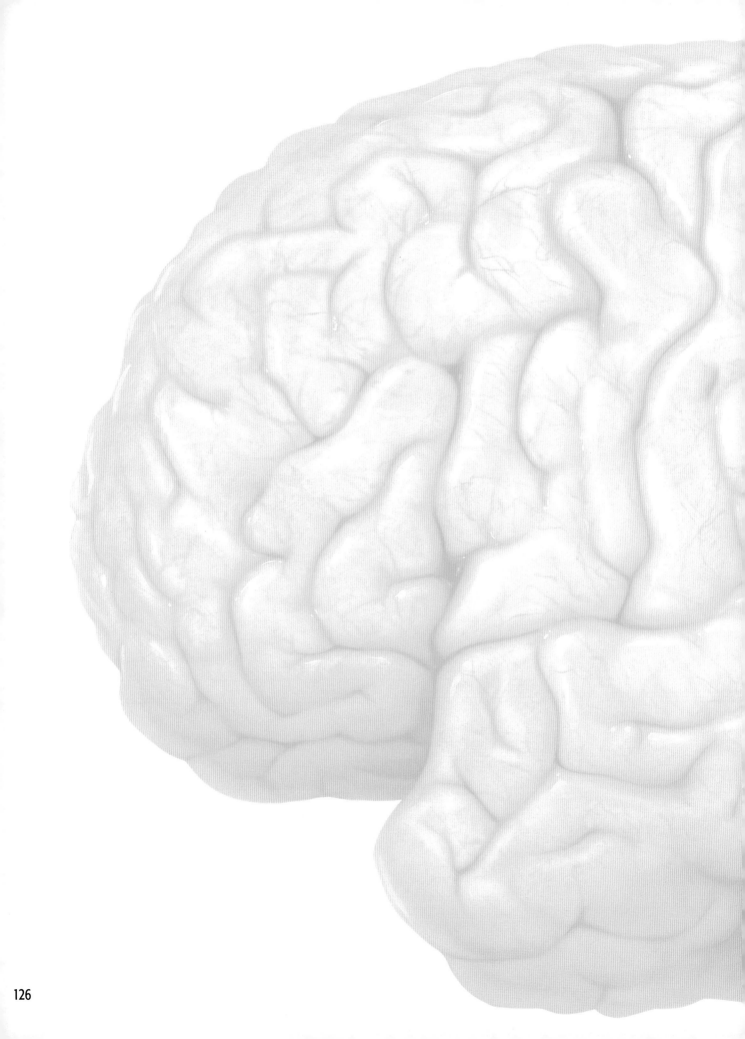

The Nervous System

The Nervous System

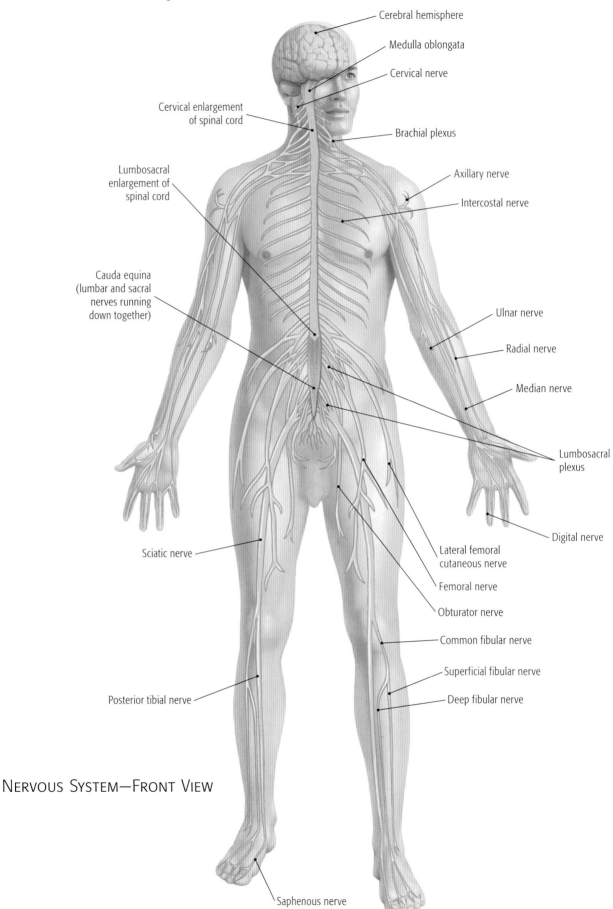

Cerebral hemisphere

Medulla oblongata

Cervical nerve

Cervical enlargement of spinal cord

Brachial plexus

Lumbosacral enlargement of spinal cord

Axillary nerve

Intercostal nerve

Cauda equina (lumbar and sacral nerves running down together)

Ulnar nerve

Radial nerve

Median nerve

Lumbosacral plexus

Digital nerve

Sciatic nerve

Lateral femoral cutaneous nerve

Femoral nerve

Obturator nerve

Common fibular nerve

Superficial fibular nerve

Posterior tibial nerve

Deep fibular nerve

Saphenous nerve

NERVOUS SYSTEM—FRONT VIEW

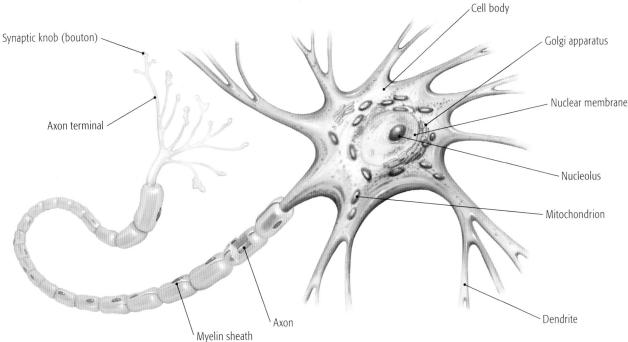

Synaptic knob (bouton)

Axon terminal

Cell body

Golgi apparatus

Nuclear membrane

Nucleolus

Mitochondrion

Dendrite

Myelin sheath

Axon

NEURON

Neurons are specialized cells that conduct nerve impulses. Each neuron has three main parts: a cell body, several branching dendrites that carry impulses to the cell body, and an axon that conveys impulses away from the cell body.

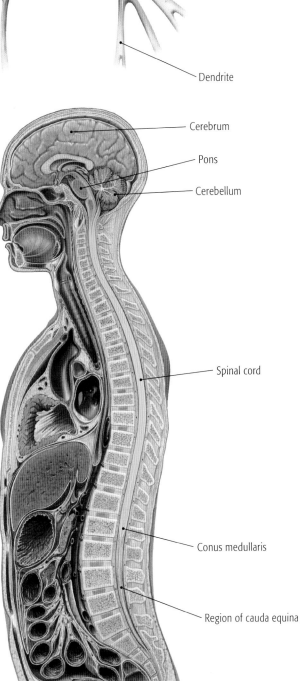

Cerebrum

Pons

Cerebellum

Spinal cord

Conus medullaris

Region of cauda equina

CENTRAL NERVOUS SYSTEM— CROSS-SECTIONAL VIEW

The central nervous system (CNS) comprises the brain and spinal cord. Nerves connect the CNS to peripheral regions such as the muscles, skin, and internal organs. Most nerve cells of the autonomic nervous system (which controls involuntary body functions) are found peripherally, but some are located in the CNS.

The Brain

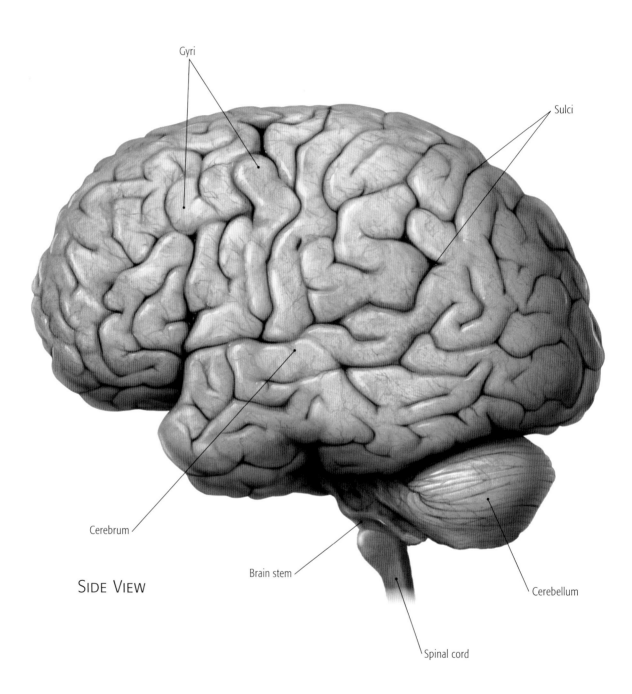

Gyri

Sulci

Cerebrum

Brain stem

Cerebellum

Spinal cord

SIDE VIEW

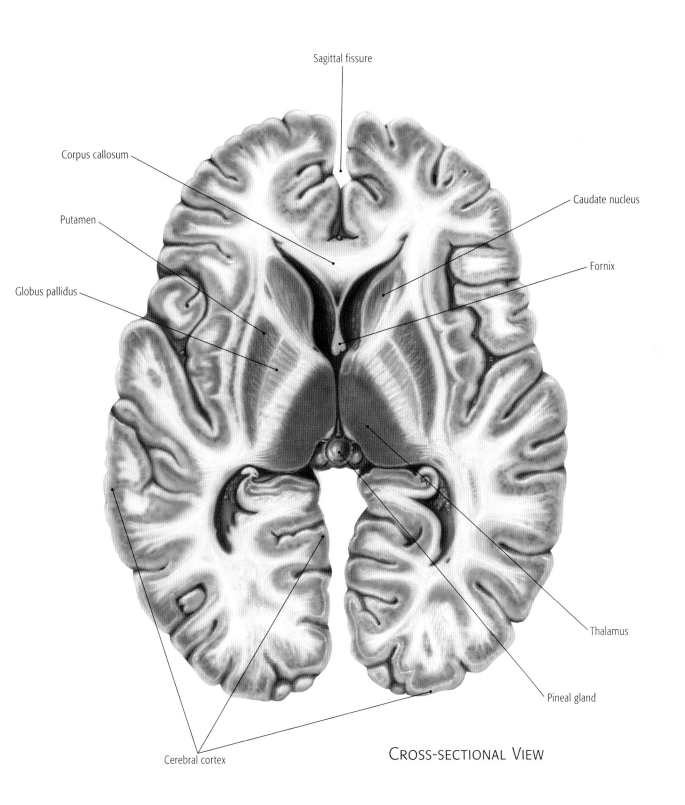

Sagittal fissure

Corpus callosum

Putamen

Globus pallidus

Caudate nucleus

Fornix

Thalamus

Pineal gland

Cerebral cortex

CROSS-SECTIONAL VIEW

The Brain

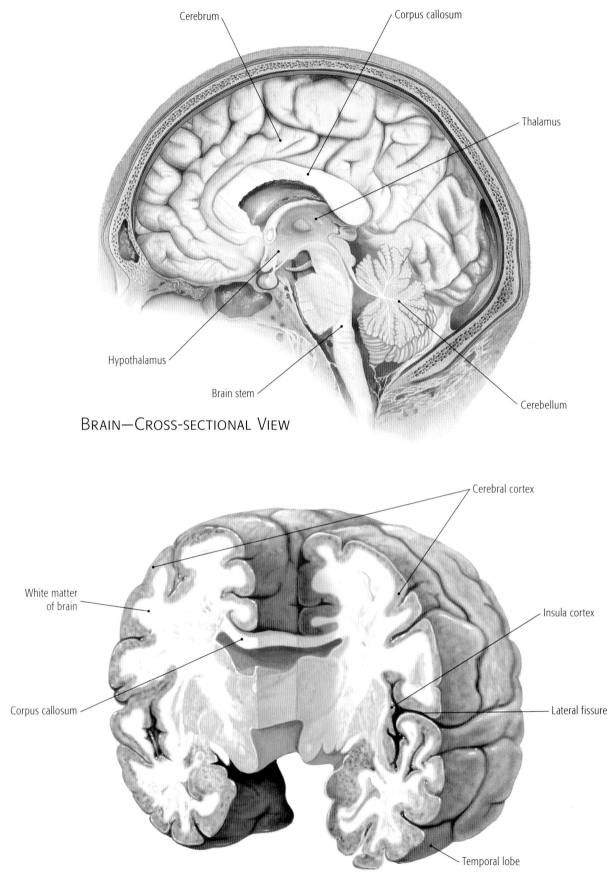

Cerebrum

Corpus callosum

Thalamus

Hypothalamus

Brain stem

Cerebellum

BRAIN—CROSS-SECTIONAL VIEW

Cerebral cortex

White matter of brain

Insula cortex

Corpus callosum

Lateral fissure

Temporal lobe

CEREBRAL CORTEX—CROSS-SECTIONAL VIEW

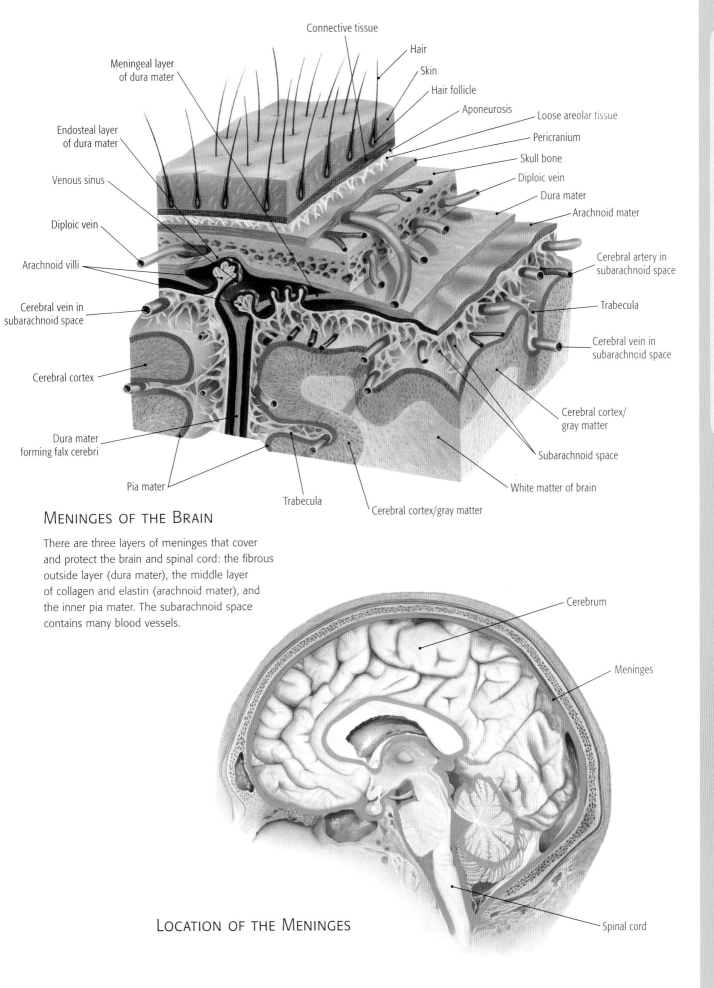

Connective tissue

Hair

Skin

Hair follicle

Aponeurosis

Loose areolar tissue

Pericranium

Skull bone

Diploic vein

Dura mater

Arachnoid mater

Meningeal layer of dura mater

Endosteal layer of dura mater

Venous sinus

Diploic vein

Arachnoid villi

Cerebral vein in subarachnoid space

Cerebral cortex

Dura mater forming falx cerebri

Pia mater

Trabecula

Cerebral cortex/gray matter

Cerebral artery in subarachnoid space

Trabecula

Cerebral vein in subarachnoid space

Cerebral cortex/gray matter

Subarachnoid space

White matter of brain

Meninges of the Brain

There are three layers of meninges that cover and protect the brain and spinal cord: the fibrous outside layer (dura mater), the middle layer of collagen and elastin (arachnoid mater), and the inner pia mater. The subarachnoid space contains many blood vessels.

Cerebrum

Meninges

Spinal cord

Location of the Meninges

Brain Functions

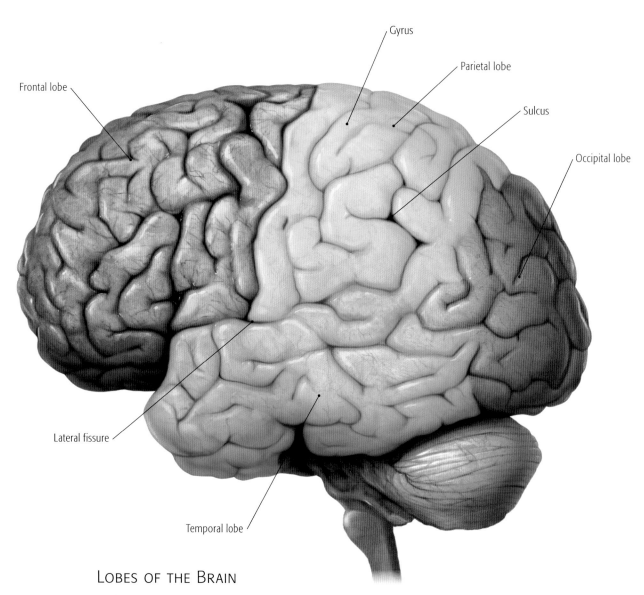

Gyrus

Parietal lobe

Sulcus

Occipital lobe

Frontal lobe

Lateral fissure

Temporal lobe

Lobes of the Brain

A ridge on the surface of the cerebral cortex is called a gyrus. A groove is called a sulcus if shallow, or a fissure if deep. Fissures and sulci divide the cortex into separate areas called lobes.

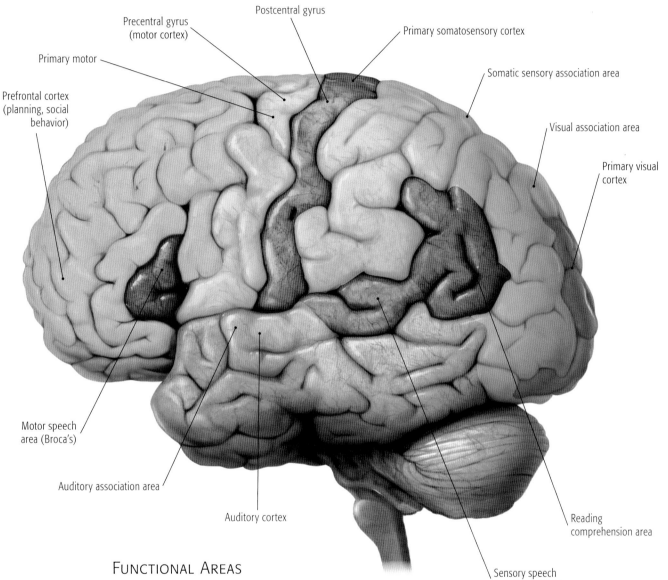

Precentral gyrus
(motor cortex)

Postcentral gyrus

Primary somatosensory cortex

Primary motor

Somatic sensory association area

Prefrontal cortex
(planning, social
behavior)

Visual association area

Primary visual
cortex

Motor speech
area (Broca's)

Auditory association area

Auditory cortex

Reading
comprehension area

Sensory speech
area (Wernicke's)

FUNCTIONAL AREAS

Particular regions of the cerebral cortex
are associated with certain functions. For
example, the precentral gyrus is associated
with the voluntary control of skeletal muscles,
while the postcentral gyrus is associated with
sensations from the skin, muscles, and joints
(somatosensory function).

Brain Functions

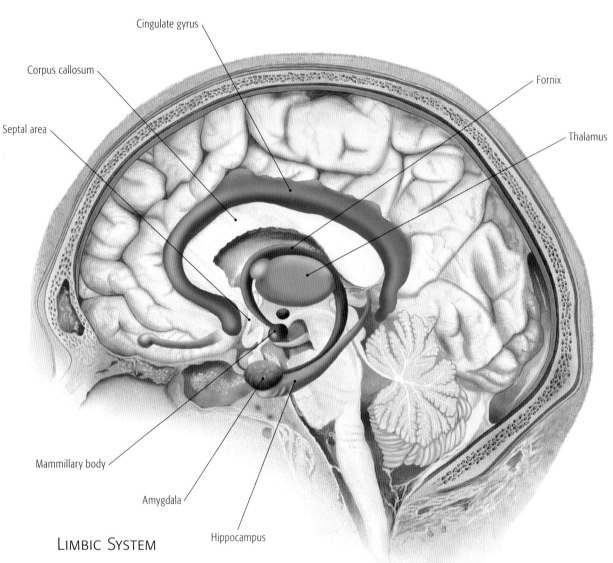

Cingulate gyrus

Corpus callosum

Septal area

Fornix

Thalamus

Mammillary body

Amygdala

Hippocampus

LIMBIC SYSTEM

This "system" refers to a group of elements in the brain. These structures are involved in behaviors associated with survival, such as feeding, defense, and reproduction, and also govern emotional states and memory storage.

Interventricular foramen

Subarachnoid space

Cerebral aqueduct

Left and right lateral ventricles

Posterior horn

Third ventricle

Anterior horn

Interthalamic adhesion

Inferior horn

Fourth ventricle

BRAIN VENTRICLES

The ventricles of the brain contain cerebrospinal fluid that acts as a shock absorber, cushioning the brain from mechanical forces. The ventricles connect via passageways (foramina and aqueducts) and with the space surrounding the outside of the brain (subarachnoid space).

Brain Functions

ORGANIZATION OF THE MOTOR AND SENSORY AREAS OF THE CEREBRAL CORTEX

Motor activity

Sensory activity

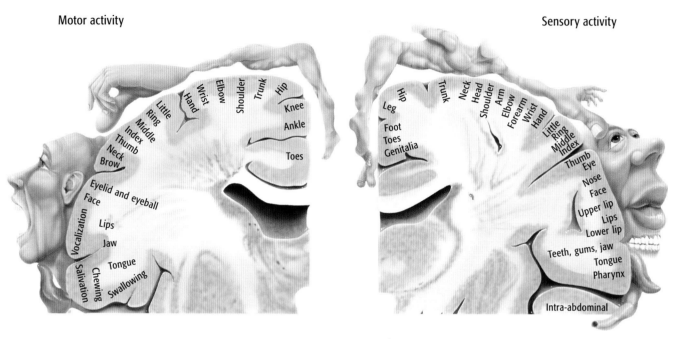

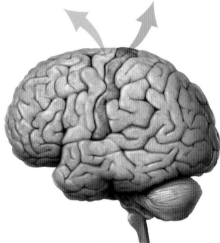

The size of the body part reflects the proportion of the precentral gyrus involved in motor activity in that specific area of the body (top left), and the proportion of the postcentral gyrus involved in sensory activity in that specific area of the body (top right).

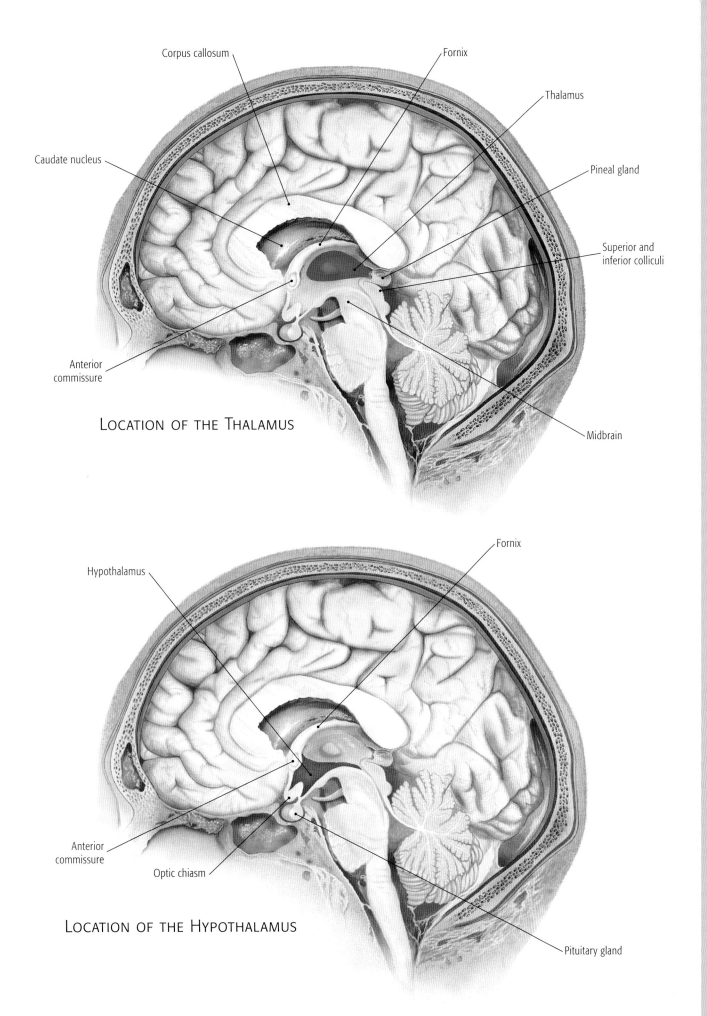

Corpus callosum

Fornix

Thalamus

Pineal gland

Caudate nucleus

Superior and
inferior colliculi

Anterior
commissure

Midbrain

LOCATION OF THE THALAMUS

Fornix

Hypothalamus

Anterior
commissure

Optic chiasm

LOCATION OF THE HYPOTHALAMUS

Pituitary gland

Cranial Nerves and Brain Stem

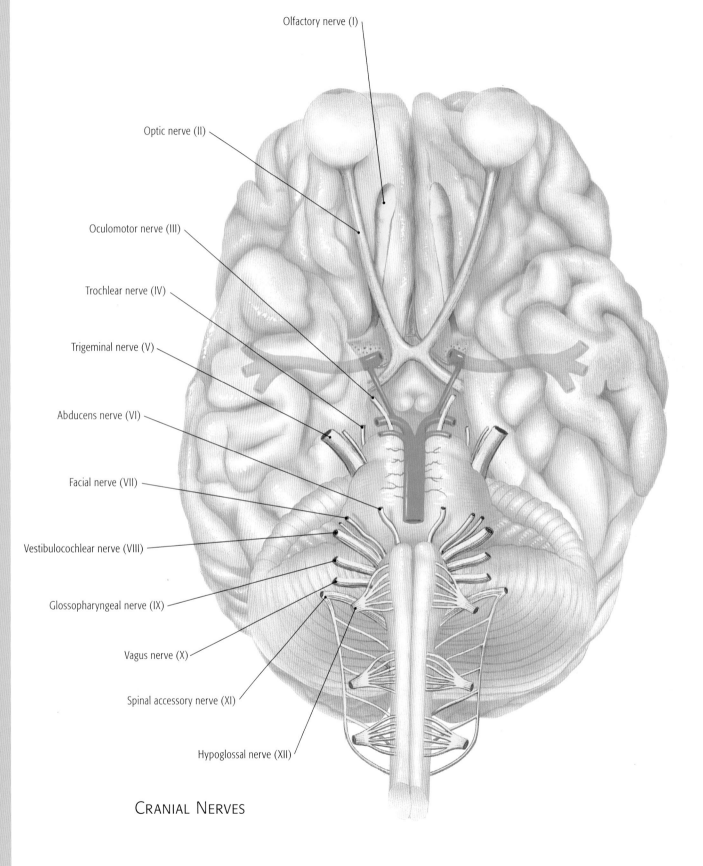

Olfactory nerve (I)

Optic nerve (II)

Oculomotor nerve (III)

Trochlear nerve (IV)

Trigeminal nerve (V)

Abducens nerve (VI)

Facial nerve (VII)

Vestibulocochlear nerve (VIII)

Glossopharyngeal nerve (IX)

Vagus nerve (X)

Spinal accessory nerve (XI)

Hypoglossal nerve (XII)

CRANIAL NERVES

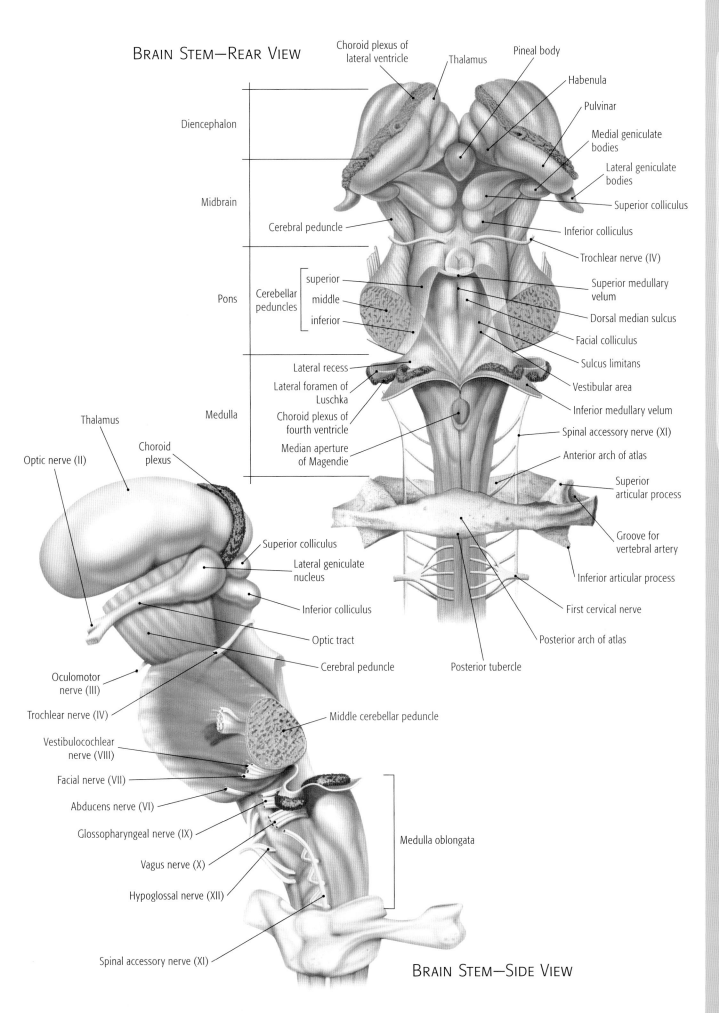

BRAIN STEM—REAR VIEW

Choroid plexus of lateral ventricle
Thalamus
Pineal body
Habenula
Pulvinar
Medial geniculate bodies
Lateral geniculate bodies
Superior colliculus
Inferior colliculus
Trochlear nerve (IV)

Diencephalon

Midbrain

Cerebral peduncle

Superior medullary velum
Dorsal median sulcus
Facial colliculus
Sulcus limitans
Vestibular area
Inferior medullary velum
Spinal accessory nerve (XI)
Anterior arch of atlas
Superior articular process
Groove for vertebral artery
Inferior articular process
First cervical nerve
Posterior arch of atlas

Pons

Cerebellar peduncles
superior
middle
inferior

Medulla

Lateral recess
Lateral foramen of Luschka
Choroid plexus of fourth ventricle
Median aperture of Magendie

Posterior tubercle

Thalamus

Optic nerve (II)

Choroid plexus

Superior colliculus
Lateral geniculate nucleus
Inferior colliculus
Optic tract
Cerebral peduncle

Oculomotor nerve (III)

Trochlear nerve (IV)

Vestibulocochlear nerve (VIII)

Facial nerve (VII)

Abducens nerve (VI)

Glossopharyngeal nerve (IX)

Vagus nerve (X)

Hypoglossal nerve (XII)

Middle cerebellar peduncle

Medulla oblongata

Spinal accessory nerve (XI)

BRAIN STEM—SIDE VIEW

141

Spinal Cord

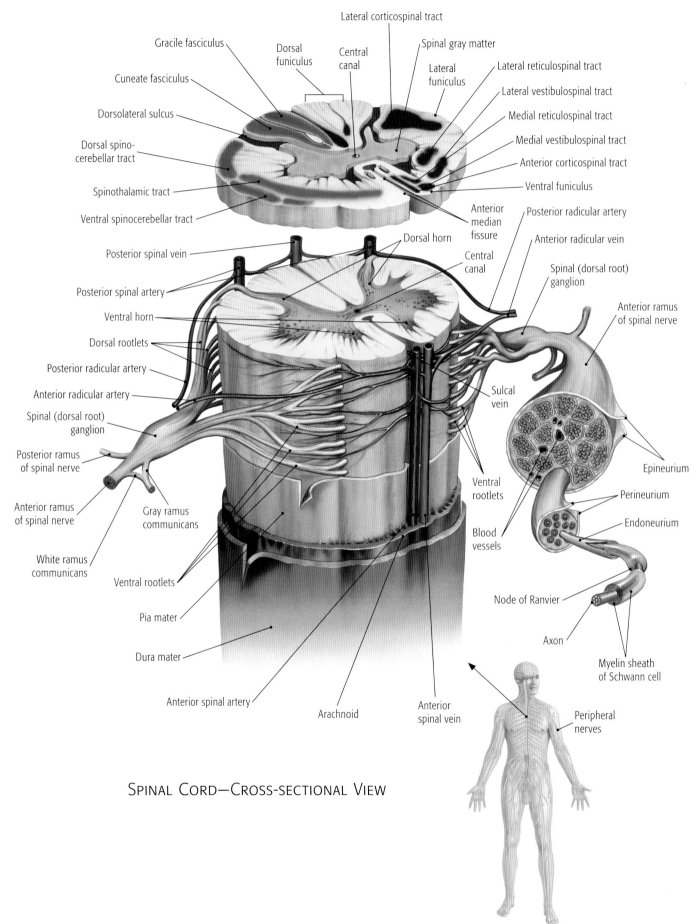

Lateral corticospinal tract

Gracile fasciculus

Dorsal funiculus

Central canal

Spinal gray matter

Lateral funiculus

Lateral reticulospinal tract

Cuneate fasciculus

Lateral vestibulospinal tract

Dorsolateral sulcus

Medial reticulospinal tract

Dorsal spino-cerebellar tract

Medial vestibulospinal tract

Anterior corticospinal tract

Spinothalamic tract

Ventral funiculus

Ventral spinocerebellar tract

Anterior median fissure

Posterior radicular artery

Dorsal horn

Anterior radicular vein

Posterior spinal vein

Central canal

Spinal (dorsal root) ganglion

Posterior spinal artery

Anterior ramus of spinal nerve

Ventral horn

Dorsal rootlets

Posterior radicular artery

Anterior radicular artery

Sulcal vein

Spinal (dorsal root) ganglion

Posterior ramus of spinal nerve

Epineurium

Anterior ramus of spinal nerve

Gray ramus communicans

Ventral rootlets

Perineurium

White ramus communicans

Blood vessels

Endoneurium

Ventral rootlets

Pia mater

Node of Ranvier

Axon

Dura mater

Myelin sheath of Schwann cell

Anterior spinal artery

Arachnoid

Anterior spinal vein

Peripheral nerves

SPINAL CORD—CROSS-SECTIONAL VIEW

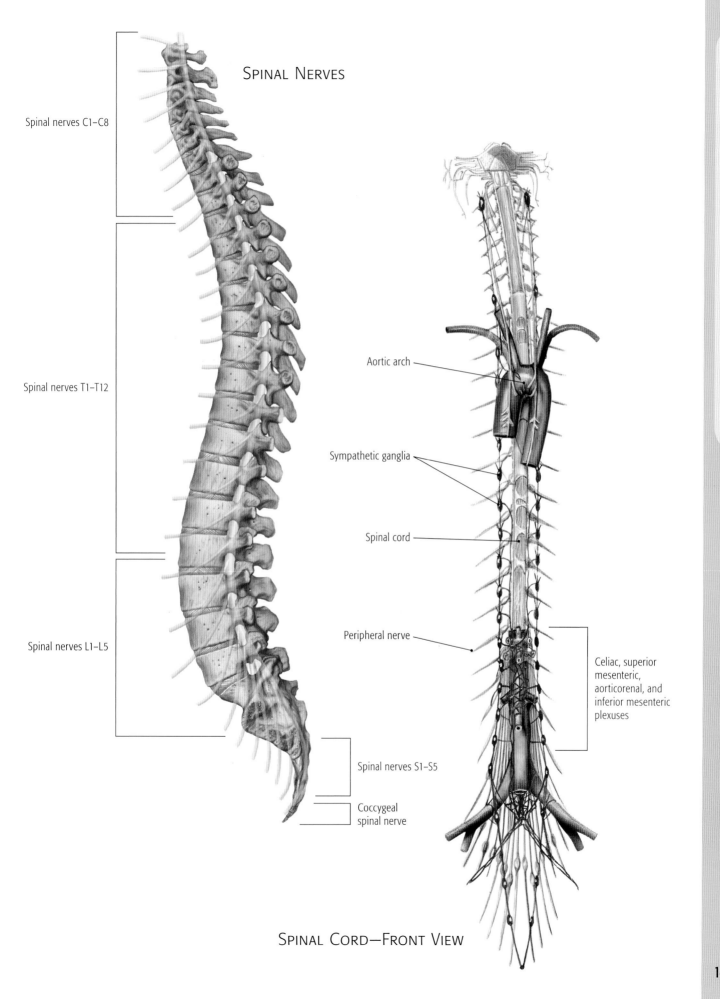

SPINAL NERVES

Spinal nerves C1–C8

Spinal nerves T1–T12

Spinal nerves L1–L5

Spinal nerves S1–S5

Coccygeal spinal nerve

Aortic arch

Sympathetic ganglia

Spinal cord

Peripheral nerve

Celiac, superior mesenteric, aorticorenal, and inferior mesenteric plexuses

SPINAL CORD—FRONT VIEW

Dermatomes

Spinal nerves are numbered and correspond closely to
the spinal vertebrae. Each pair of nerves supplies a specific
dermatome (skin area) of the body. However, there is usually
some overlap between adjacent dermatomes. The skin of the
face is supplied by branches of the trigeminal nerve (cranial
nerves V1, V2, and V3).

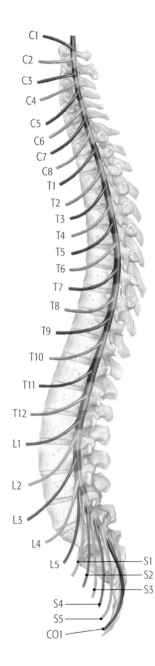

NERVE TO SKIN LINK

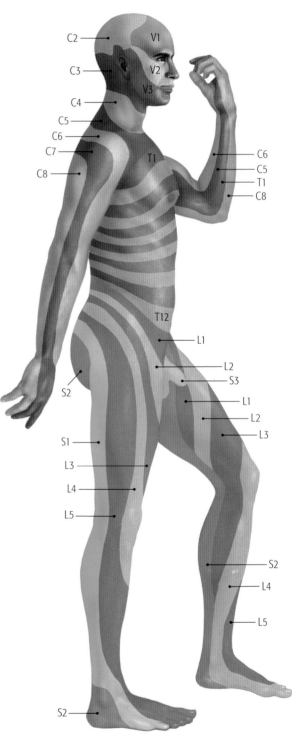

DERMATOMES—SIDE VIEW

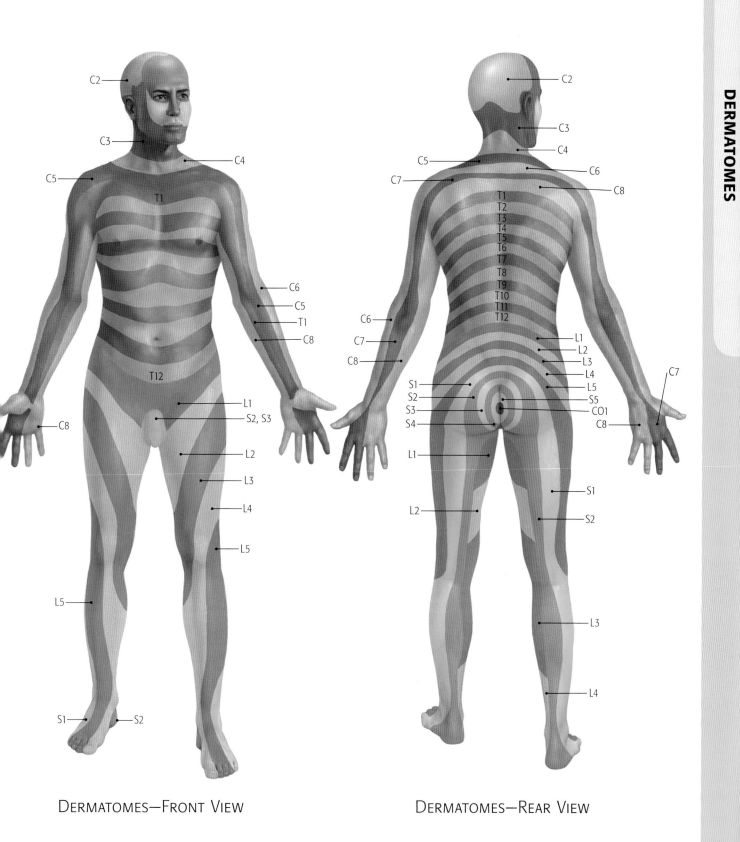

DERMATOMES—FRONT VIEW

DERMATOMES—REAR VIEW

Nerves of the Head, Arms, and Legs

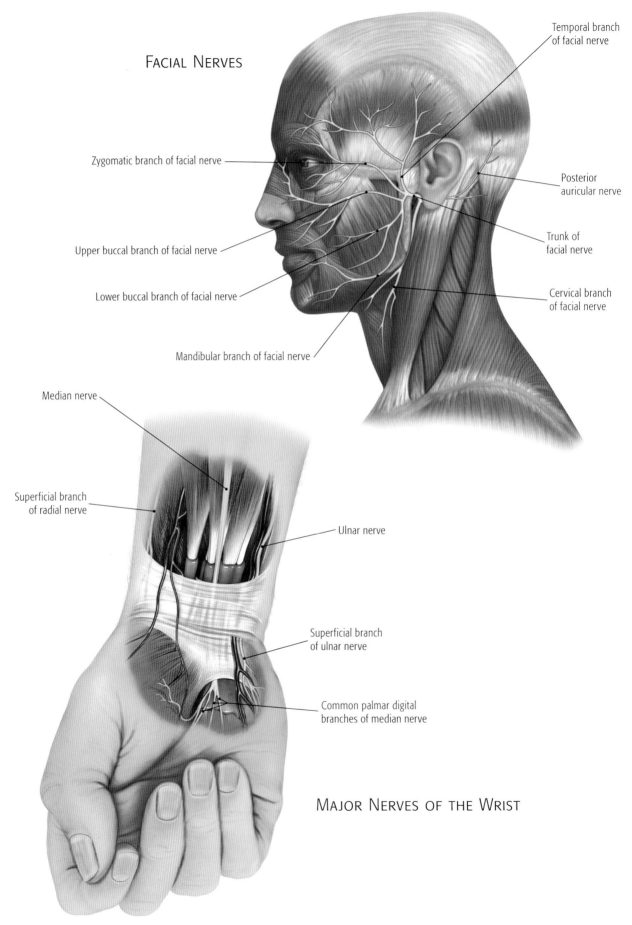

FACIAL NERVES

Temporal branch of facial nerve

Zygomatic branch of facial nerve

Posterior auricular nerve

Upper buccal branch of facial nerve

Trunk of facial nerve

Lower buccal branch of facial nerve

Cervical branch of facial nerve

Mandibular branch of facial nerve

Median nerve

Superficial branch of radial nerve

Ulnar nerve

Superficial branch of ulnar nerve

Common palmar digital branches of median nerve

MAJOR NERVES OF THE WRIST

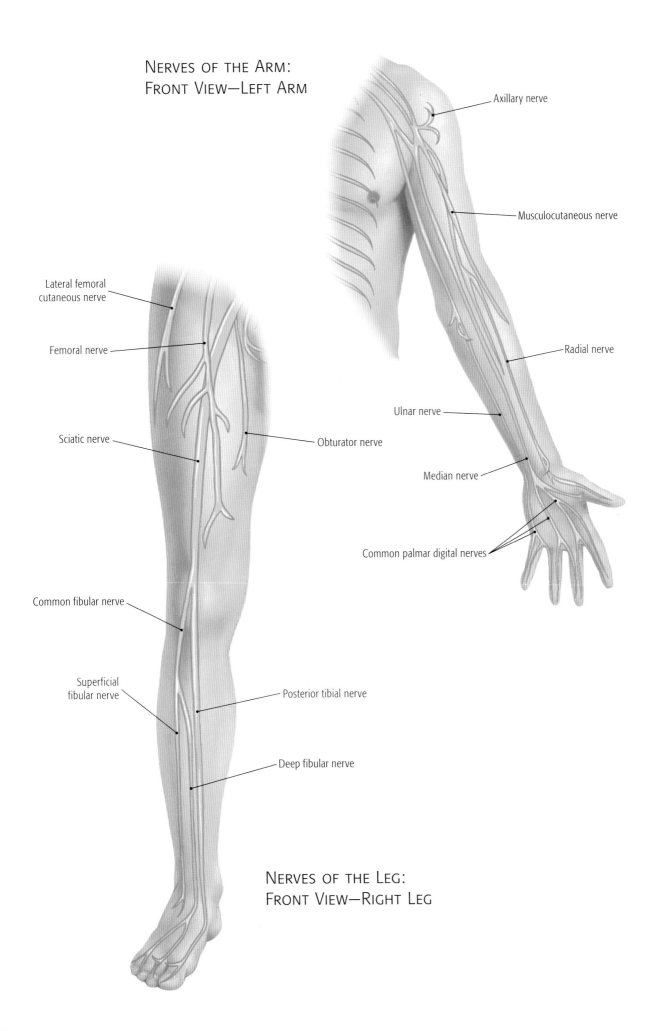

NERVES OF THE ARM:
FRONT VIEW—LEFT ARM

Axillary nerve

Musculocutaneous nerve

Radial nerve

Ulnar nerve

Median nerve

Common palmar digital nerves

Lateral femoral
cutaneous nerve

Femoral nerve

Sciatic nerve

Obturator nerve

Common fibular nerve

Superficial
fibular nerve

Posterior tibial nerve

Deep fibular nerve

NERVES OF THE LEG:
FRONT VIEW—RIGHT LEG

Autonomic Nervous System

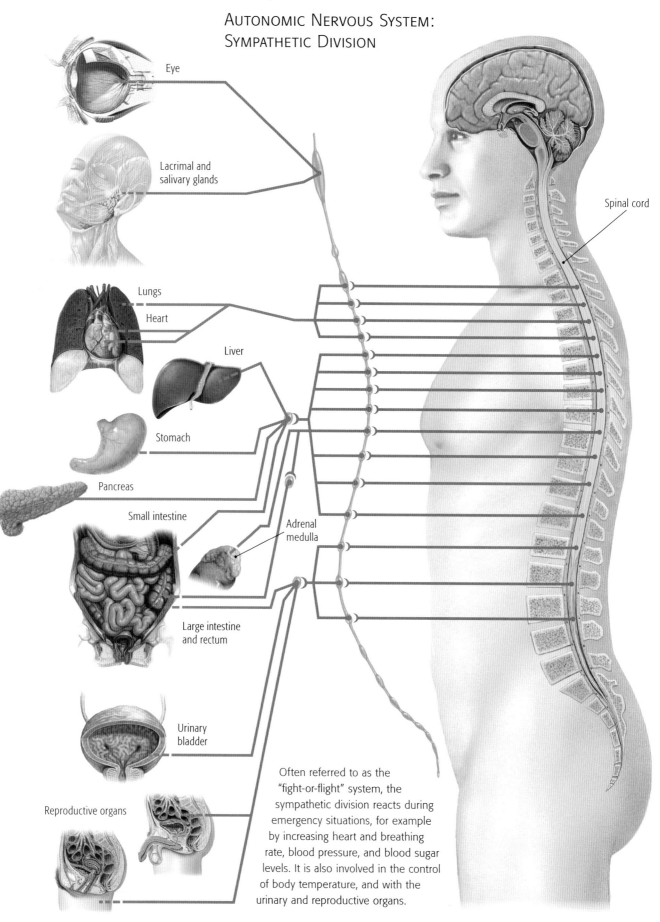

AUTONOMIC NERVOUS SYSTEM: SYMPATHETIC DIVISION

Eye

Lacrimal and salivary glands

Lungs

Heart

Liver

Stomach

Pancreas

Small intestine

Adrenal medulla

Large intestine and rectum

Urinary bladder

Reproductive organs

Spinal cord

Often referred to as the "fight-or-flight" system, the sympathetic division reacts during emergency situations, for example by increasing heart and breathing rate, blood pressure, and blood sugar levels. It is also involved in the control of body temperature, and with the urinary and reproductive organs.

148

AUTONOMIC NERVOUS SYSTEM: PARASYMPATHETIC DIVISION

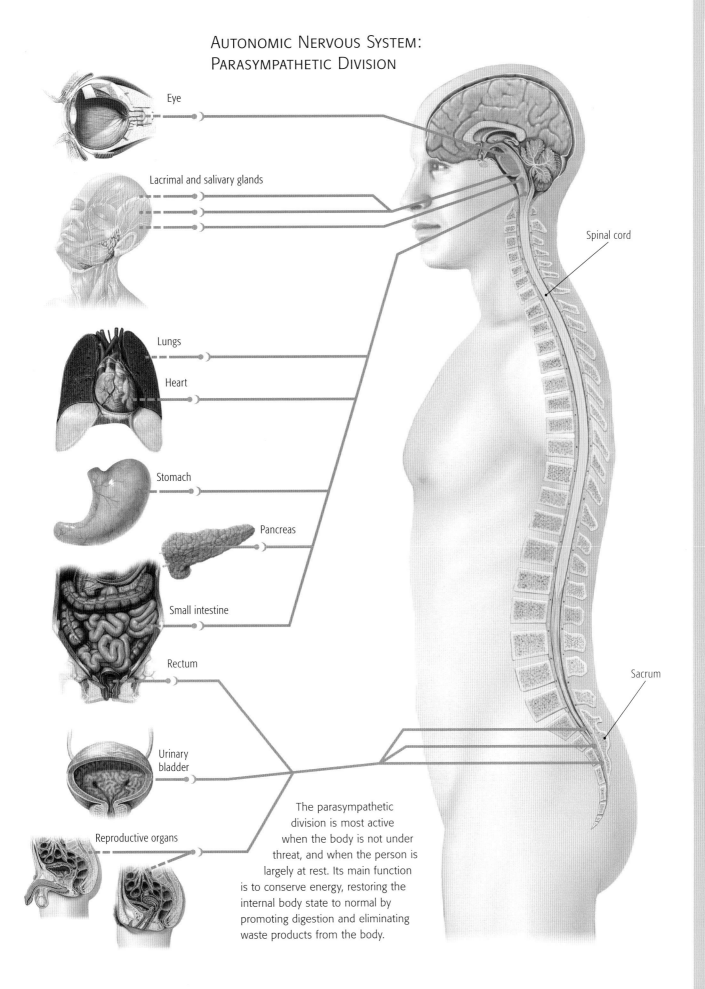

Eye

Lacrimal and salivary glands

Lungs

Heart

Stomach

Pancreas

Small intestine

Rectum

Urinary bladder

Reproductive organs

Spinal cord

Sacrum

The parasympathetic division is most active when the body is not under threat, and when the person is largely at rest. Its main function is to conserve energy, restoring the internal body state to normal by promoting digestion and eliminating waste products from the body.

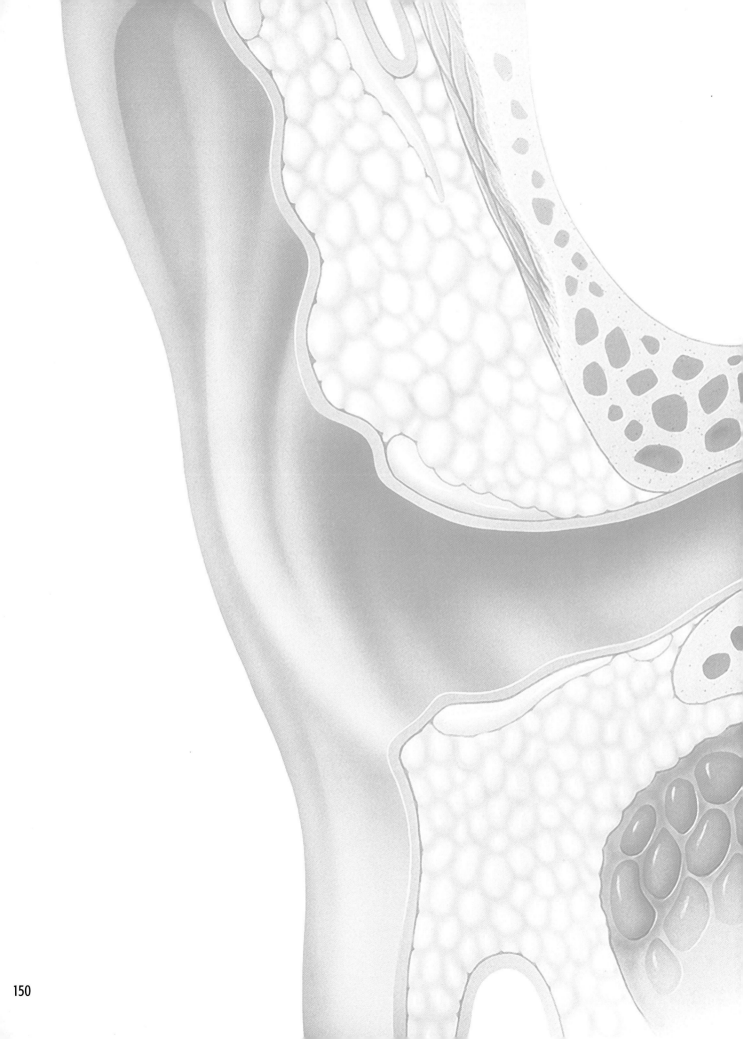

Special Sense Organs

The Eye

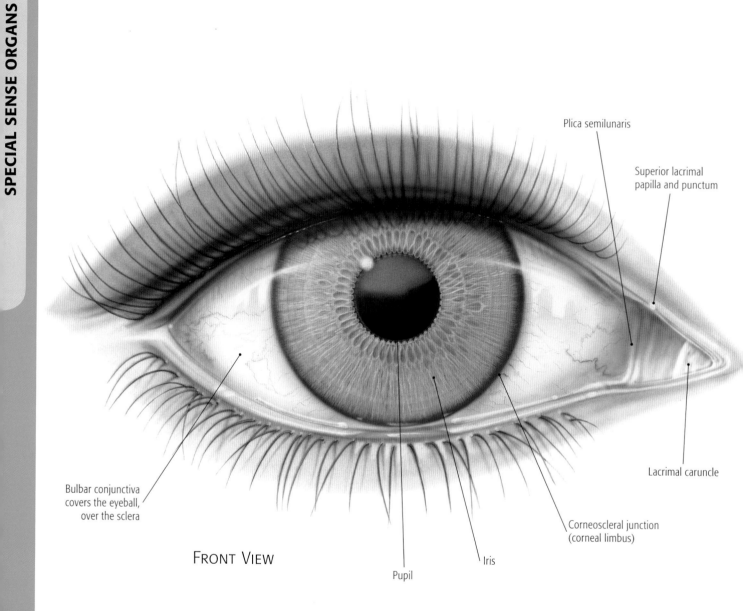

Plica semilunaris

Superior lacrimal
papilla and punctum

Lacrimal caruncle

Bulbar conjunctiva
covers the eyeball,
over the sclera

Corneoscleral junction
(corneal limbus)

FRONT VIEW

Iris

Pupil

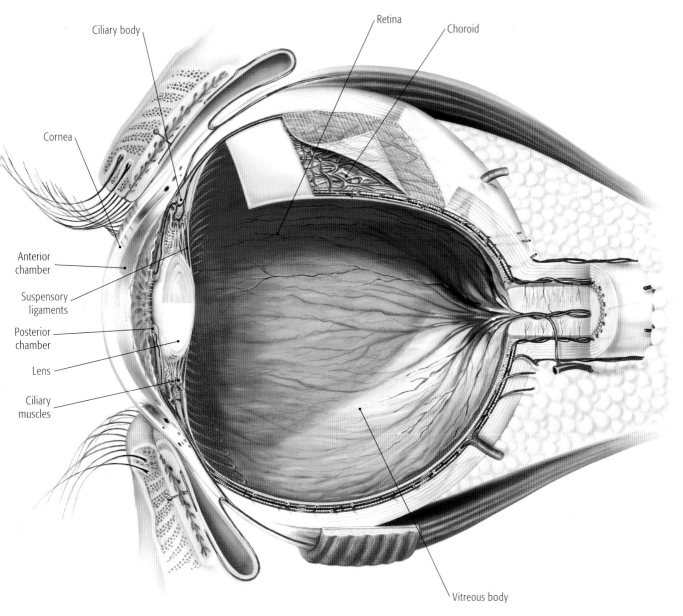

Ciliary body

Retina

Choroid

Cornea

Anterior
chamber

Suspensory
ligaments

Posterior
chamber

Lens

Ciliary
muscles

Vitreous body

SIDE VIEW

Sight

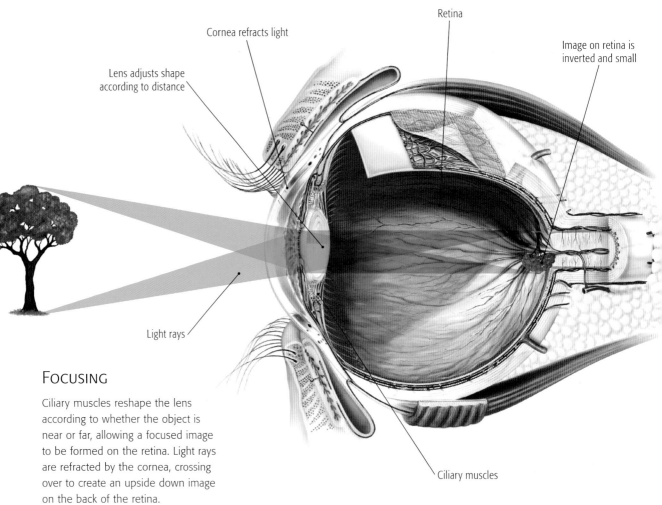

Lens adjusts shape according to distance

Cornea refracts light

Retina

Image on retina is inverted and small

Light rays

Ciliary muscles

FOCUSING

Ciliary muscles reshape the lens according to whether the object is near or far, allowing a focused image to be formed on the retina. Light rays are refracted by the cornea, crossing over to create an upside down image on the back of the retina.

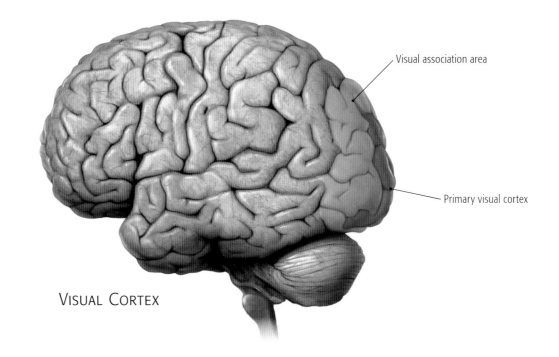

Visual association area

Primary visual cortex

VISUAL CORTEX

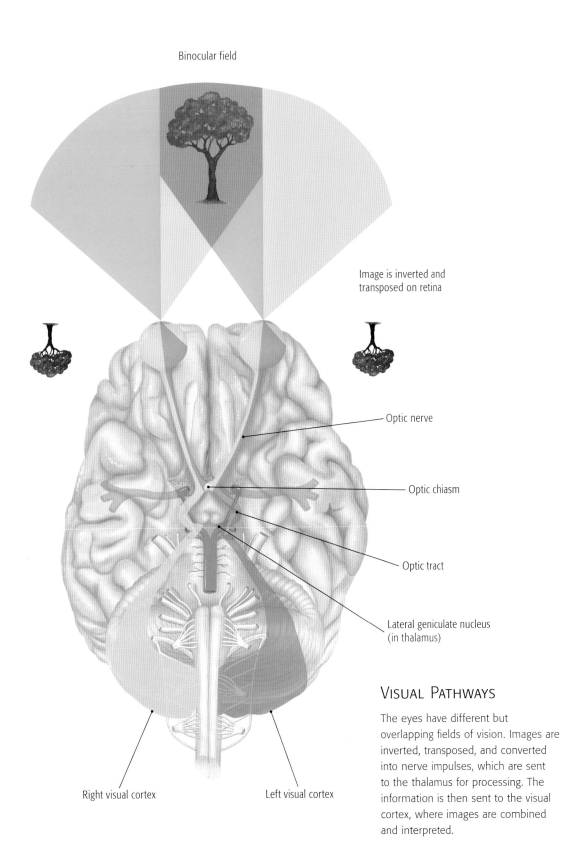

Binocular field

Image is inverted and transposed on retina

Optic nerve

Optic chiasm

Optic tract

Lateral geniculate nucleus (in thalamus)

Right visual cortex

Left visual cortex

VISUAL PATHWAYS

The eyes have different but overlapping fields of vision. Images are inverted, transposed, and converted into nerve impulses, which are sent to the thalamus for processing. The information is then sent to the visual cortex, where images are combined and interpreted.

The Ear

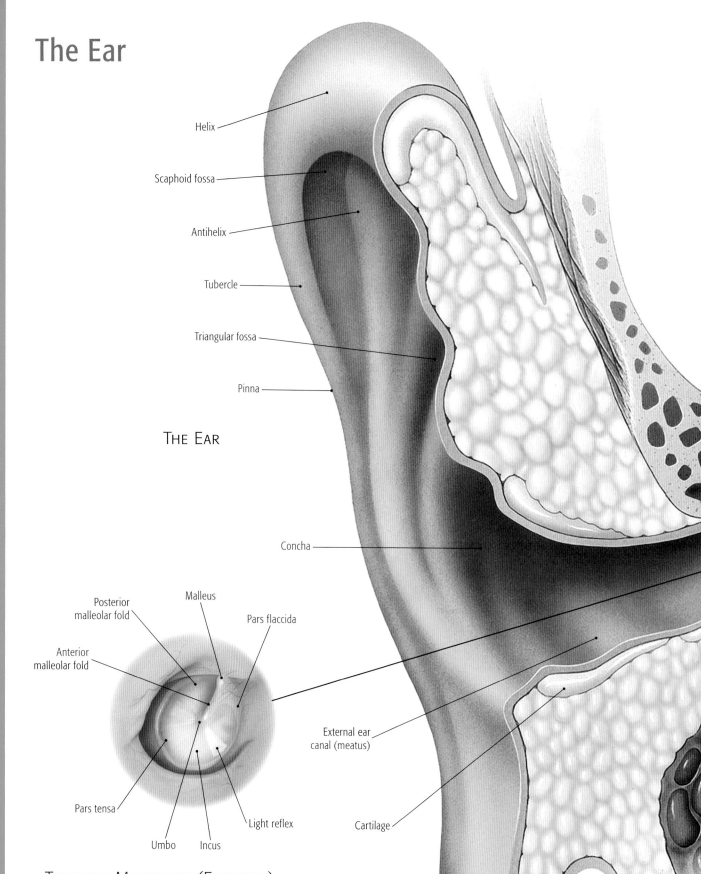

Helix

Scaphoid fossa

Antihelix

Tubercle

Triangular fossa

Pinna

THE EAR

Concha

Posterior malleolar fold

Malleus

Pars flaccida

Anterior malleolar fold

External ear canal (meatus)

Pars tensa

Light reflex

Cartilage

Umbo   Incus

Lobule

TYMPANIC MEMBRANE (EARDRUM)

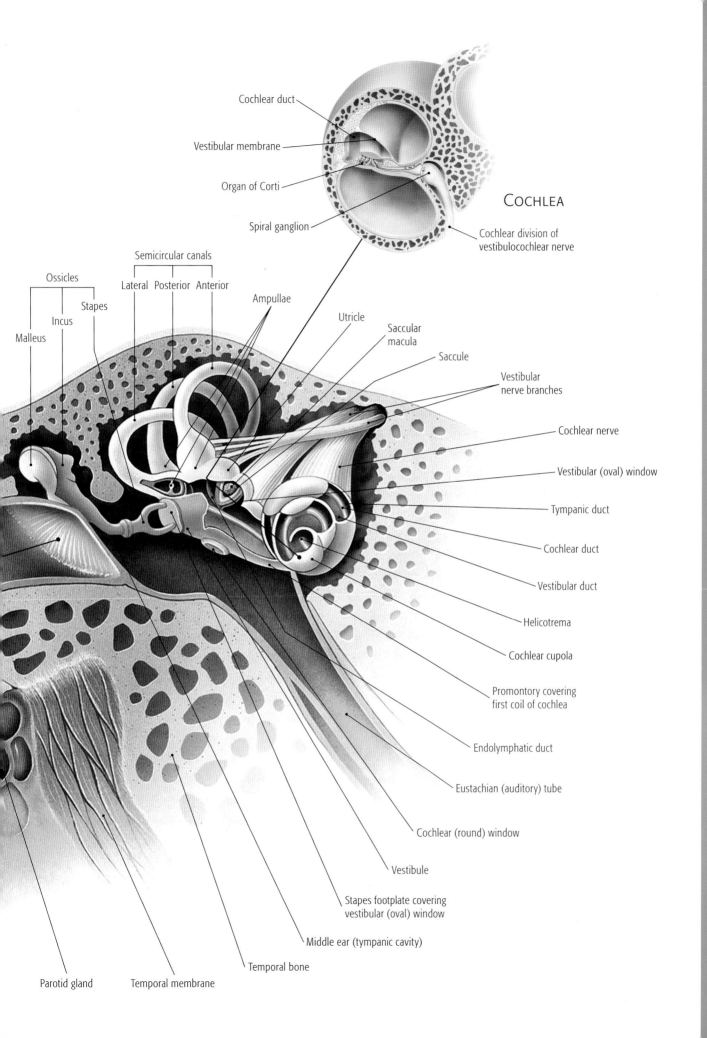

Cochlear duct

Vestibular membrane

Organ of Corti

Spiral ganglion

COCHLEA

Cochlear division of
vestibulocochlear nerve

Ossicles

Stapes

Incus

Malleus

Semicircular canals

Lateral Posterior Anterior

Ampullae

Utricle

Saccular
macula

Saccule

Vestibular
nerve branches

Cochlear nerve

Vestibular (oval) window

Tympanic duct

Cochlear duct

Vestibular duct

Helicotrema

Cochlear cupola

Promontory covering
first coil of cochlea

Endolymphatic duct

Eustachian (auditory) tube

Cochlear (round) window

Vestibule

Stapes footplate covering
vestibular (oval) window

Middle ear (tympanic cavity)

Temporal bone

Parotid gland

Temporal membrane

Hearing and Balance

HEARING: AUDITORY CENTERS

Auditory association area

Auditory cortex

Temporal lobe

Brain stem

HEARING: EAR

Sound waves enter the ear canal and hit the eardrum (a). The eardrum vibrates and passes vibrations to the ossicles (b). The ossicles amplify the sound waves and transmit vibrations to the vestibular (oval) window (c). The vibrations pass into the cochlear spiral, where fluid displaces tiny hairlike receptor cells in the organ of Corti (d). These cells send nerve impulses (e) to the auditory centers in the temporal lobe of the brain, where sounds are interpreted.

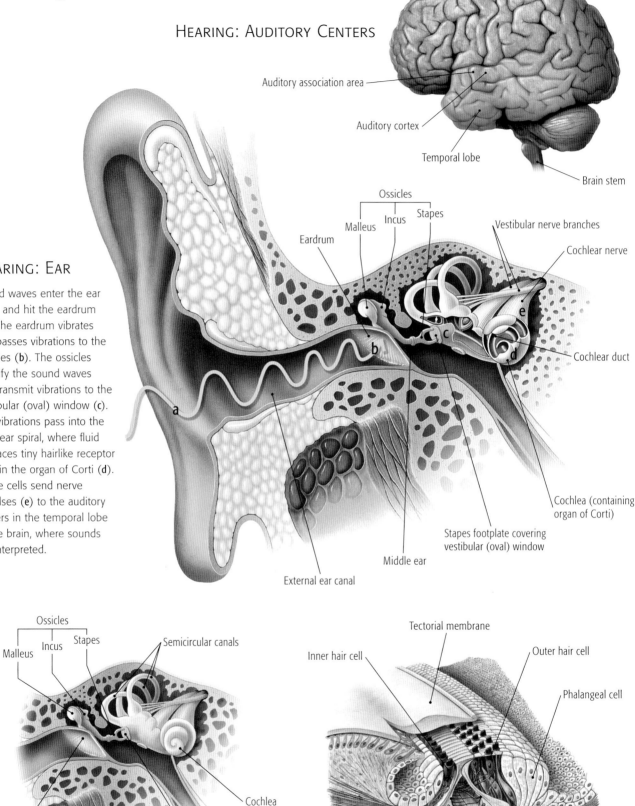

Ossicles

Malleus Incus Stapes

Eardrum

Vestibular nerve branches

Cochlear nerve

Cochlear duct

Cochlea (containing organ of Corti)

Stapes footplate covering vestibular (oval) window

Middle ear

External ear canal

HEARING: AUDITORY OSSICLES

Ossicles

Malleus Incus Stapes

Semicircular canals

Cochlea

Eardrum

Stapes footplate covering vestibular (oval) window

HEARING: ORGAN OF CORTI

Tectorial membrane

Inner hair cell

Outer hair cell

Phalangeal cell

Nerve fibers

Pillar cell

Basilar membrane

BALANCE: BALANCE MECHANISM IN THE EAR

Semicircular canals and otolith organs in the inner ear contain tiny hairs that are sensitive to the body's position. Changes in position cause the hairs to send nerve signals to the brain, which uses this information to help balance the body.

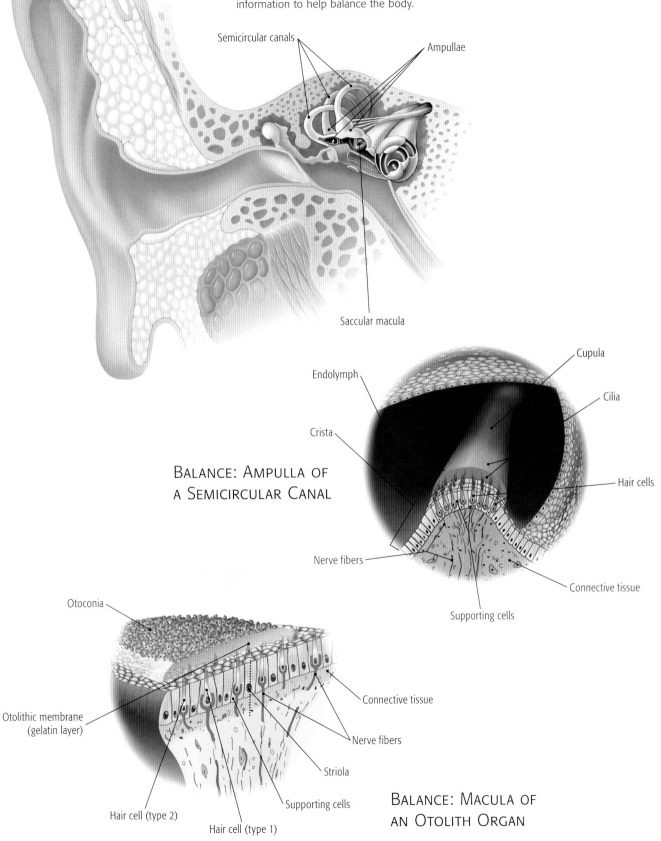

Semicircular canals

Ampullae

Saccular macula

Endolymph

Cupula

Crista

Cilia

BALANCE: AMPULLA OF A SEMICIRCULAR CANAL

Hair cells

Nerve fibers

Connective tissue

Supporting cells

Otoconia

Connective tissue

Otolithic membrane (gelatin layer)

Nerve fibers

Striola

Supporting cells

Hair cell (type 2)

Hair cell (type 1)

BALANCE: MACULA OF AN OTOLITH ORGAN

159

Taste

TASTE PATHWAYS

Taste buds on the tongue and in the throat send nerve impulses via the medulla and thalamus to taste-receiving areas in the parietal lobe, where the taste is identified. The olfactory organs provide additional information vital for interpreting different tastes.

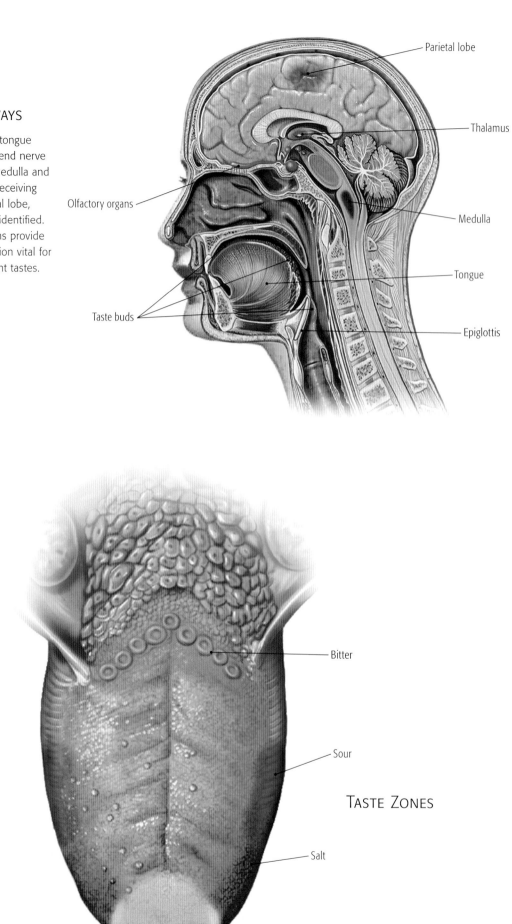

Parietal lobe

Thalamus

Olfactory organs

Medulla

Tongue

Taste buds

Epiglottis

Bitter

Sour

TASTE ZONES

Salt

Sweet

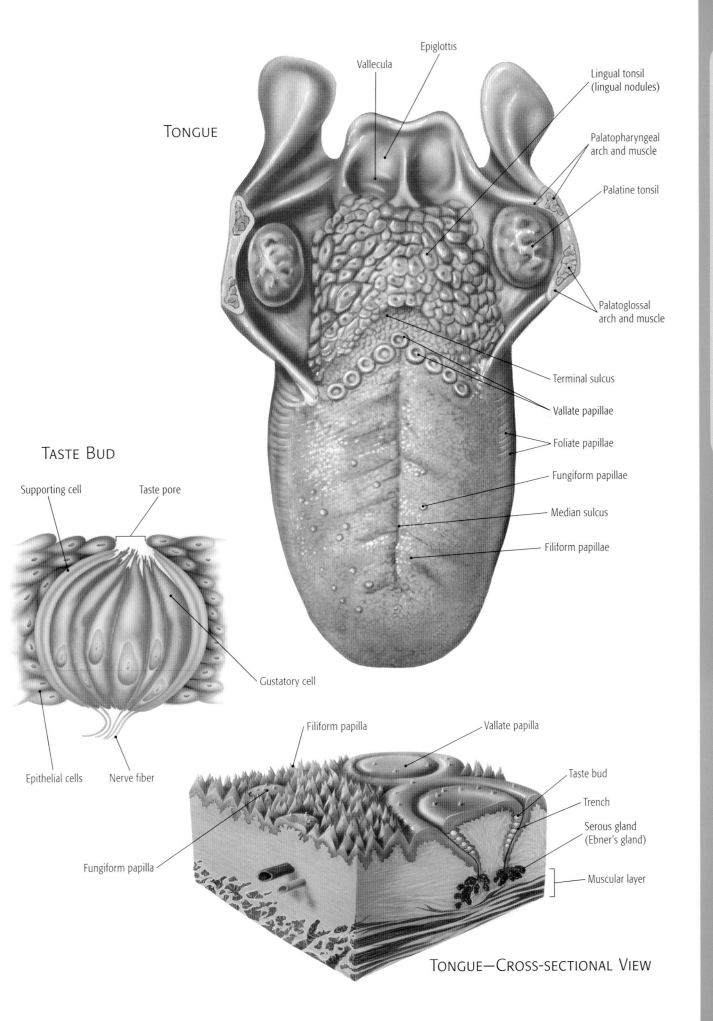

TONGUE

Epiglottis

Vallecula

Lingual tonsil
(lingual nodules)

Palatopharyngeal
arch and muscle

Palatine tonsil

Palatoglossal
arch and muscle

Terminal sulcus

Vallate papillae

Foliate papillae

Fungiform papillae

Median sulcus

Filiform papillae

TASTE BUD

Supporting cell

Taste pore

Gustatory cell

Epithelial cells

Nerve fiber

Filiform papilla

Vallate papilla

Taste bud

Trench

Serous gland
(Ebner's gland)

Muscular layer

Fungiform papilla

TONGUE—CROSS-SECTIONAL VIEW

Smell

OLFACTORY PATHWAY

Odor molecules enter the nostrils and pass into the nasal cavity, where they dissolve in olfactory mucosa in the nasal lining. Receptors send nerve signals via the olfactory bulb to the olfactory center in the brain, where smells are identified.

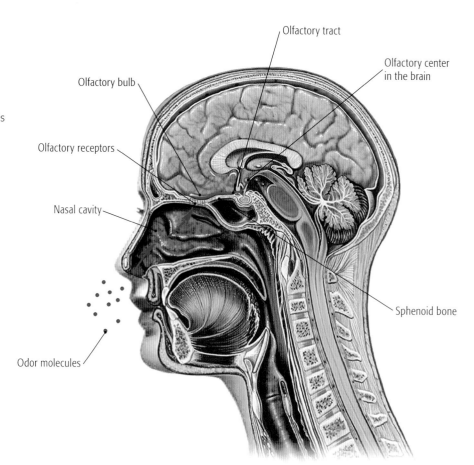

Olfactory tract

Olfactory center in the brain

Olfactory bulb

Olfactory receptors

Nasal cavity

Sphenoid bone

Odor molecules

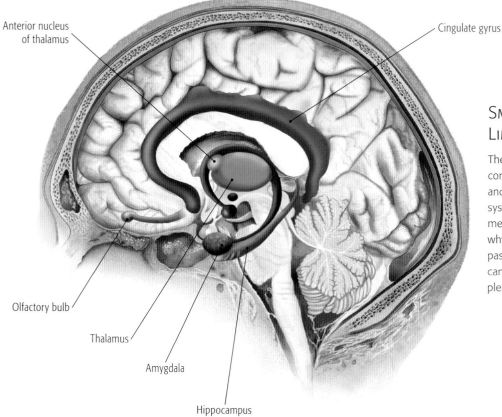

Anterior nucleus of thalamus

Cingulate gyrus

Olfactory bulb

Thalamus

Amygdala

Hippocampus

SMELL AND THE LIMBIC SYSTEM

The olfactory bulb is directly connected to the hippocampus and amygdala in the limbic system, which is important for memory and emotion. This is why smells are evocative of past places and feelings, and can trigger responses like pleasure and fear.

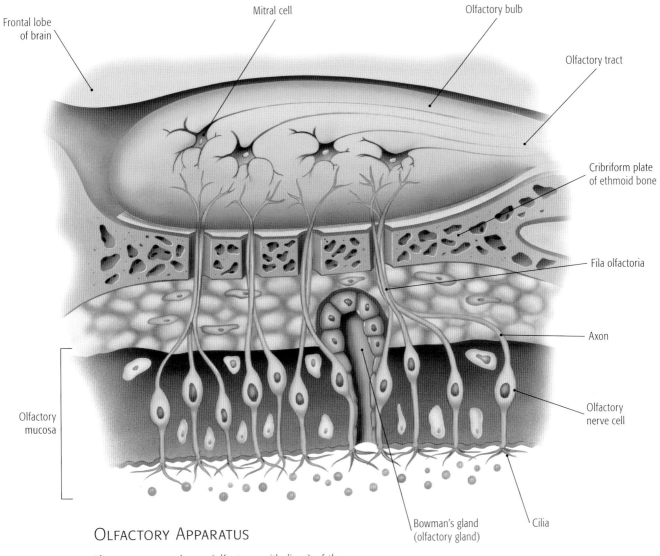

Frontal lobe of brain

Mitral cell

Olfactory bulb

Olfactory tract

Cribriform plate of ethmoid bone

Fila olfactoria

Axon

Olfactory nerve cell

Cilia

Bowman's gland (olfactory gland)

Olfactory mucosa

OLFACTORY APPARATUS

The mucous membrane (olfactory epithelium) of the olfactory receptors contains millions of nerve cells bearing cilia. Odor molecules stimulate the nerve cells to send impulses along the nerve fibers through holes in the cribriform plate of the ethmoid bone to the olfactory bulb.

Pain

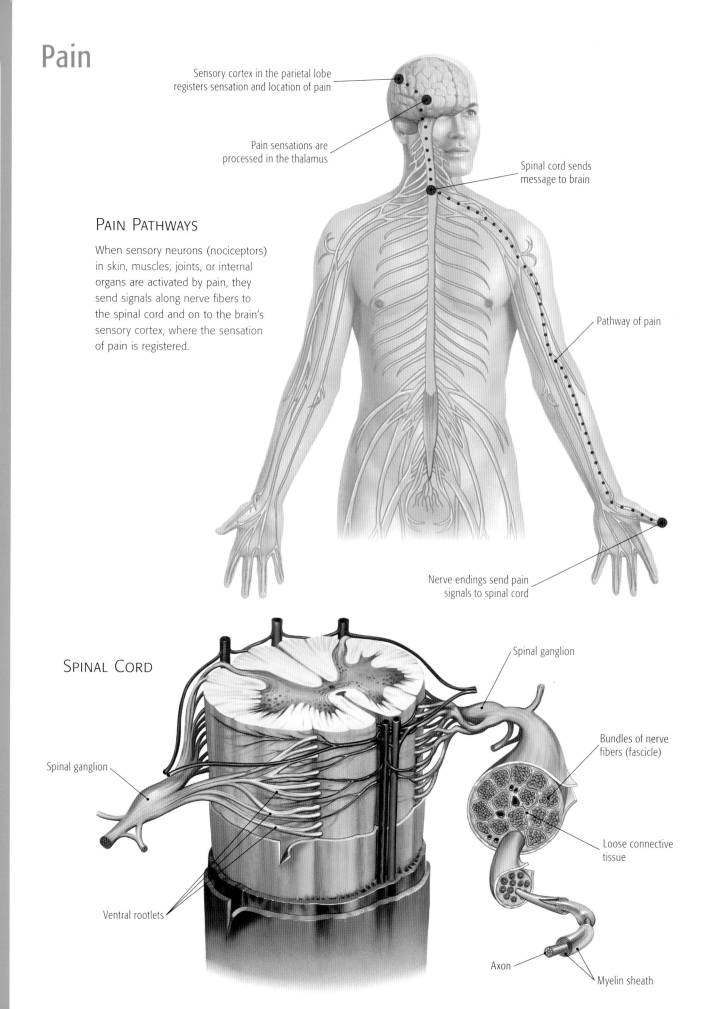

Sensory cortex in the parietal lobe registers sensation and location of pain

Pain sensations are processed in the thalamus

Spinal cord sends message to brain

PAIN PATHWAYS

When sensory neurons (nociceptors) in skin, muscles, joints, or internal organs are activated by pain, they send signals along nerve fibers to the spinal cord and on to the brain's sensory cortex, where the sensation of pain is registered.

Pathway of pain

Nerve endings send pain signals to spinal cord

SPINAL CORD

Spinal ganglion

Spinal ganglion

Bundles of nerve fibers (fascicle)

Loose connective tissue

Ventral rootlets

Axon

Myelin sheath

REFERRED PAIN

The pain from internal organs may be felt on the surface of the skin as well as internally. This is because the skin and internal organs may share the same pain pathways.

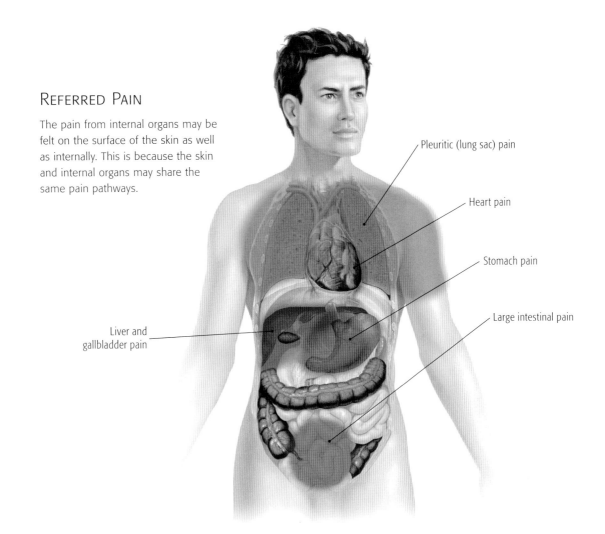

Pleuritic (lung sac) pain

Heart pain

Stomach pain

Large intestinal pain

Liver and gallbladder pain

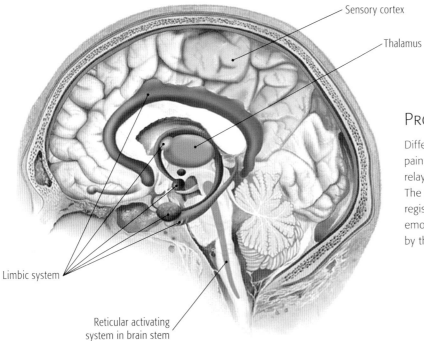

Sensory cortex

Thalamus

Limbic system

Reticular activating system in brain stem

PROCESSING PAIN

Different areas of the brain control pain perception. Pain signals are relayed to the brain via the thalamus. The sensation and location of pain is registered in the sensory cortex, and emotional responses are governed by the limbic system.

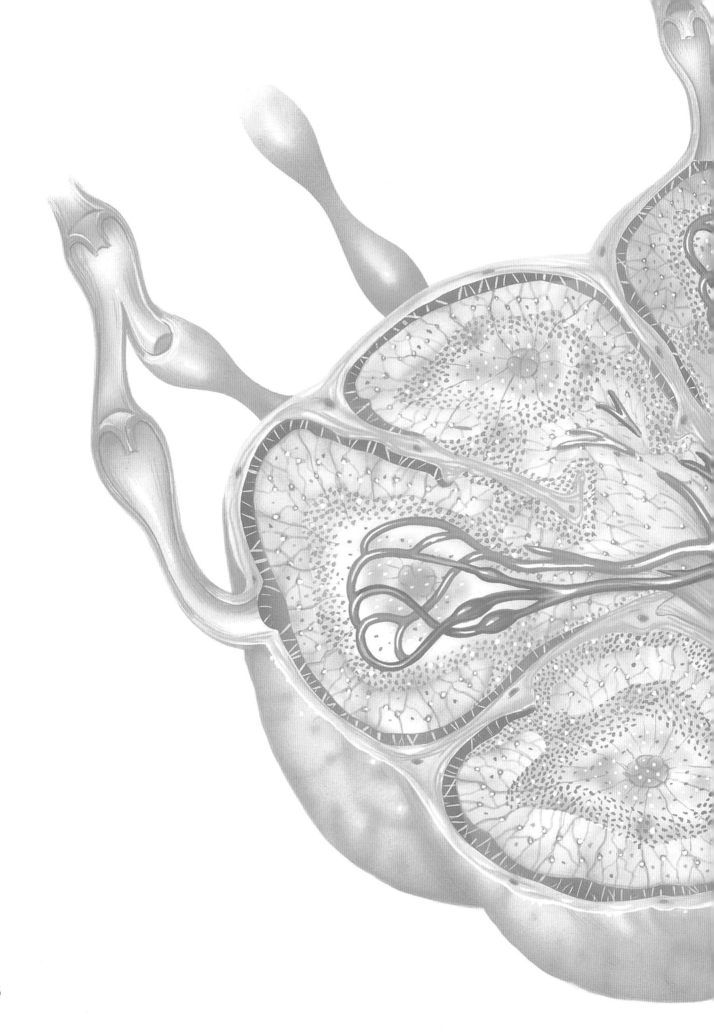

The Lymphatic System

The Lymphatic System

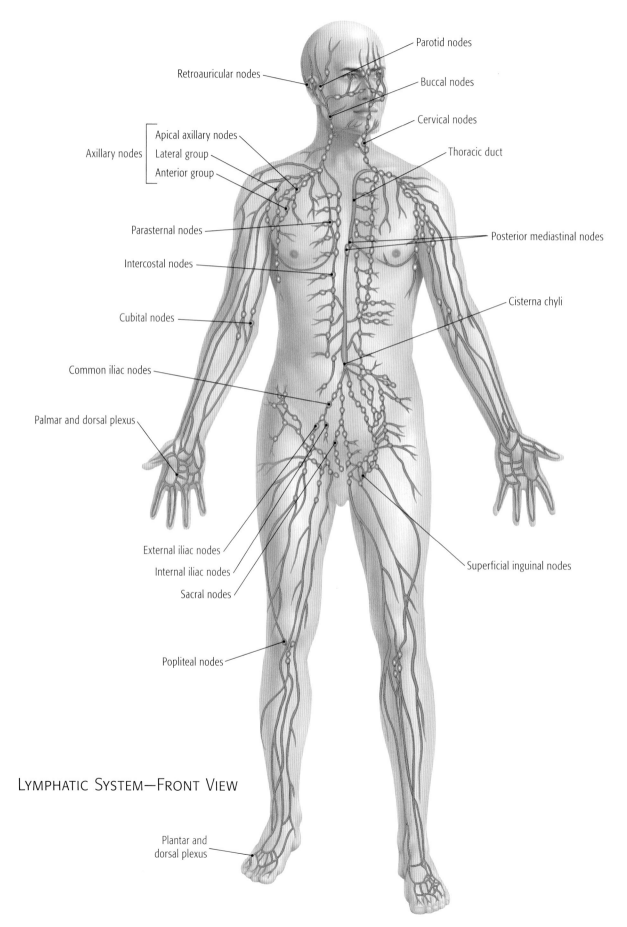

Parotid nodes

Retroauricular nodes

Buccal nodes

Cervical nodes

Axillary nodes
Apical axillary nodes
Lateral group
Anterior group

Thoracic duct

Parasternal nodes

Posterior mediastinal nodes

Intercostal nodes

Cisterna chyli

Cubital nodes

Common iliac nodes

Palmar and dorsal plexus

External iliac nodes

Internal iliac nodes

Sacral nodes

Superficial inguinal nodes

Popliteal nodes

LYMPHATIC SYSTEM—FRONT VIEW

Plantar and
dorsal plexus

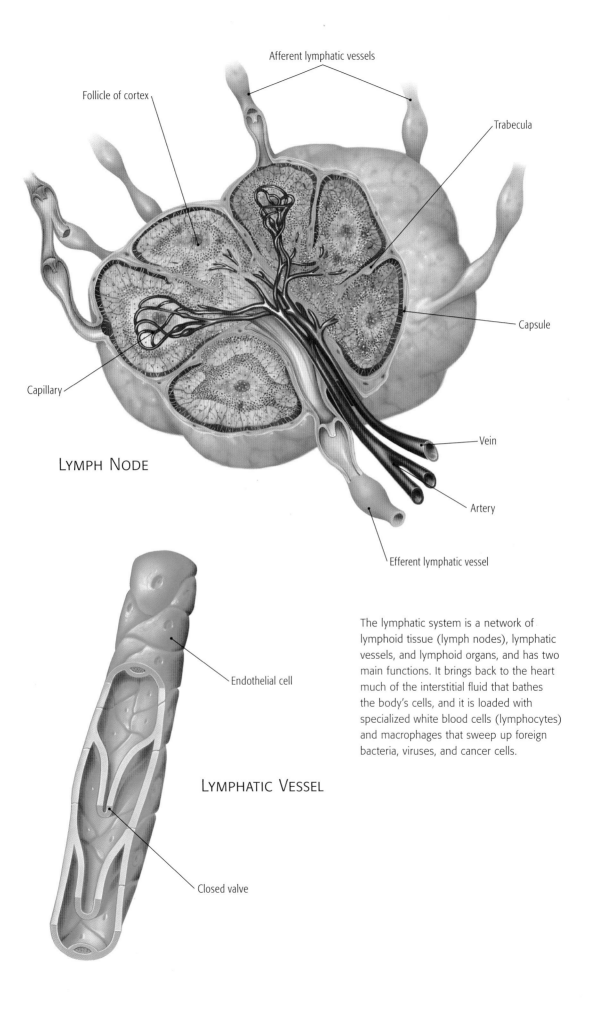

Afferent lymphatic vessels

Follicle of cortex

Trabecula

Capsule

Capillary

Vein

Artery

LYMPH NODE

Efferent lymphatic vessel

Endothelial cell

The lymphatic system is a network of lymphoid tissue (lymph nodes), lymphatic vessels, and lymphoid organs, and has two main functions. It brings back to the heart much of the interstitial fluid that bathes the body's cells, and it is loaded with specialized white blood cells (lymphocytes) and macrophages that sweep up foreign bacteria, viruses, and cancer cells.

LYMPHATIC VESSEL

Closed valve

Lymphoid Organs

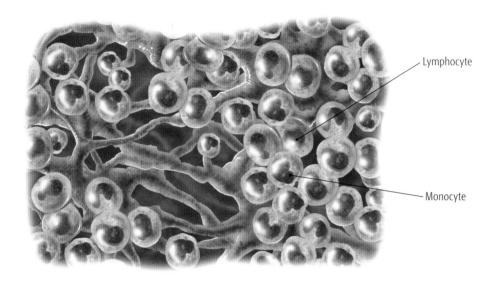

Lymphocyte

Monocyte

LYMPHATIC TISSUE

The spleen is the largest concentration of lymphatic tissue in the body; lymphatic tissue is also found in the lymphatic nodules of the gut and tonsils, and in the linings (mucosa) of the respiratory system, urogenital tract, and digestive tract.

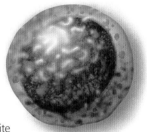

LYMPHOCYTE

A lymphocyte is a type of white blood cell that plays an important role in the immune response. There are several types, including B cells, T cells, and natural killer cells.

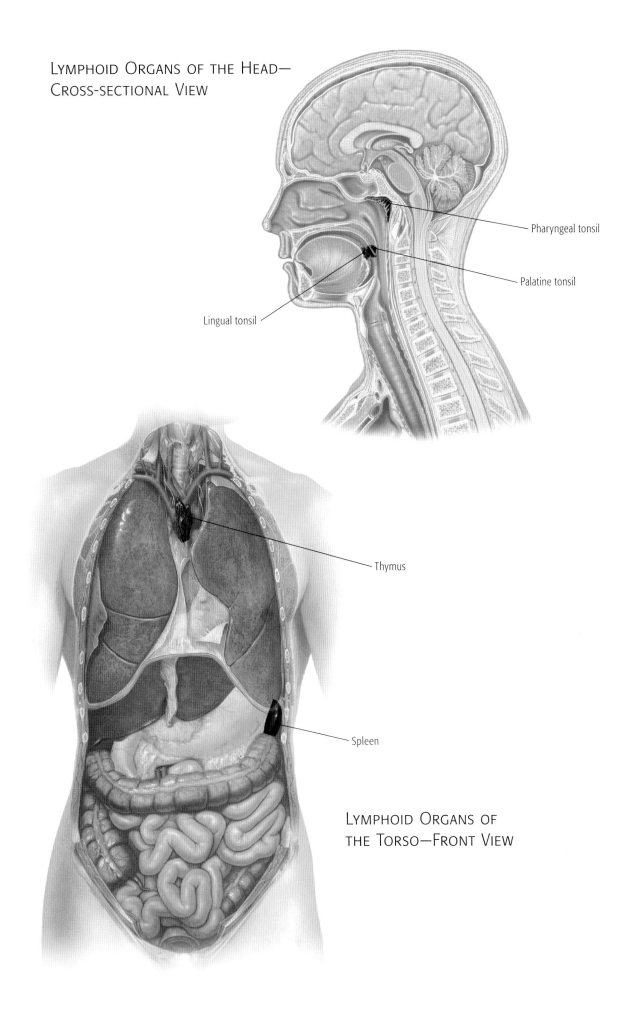

LYMPHOID ORGANS OF THE HEAD—
CROSS-SECTIONAL VIEW

Pharyngeal tonsil

Palatine tonsil

Lingual tonsil

Thymus

Spleen

LYMPHOID ORGANS OF
THE TORSO—FRONT VIEW

Lymphoid Organs

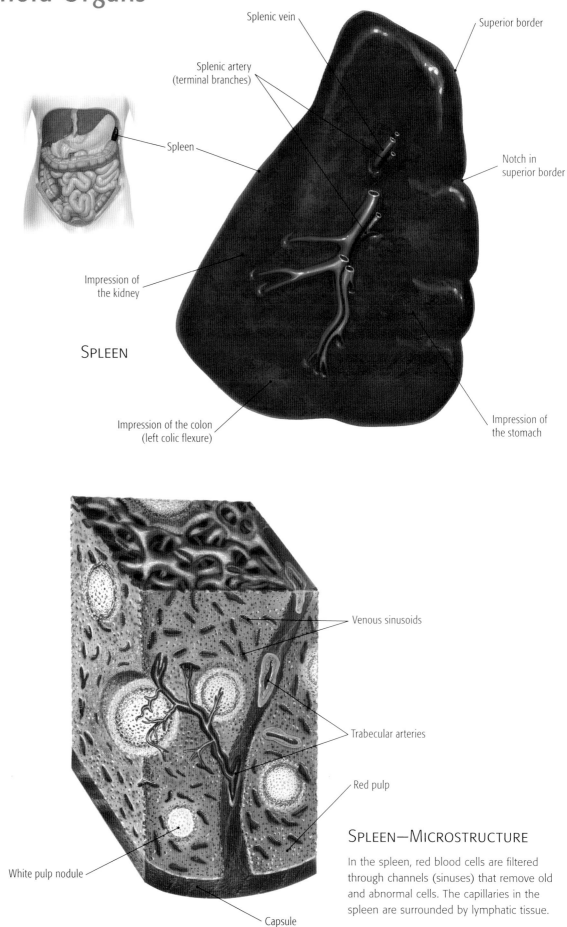

Splenic vein

Splenic artery
(terminal branches)

Superior border

Spleen

Notch in
superior border

Impression of
the kidney

Impression of
the stomach

SPLEEN

Impression of the colon
(left colic flexure)

Venous sinusoids

Trabecular arteries

Red pulp

White pulp nodule

Capsule

SPLEEN—MICROSTRUCTURE

In the spleen, red blood cells are filtered
through channels (sinuses) that remove old
and abnormal cells. The capillaries in the
spleen are surrounded by lymphatic tissue.

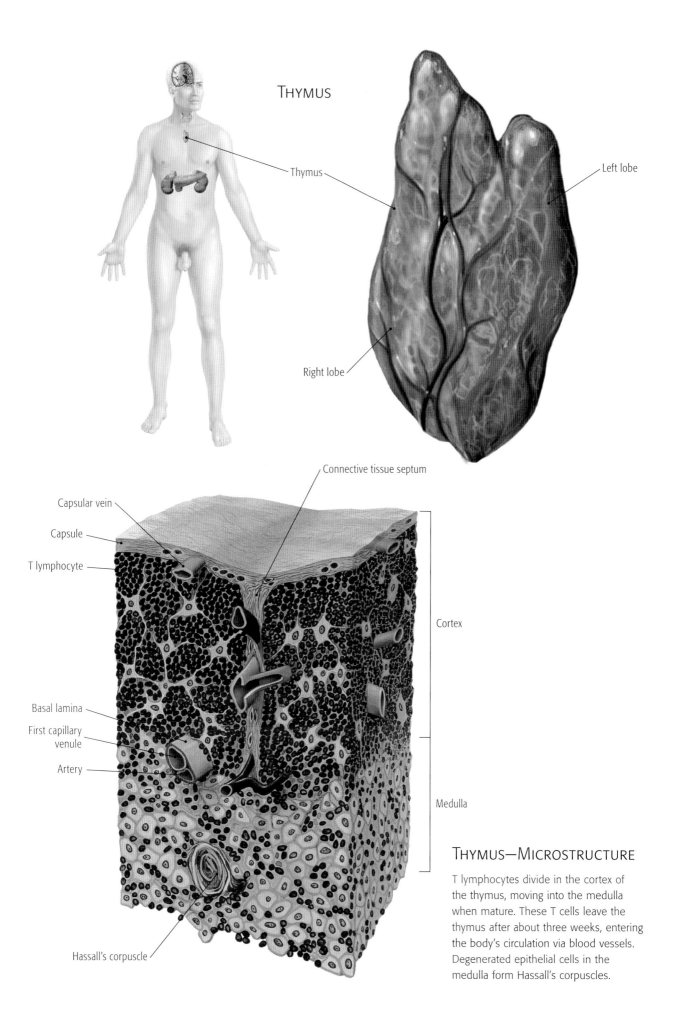

Thymus

Thymus

Left lobe

Right lobe

Connective tissue septum

Capsular vein

Capsule

T lymphocyte

Cortex

Basal lamina

First capillary venule

Artery

Medulla

Hassall's corpuscle

Thymus—Microstructure

T lymphocytes divide in the cortex of the thymus, moving into the medulla when mature. These T cells leave the thymus after about three weeks, entering the body's circulation via blood vessels. Degenerated epithelial cells in the medulla form Hassall's corpuscles.

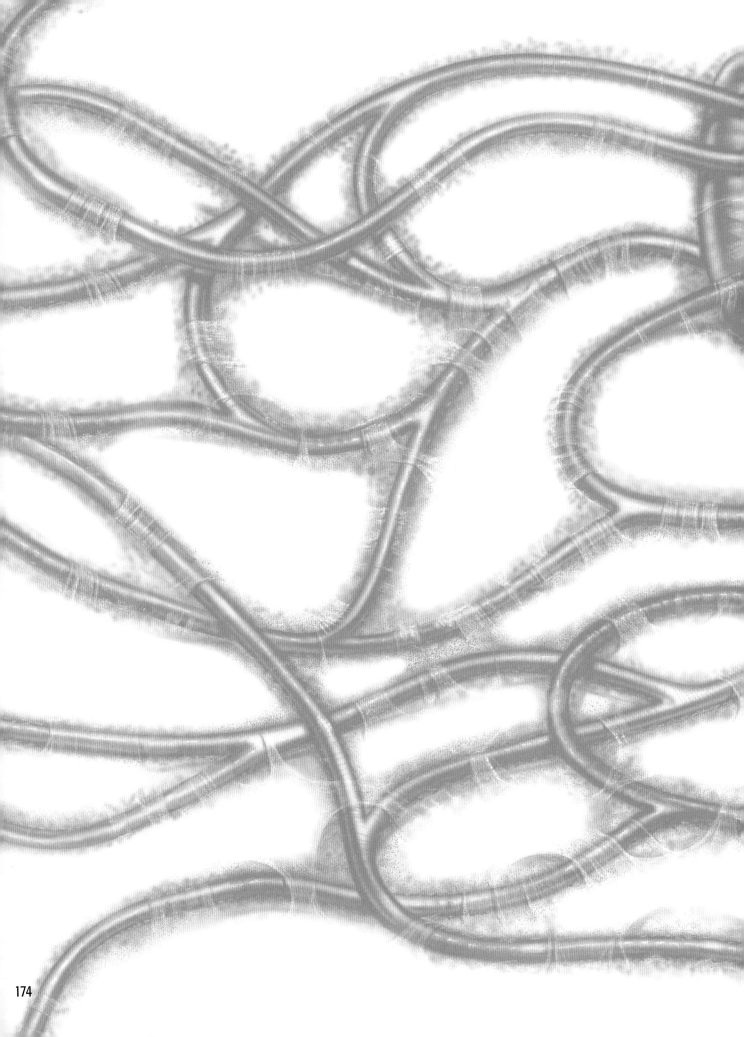

The Circulatory System

The Circulatory System

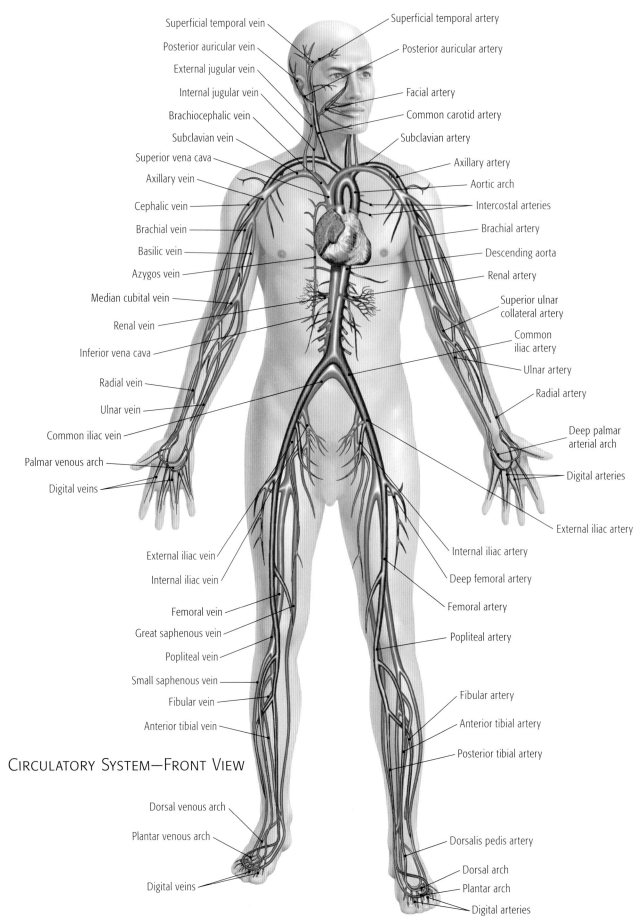

Superficial temporal vein

Posterior auricular vein

External jugular vein

Internal jugular vein

Brachiocephalic vein

Subclavian vein

Superior vena cava

Axillary vein

Cephalic vein

Brachial vein

Basilic vein

Azygos vein

Median cubital vein

Renal vein

Inferior vena cava

Radial vein

Ulnar vein

Common iliac vein

Palmar venous arch

Digital veins

Superficial temporal artery

Posterior auricular artery

Facial artery

Common carotid artery

Subclavian artery

Axillary artery

Aortic arch

Intercostal arteries

Brachial artery

Descending aorta

Renal artery

Superior ulnar collateral artery

Common iliac artery

Ulnar artery

Radial artery

Deep palmar arterial arch

Digital arteries

External iliac artery

External iliac vein

Internal iliac vein

Femoral vein

Great saphenous vein

Popliteal vein

Small saphenous vein

Fibular vein

Anterior tibial vein

Internal iliac artery

Deep femoral artery

Femoral artery

Popliteal artery

Fibular artery

Anterior tibial artery

Posterior tibial artery

CIRCULATORY SYSTEM—FRONT VIEW

Dorsal venous arch

Plantar venous arch

Digital veins

Dorsalis pedis artery

Dorsal arch

Plantar arch

Digital arteries

BLOOD COMPOSITION

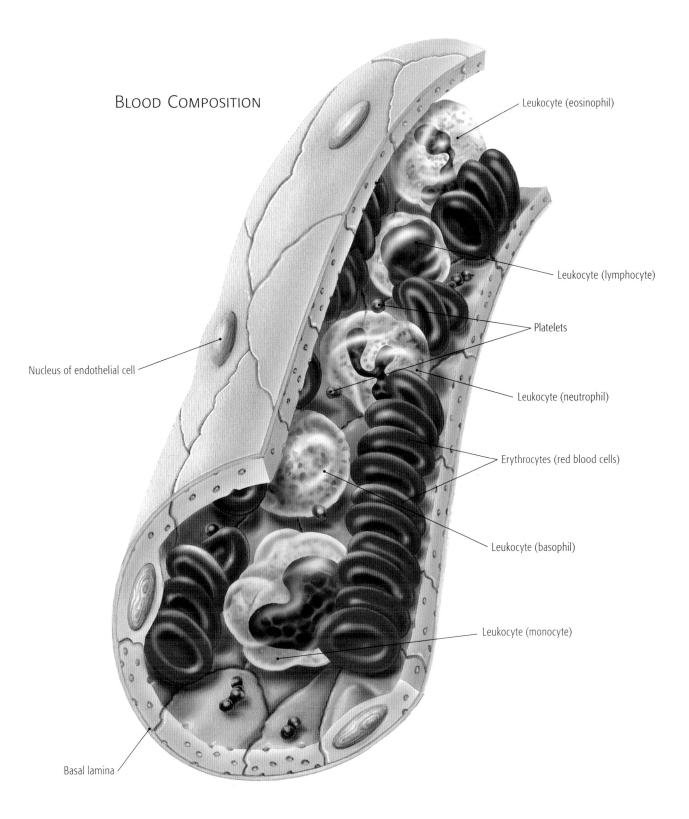

Leukocyte (eosinophil)

Leukocyte (lymphocyte)

Platelets

Leukocyte (neutrophil)

Nucleus of endothelial cell

Erythrocytes (red blood cells)

Leukocyte (basophil)

Leukocyte (monocyte)

Basal lamina

Blood Vessels

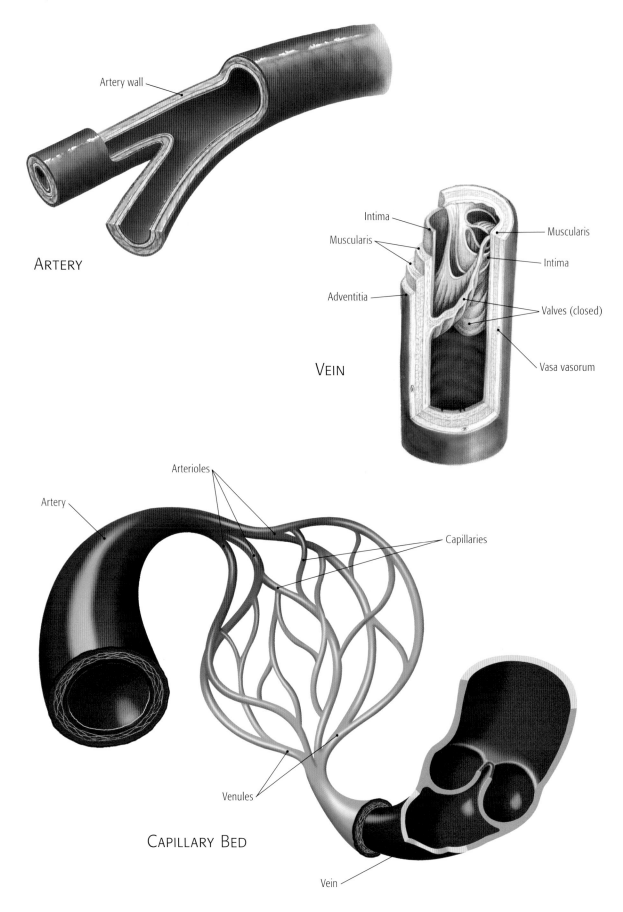

Artery wall

ARTERY

Intima

Muscularis

Adventitia

Muscularis

Intima

Valves (closed)

Vasa vasorum

VEIN

Arterioles

Artery

Capillaries

Venules

Vein

CAPILLARY BED

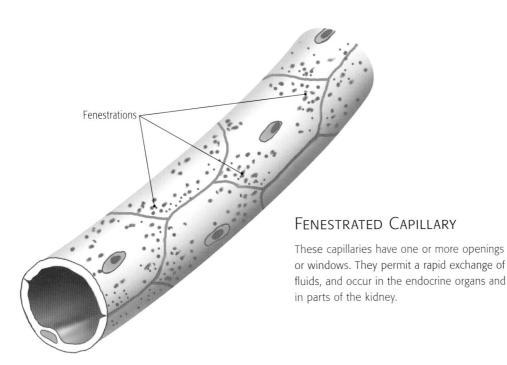

Fenestrations

FENESTRATED CAPILLARY

These capillaries have one or more openings or windows. They permit a rapid exchange of fluids, and occur in the endocrine organs and in parts of the kidney.

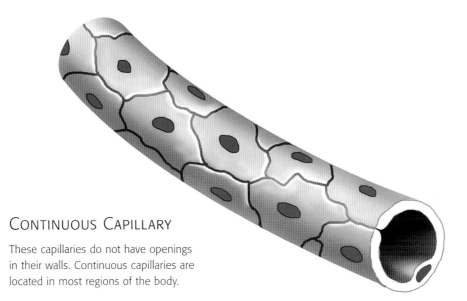

CONTINUOUS CAPILLARY

These capillaries do not have openings in their walls. Continuous capillaries are located in most regions of the body.

Major Arteries and Veins of the Body

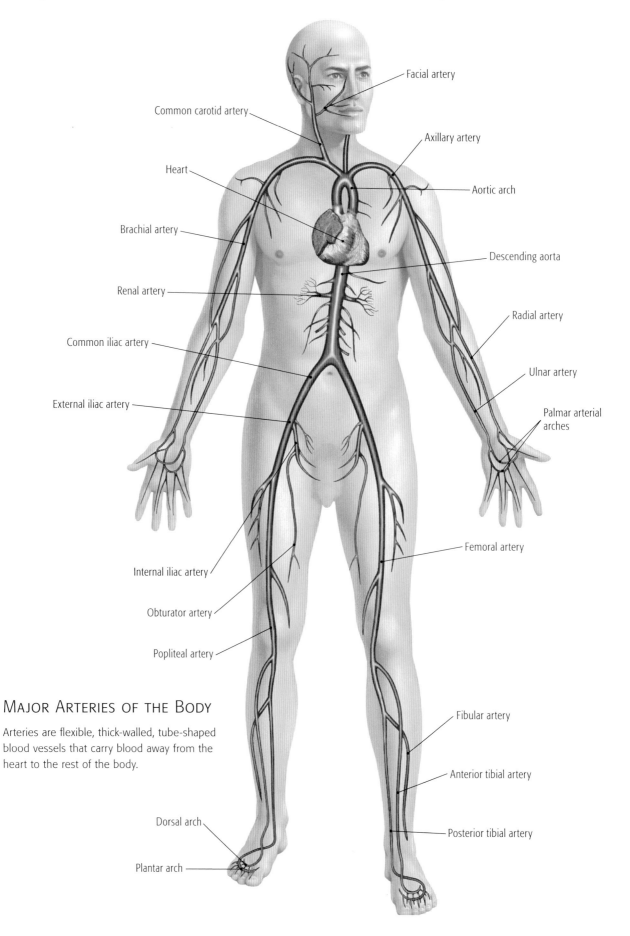

Facial artery

Common carotid artery

Axillary artery

Heart

Aortic arch

Brachial artery

Descending aorta

Renal artery

Radial artery

Common iliac artery

Ulnar artery

External iliac artery

Palmar arterial arches

Internal iliac artery

Femoral artery

Obturator artery

Popliteal artery

Fibular artery

Anterior tibial artery

Dorsal arch

Posterior tibial artery

Plantar arch

MAJOR ARTERIES OF THE BODY

Arteries are flexible, thick-walled, tube-shaped blood vessels that carry blood away from the heart to the rest of the body.

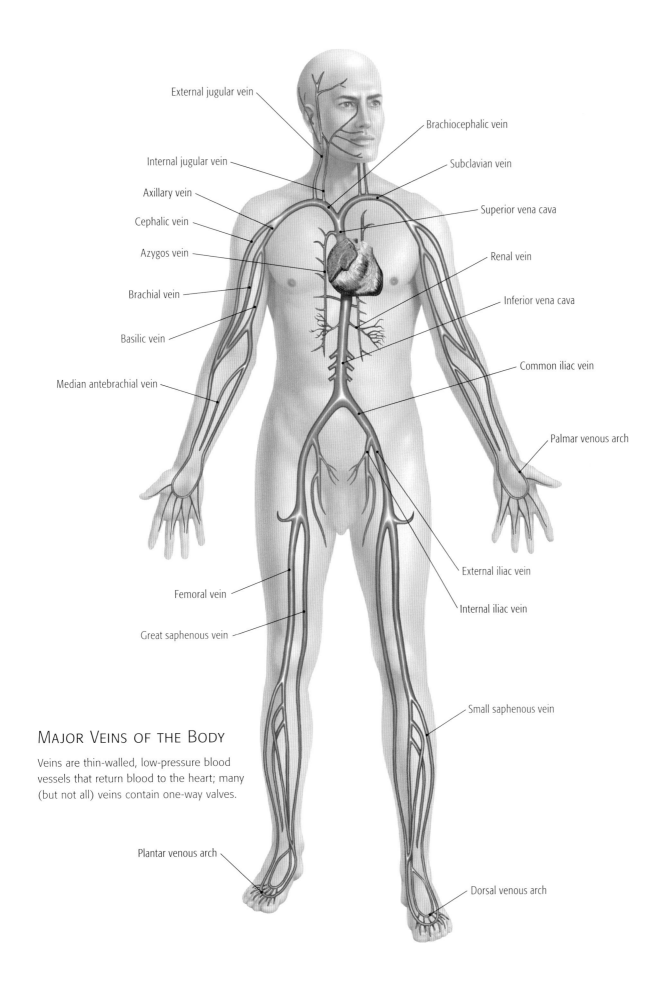

External jugular vein

Brachiocephalic vein

Internal jugular vein

Subclavian vein

Axillary vein

Superior vena cava

Cephalic vein

Azygos vein

Renal vein

Brachial vein

Inferior vena cava

Basilic vein

Common iliac vein

Median antebrachial vein

Palmar venous arch

External iliac vein

Internal iliac vein

Femoral vein

Great saphenous vein

Small saphenous vein

MAJOR VEINS OF THE BODY

Veins are thin-walled, low-pressure blood vessels that return blood to the heart; many (but not all) veins contain one-way valves.

Plantar venous arch

Dorsal venous arch

Arteries of the Brain

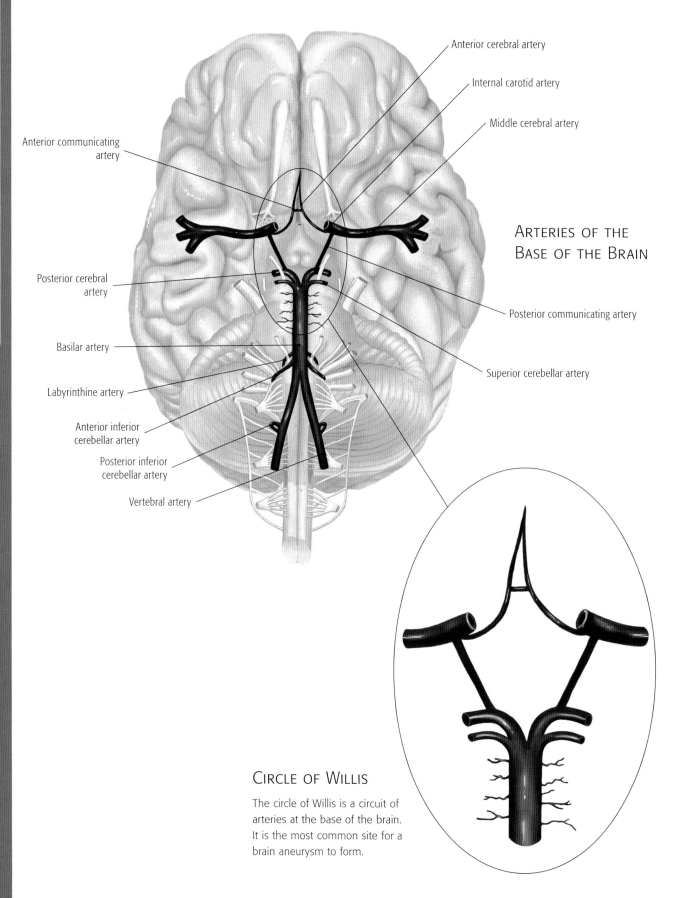

Anterior cerebral artery

Internal carotid artery

Middle cerebral artery

Anterior communicating artery

ARTERIES OF THE BASE OF THE BRAIN

Posterior cerebral artery

Posterior communicating artery

Basilar artery

Superior cerebellar artery

Labyrinthine artery

Anterior inferior cerebellar artery

Posterior inferior cerebellar artery

Vertebral artery

CIRCLE OF WILLIS

The circle of Willis is a circuit of arteries at the base of the brain. It is the most common site for a brain aneurysm to form.

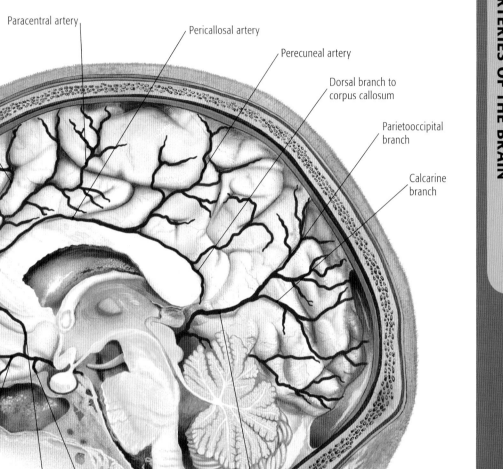

Medial frontal branches {
Posterior
Intermediate
Anterior

Paracentral artery

Pericallosal artery

Perecuneal artery

Dorsal branch to corpus callosum

Parietooccipital branch

Calcarine branch

Callosomarginal artery

Polar frontal artery

Medial frontobasal artery

Right anterior cerebral artery

Medial striate artery

Medial occipital artery (branch of posterior cerebral artery)

BRAIN ARTERIES—CROSS-SECTIONAL VIEW

Blood Vessels of the Head and Neck

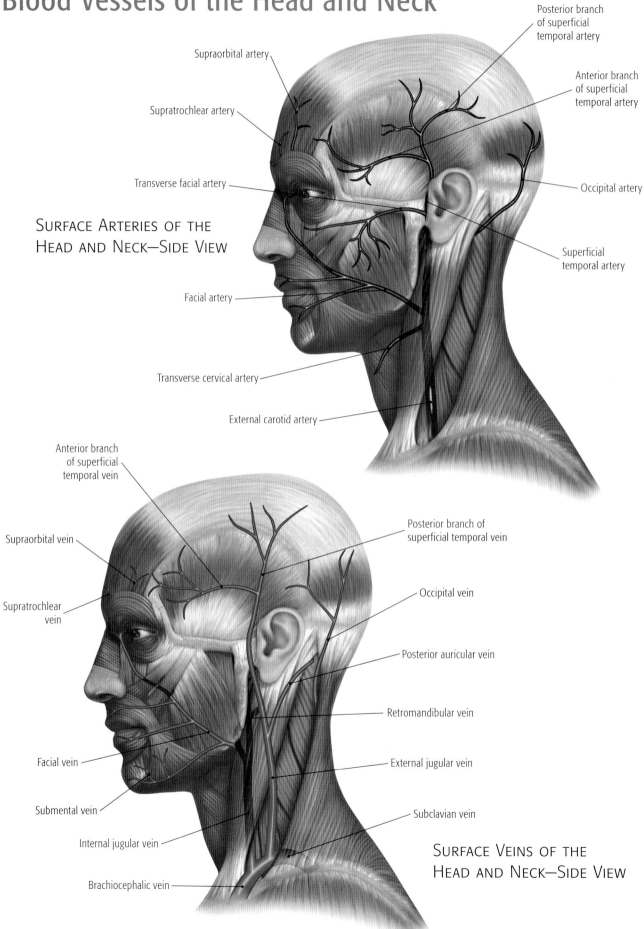

Posterior branch of superficial temporal artery

Supraorbital artery

Anterior branch of superficial temporal artery

Supratrochlear artery

Transverse facial artery

Occipital artery

SURFACE ARTERIES OF THE HEAD AND NECK—SIDE VIEW

Superficial temporal artery

Facial artery

Transverse cervical artery

External carotid artery

Anterior branch of superficial temporal vein

Supraorbital vein

Posterior branch of superficial temporal vein

Supratrochlear vein

Occipital vein

Posterior auricular vein

Retromandibular vein

Facial vein

External jugular vein

Submental vein

Subclavian vein

Internal jugular vein

SURFACE VEINS OF THE HEAD AND NECK—SIDE VIEW

Brachiocephalic vein

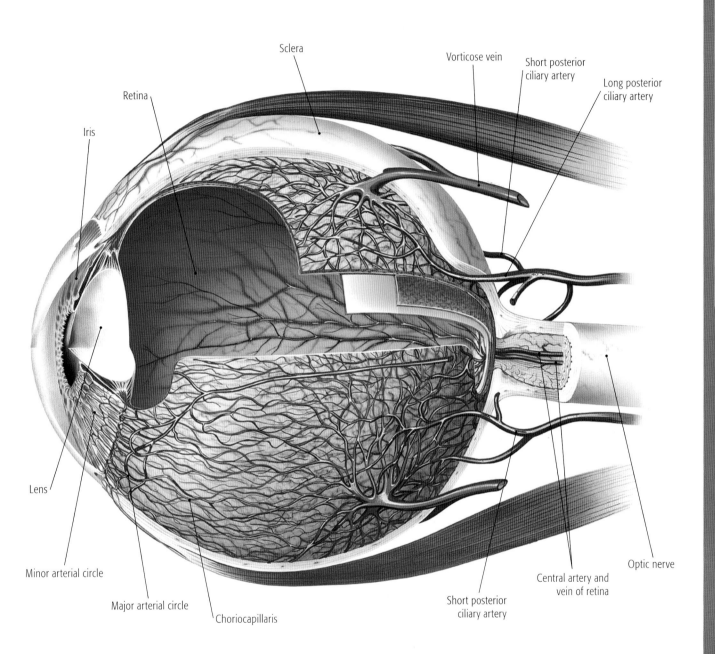

Sclera

Vorticose vein

Short posterior
ciliary artery

Long posterior
ciliary artery

Retina

Iris

Lens

Minor arterial circle

Major arterial circle

Choriocapillaris

Short posterior
ciliary artery

Central artery and
vein of retina

Optic nerve

SURFACE ARTERIES OF THE EYE—SIDE VIEW

The Heart

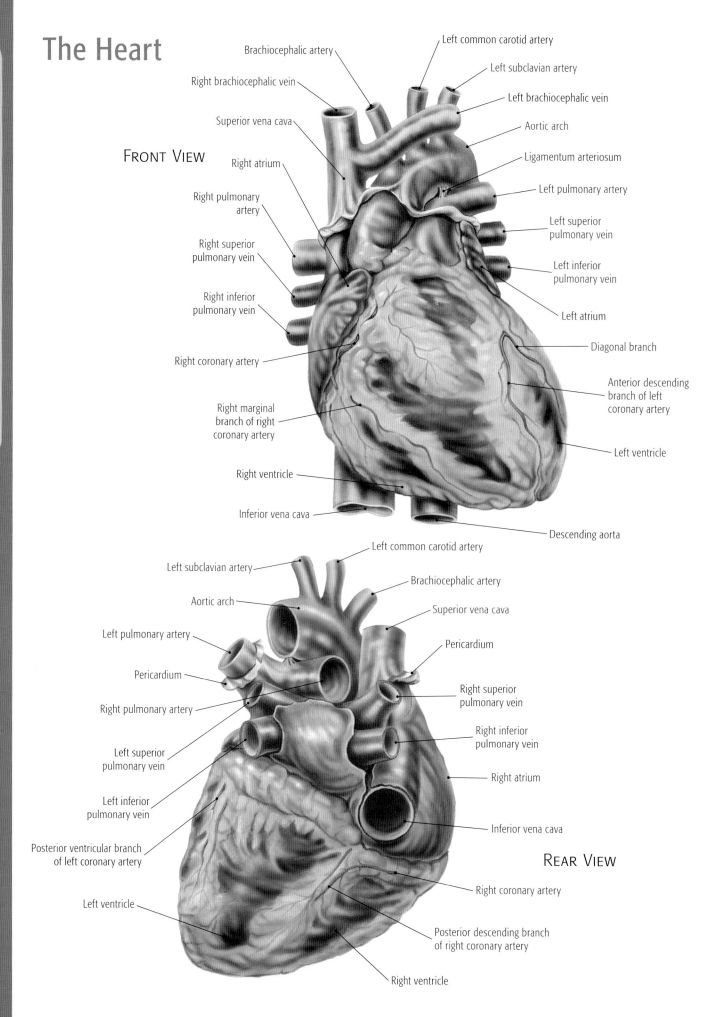

FRONT VIEW

Brachiocephalic artery

Right brachiocephalic vein

Superior vena cava

Right atrium

Right pulmonary artery

Right superior pulmonary vein

Right inferior pulmonary vein

Right coronary artery

Right marginal branch of right coronary artery

Right ventricle

Inferior vena cava

Left common carotid artery

Left subclavian artery

Left brachiocephalic vein

Aortic arch

Ligamentum arteriosum

Left pulmonary artery

Left superior pulmonary vein

Left inferior pulmonary vein

Left atrium

Diagonal branch

Anterior descending branch of left coronary artery

Left ventricle

Descending aorta

Left subclavian artery

Aortic arch

Left pulmonary artery

Pericardium

Right pulmonary artery

Left superior pulmonary vein

Left inferior pulmonary vein

Posterior ventricular branch of left coronary artery

Left ventricle

Left common carotid artery

Brachiocephalic artery

Superior vena cava

Pericardium

Right superior pulmonary vein

Right inferior pulmonary vein

Right atrium

Inferior vena cava

REAR VIEW

Right coronary artery

Posterior descending branch of right coronary artery

Right ventricle

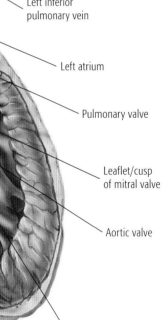

Left common carotid artery

Brachiocephalic artery

Right brachiocephalic vein

Left subclavian artery

Left brachiocephalic vein

Aortic arch

Superior vena cava

Ascending aorta

Left pulmonary artery

Pericardium

Right pulmonary artery

Left superior
pulmonary vein

Right superior
pulmonary vein

Left inferior
pulmonary vein

Right inferior
pulmonary vein

Left atrium

Right atrium

Pulmonary valve

Leaflet/cusp
of tricuspid valve

Leaflet/cusp
of mitral valve

Right ventricle

Aortic valve

Chordae tendineae

Papillary muscle

Papillary muscle

Inferior vena cava

Descending aorta

CROSS-SECTIONAL VIEW

Heart Valves

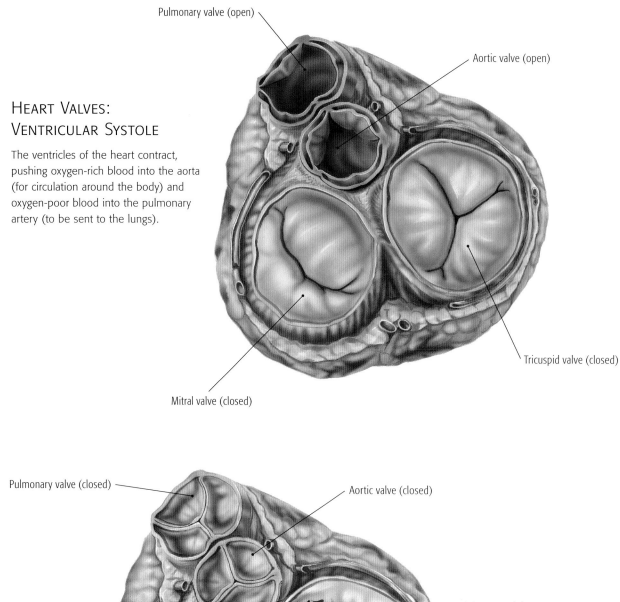

Pulmonary valve (open)

Aortic valve (open)

Tricuspid valve (closed)

Mitral valve (closed)

HEART VALVES: VENTRICULAR SYSTOLE

The ventricles of the heart contract, pushing oxygen-rich blood into the aorta (for circulation around the body) and oxygen-poor blood into the pulmonary artery (to be sent to the lungs).

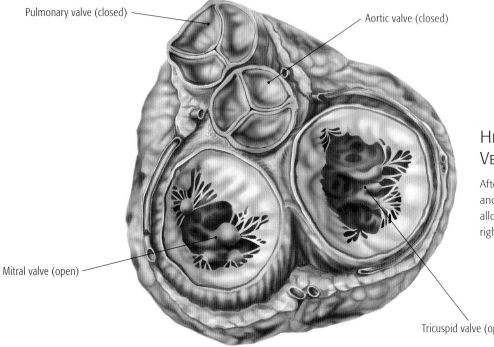

Pulmonary valve (closed)

Aortic valve (closed)

Mitral valve (open)

Tricuspid valve (open)

HEART VALVES: VENTRICULAR DIASTOLE

After a contraction, the mitral and tricuspid valves open. This allows blood to fill the left and right ventricles of the heart.

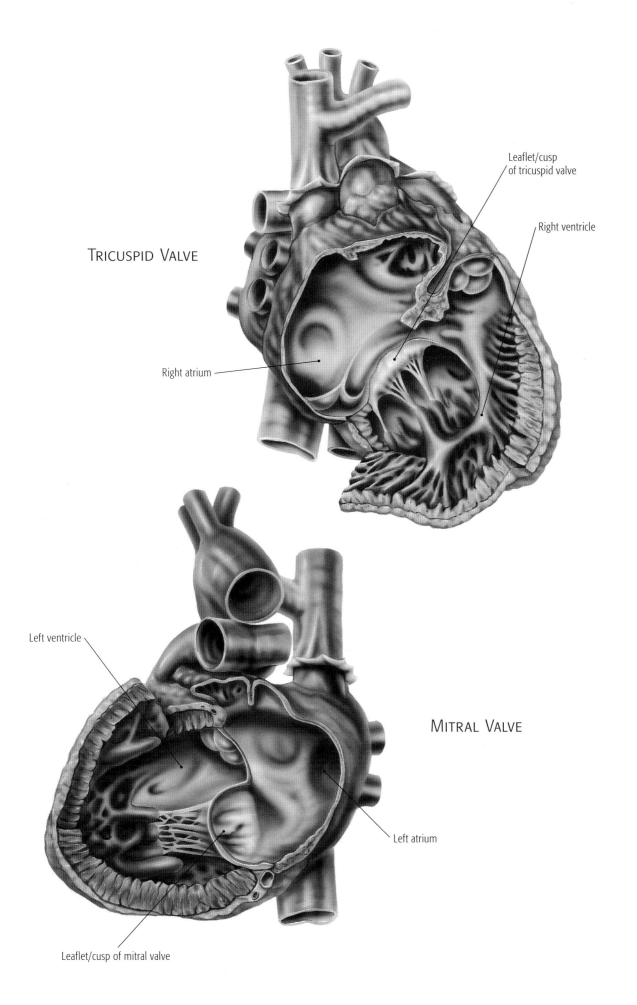

TRICUSPID VALVE

Leaflet/cusp
of tricuspid valve

Right ventricle

Right atrium

Left ventricle

MITRAL VALVE

Left atrium

Leaflet/cusp of mitral valve

Heart Cycle

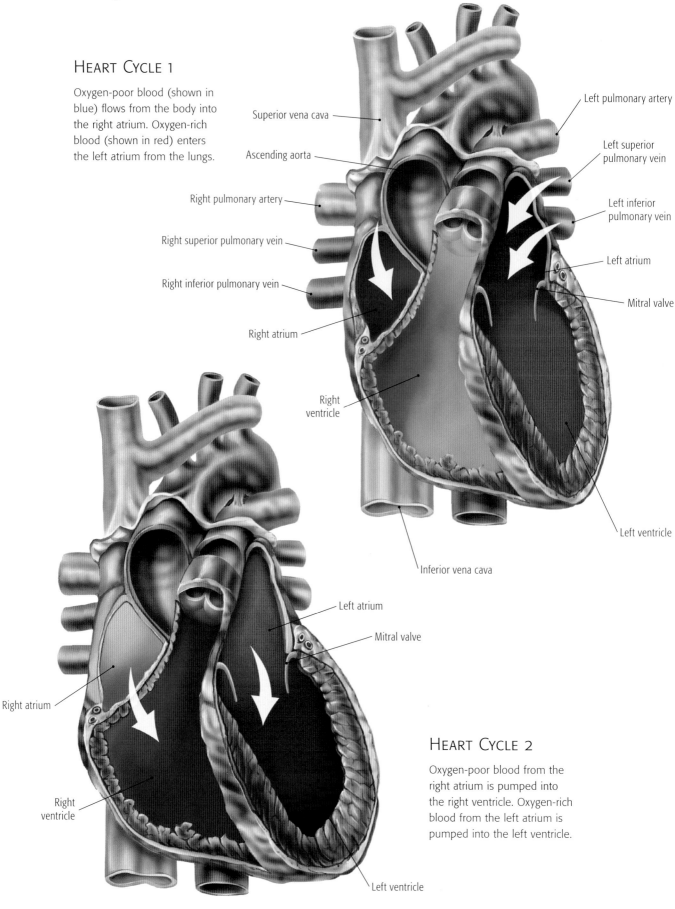

HEART CYCLE 1

Oxygen-poor blood (shown in blue) flows from the body into the right atrium. Oxygen-rich blood (shown in red) enters the left atrium from the lungs.

Superior vena cava

Ascending aorta

Right pulmonary artery

Right superior pulmonary vein

Right inferior pulmonary vein

Right atrium

Right ventricle

Inferior vena cava

Left pulmonary artery

Left superior pulmonary vein

Left inferior pulmonary vein

Left atrium

Mitral valve

Left ventricle

Left atrium

Mitral valve

Right atrium

Right ventricle

Left ventricle

HEART CYCLE 2

Oxygen-poor blood from the right atrium is pumped into the right ventricle. Oxygen-rich blood from the left atrium is pumped into the left ventricle.

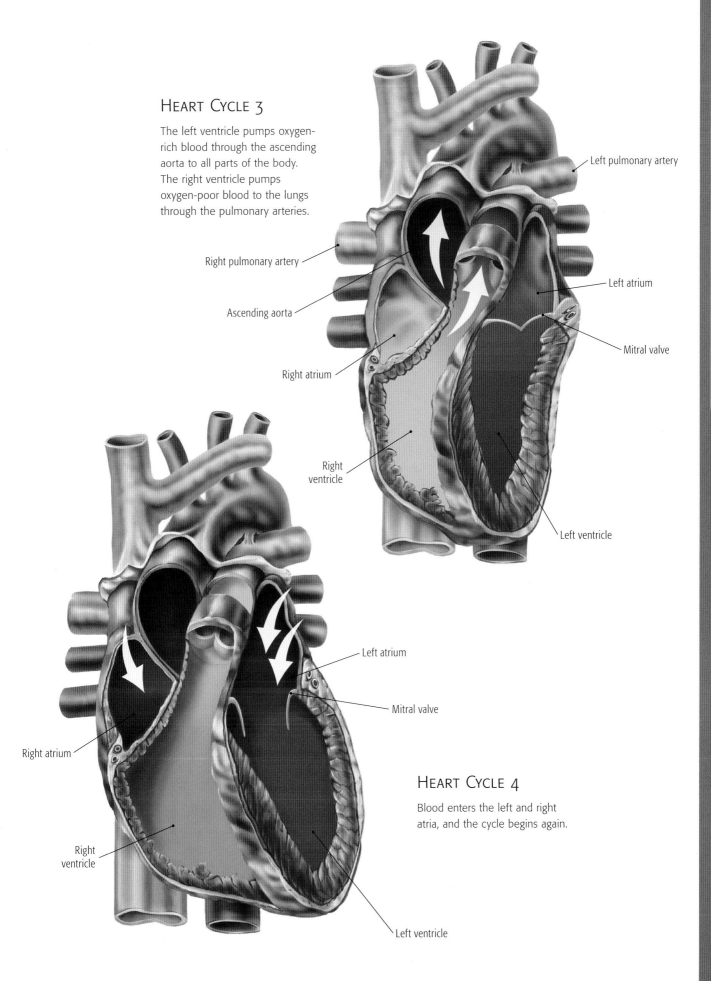

HEART CYCLE 3

The left ventricle pumps oxygen-rich blood through the ascending aorta to all parts of the body. The right ventricle pumps oxygen-poor blood to the lungs through the pulmonary arteries.

Left pulmonary artery

Right pulmonary artery

Left atrium

Ascending aorta

Mitral valve

Right atrium

Right ventricle

Left ventricle

Left atrium

Mitral valve

Right atrium

HEART CYCLE 4

Blood enters the left and right atria, and the cycle begins again.

Right ventricle

Left ventricle

Blood Vessels of the Abdomen

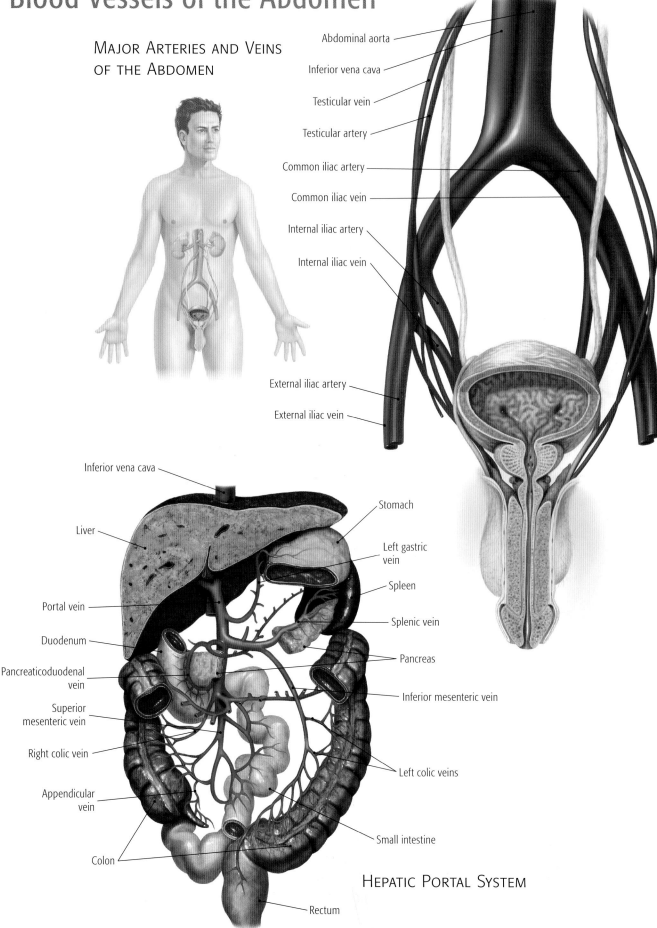

MAJOR ARTERIES AND VEINS
OF THE ABDOMEN

Abdominal aorta

Inferior vena cava

Testicular vein

Testicular artery

Common iliac artery

Common iliac vein

Internal iliac artery

Internal iliac vein

External iliac artery

External iliac vein

Inferior vena cava

Liver

Portal vein

Duodenum

Pancreaticoduodenal
vein

Superior
mesenteric vein

Right colic vein

Appendicular
vein

Colon

Rectum

Stomach

Left gastric
vein

Spleen

Splenic vein

Pancreas

Inferior mesenteric vein

Left colic veins

Small intestine

HEPATIC PORTAL SYSTEM

HEPATIC ARTERY

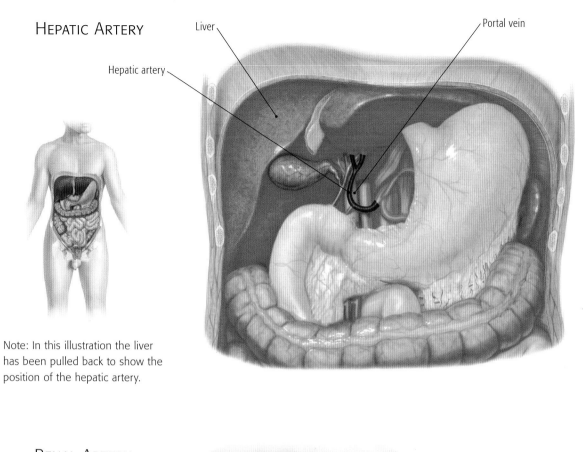

Liver

Portal vein

Hepatic artery

Note: In this illustration the liver has been pulled back to show the position of the hepatic artery.

RENAL ARTERY

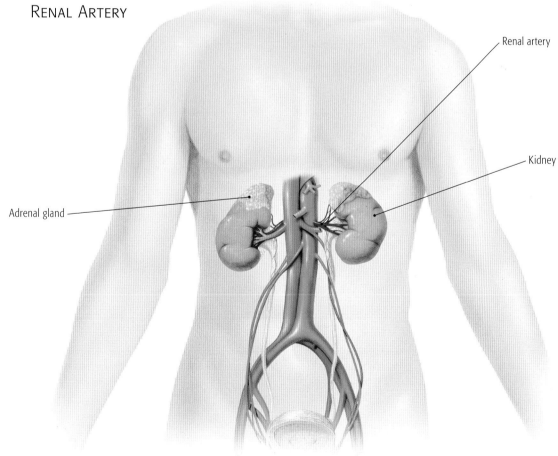

Renal artery

Kidney

Adrenal gland

Blood Vessels of the Arms and Legs

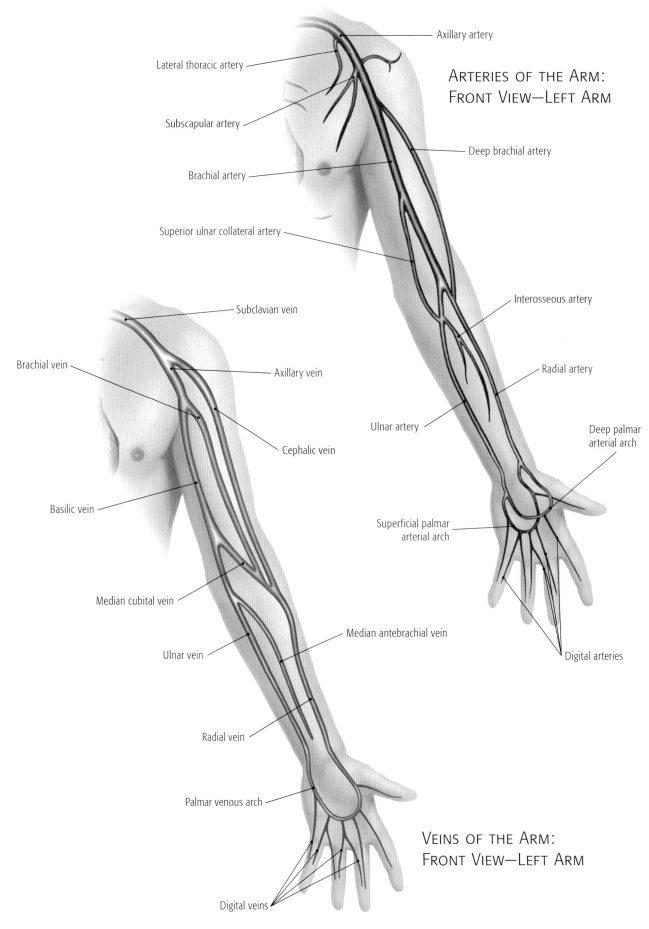

Axillary artery

Lateral thoracic artery

Subscapular artery

Brachial artery

Superior ulnar collateral artery

ARTERIES OF THE ARM:
FRONT VIEW—LEFT ARM

Deep brachial artery

Interosseous artery

Radial artery

Ulnar artery

Deep palmar
arterial arch

Superficial palmar
arterial arch

Digital arteries

Subclavian vein

Brachial vein

Axillary vein

Cephalic vein

Basilic vein

Median cubital vein

Median antebrachial vein

Ulnar vein

Radial vein

Palmar venous arch

VEINS OF THE ARM:
FRONT VIEW—LEFT ARM

Digital veins

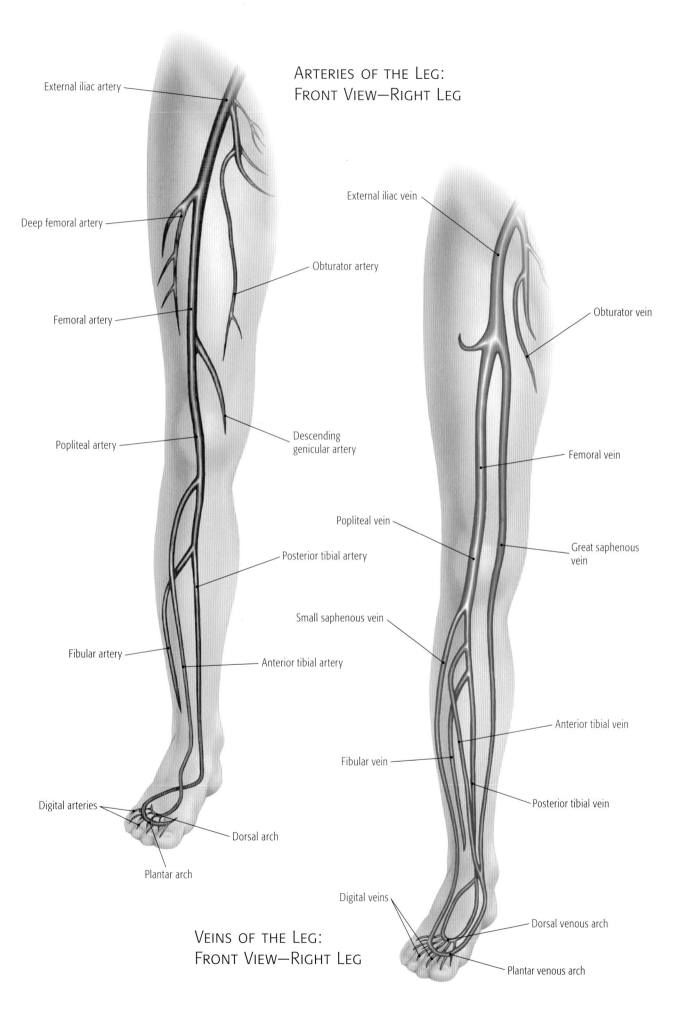

ARTERIES OF THE LEG:
FRONT VIEW—RIGHT LEG

External iliac artery

Deep femoral artery

Femoral artery

Popliteal artery

Fibular artery

Digital arteries

Plantar arch

Obturator artery

Descending
genicular artery

Posterior tibial artery

Anterior tibial artery

Dorsal arch

External iliac vein

Obturator vein

Femoral vein

Popliteal vein

Great saphenous
vein

Small saphenous vein

Anterior tibial vein

Fibular vein

Posterior tibial vein

Digital veins

Dorsal venous arch

Plantar venous arch

VEINS OF THE LEG:
FRONT VIEW—RIGHT LEG

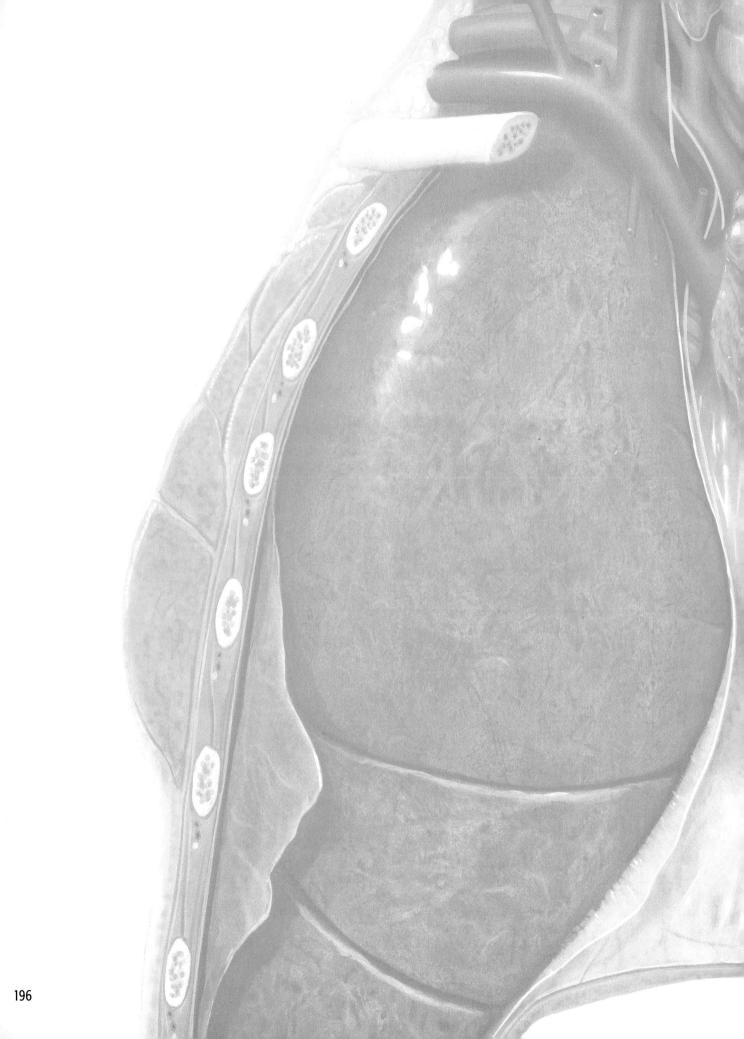

The Respiratory System

The Respiratory System

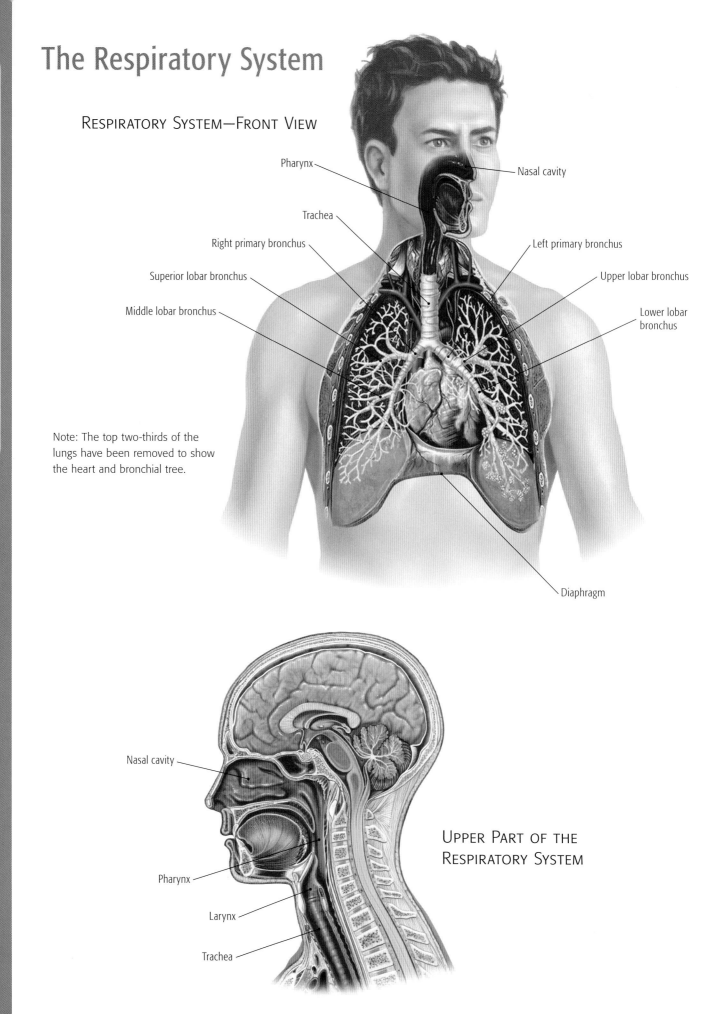

RESPIRATORY SYSTEM—FRONT VIEW

Pharynx

Nasal cavity

Trachea

Right primary bronchus

Left primary bronchus

Superior lobar bronchus

Upper lobar bronchus

Middle lobar bronchus

Lower lobar bronchus

Note: The top two-thirds of the lungs have been removed to show the heart and bronchial tree.

Diaphragm

Nasal cavity

UPPER PART OF THE RESPIRATORY SYSTEM

Pharynx

Larynx

Trachea

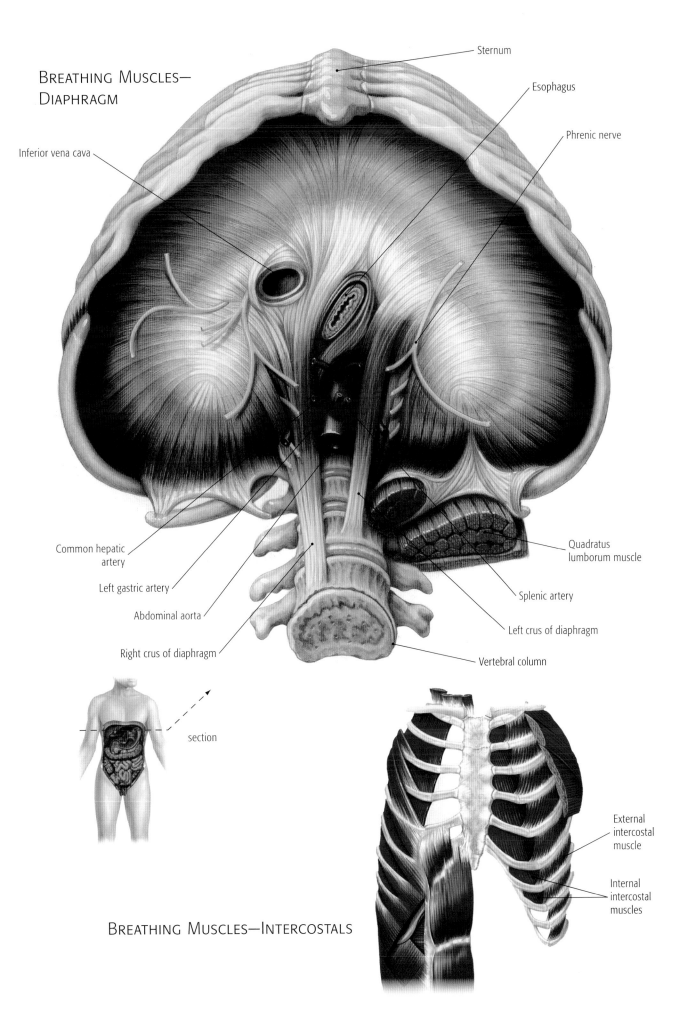

BREATHING MUSCLES—
DIAPHRAGM

Sternum

Esophagus

Phrenic nerve

Inferior vena cava

Common hepatic artery

Left gastric artery

Abdominal aorta

Right crus of diaphragm

Quadratus lumborum muscle

Splenic artery

Left crus of diaphragm

Vertebral column

section

BREATHING MUSCLES—INTERCOSTALS

External intercostal muscle

Internal intercostal muscles

Nose and Throat

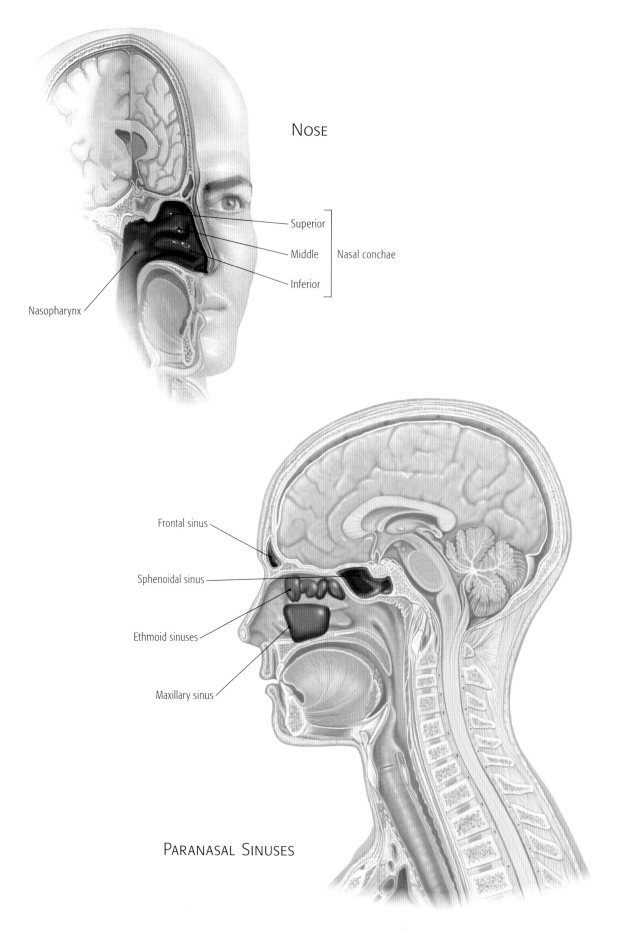

NOSE

Superior
Middle
Inferior

Nasal conchae

Nasopharynx

Frontal sinus

Sphenoidal sinus

Ethmoid sinuses

Maxillary sinus

PARANASAL SINUSES

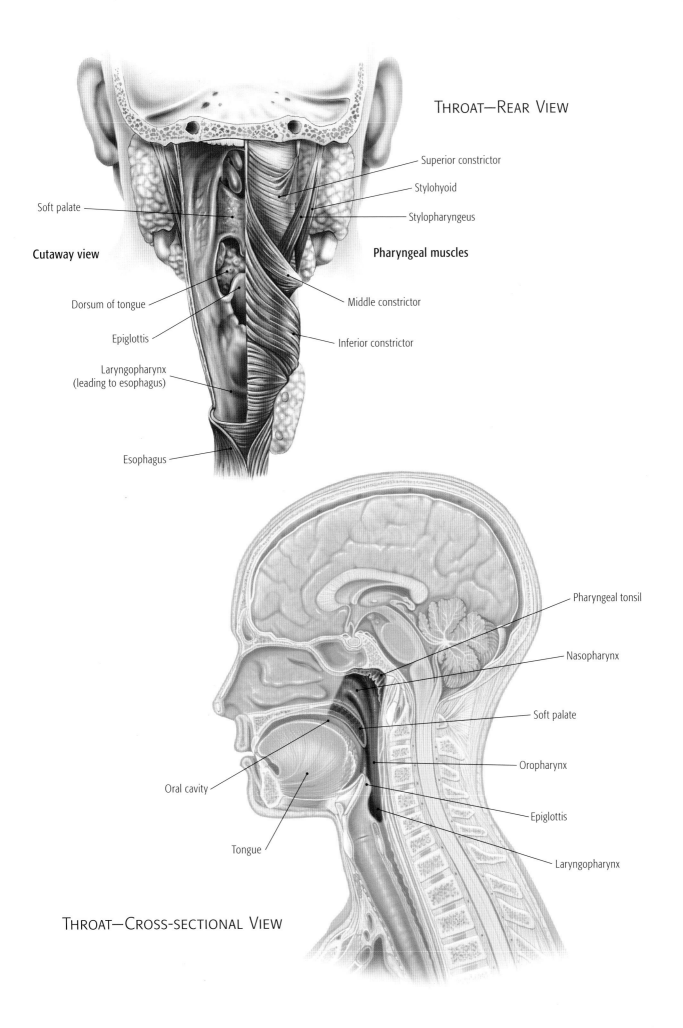

THROAT—REAR VIEW

Superior constrictor

Stylohyoid

Stylopharyngeus

Soft palate

Cutaway view

Pharyngeal muscles

Dorsum of tongue

Middle constrictor

Epiglottis

Inferior constrictor

Laryngopharynx
(leading to esophagus)

Esophagus

Pharyngeal tonsil

Nasopharynx

Soft palate

Oropharynx

Oral cavity

Epiglottis

Tongue

Laryngopharynx

THROAT—CROSS-SECTIONAL VIEW

Larynx

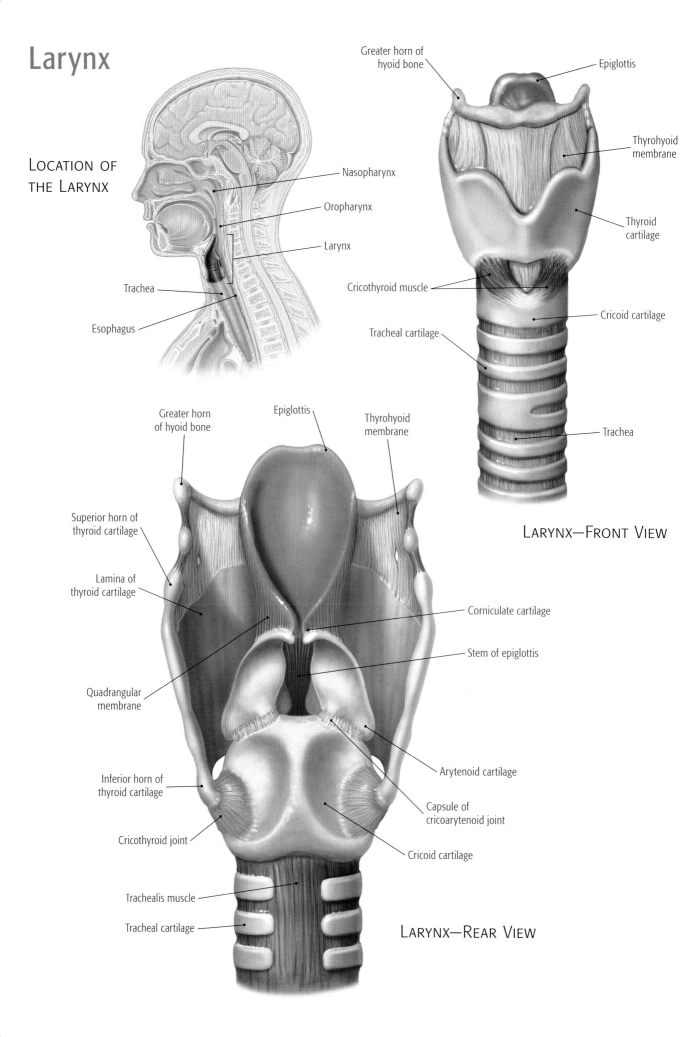

LOCATION OF
THE LARYNX

Nasopharynx

Oropharynx

Larynx

Trachea

Esophagus

Greater horn of
hyoid bone

Epiglottis

Thyrohyoid
membrane

Thyroid
cartilage

Cricothyroid muscle

Cricoid cartilage

Tracheal cartilage

Trachea

LARYNX—FRONT VIEW

Greater horn
of hyoid bone

Epiglottis

Thyrohyoid
membrane

Superior horn of
thyroid cartilage

Lamina of
thyroid cartilage

Corniculate cartilage

Stem of epiglottis

Quadrangular
membrane

Arytenoid cartilage

Inferior horn of
thyroid cartilage

Capsule of
cricoarytenoid joint

Cricothyroid joint

Cricoid cartilage

Trachealis muscle

Tracheal cartilage

LARYNX—REAR VIEW

Epiglottis: Swallowing

The epiglottis is a flap of elastic cartilage in the larynx. During swallowing it folds down over the glottis to prevent food and drink passing into the airway.

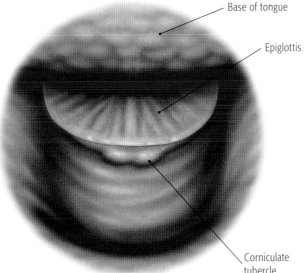

Base of tongue

Epiglottis

Corniculate tubercle

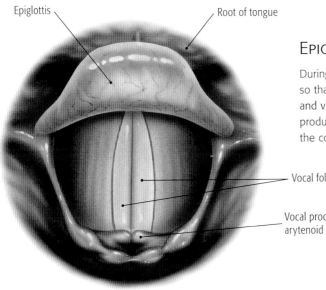

Epiglottis

Root of tongue

Vocal folds

Vocal process of arytenoid cartilage

Epiglottis: Speaking

During speaking, the epiglottis remains upright so that exhaled air can flow through the larynx and vibrate the vocal folds (vocal cords), producing sound. The tension and length of the cords determines the pitch of the sound.

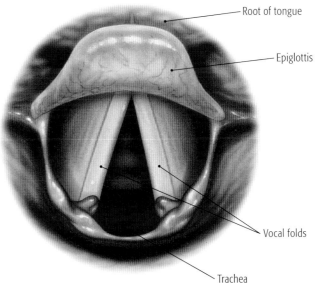

Root of tongue

Epiglottis

Vocal folds

Trachea

Epiglottis: Breathing

During breathing, the epiglottis remains upright, and the vocal folds (vocal cords) are moved apart by muscles in the larynx, allowing air to flow downward into the trachea.

Trachea and Bronchi

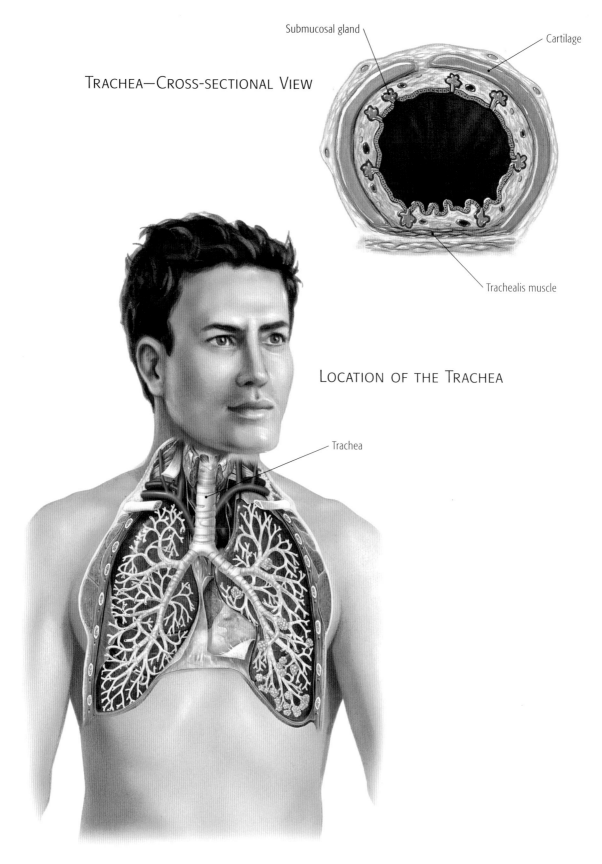

TRACHEA—CROSS-SECTIONAL VIEW

Submucosal gland

Cartilage

Trachealis muscle

LOCATION OF THE TRACHEA

Trachea

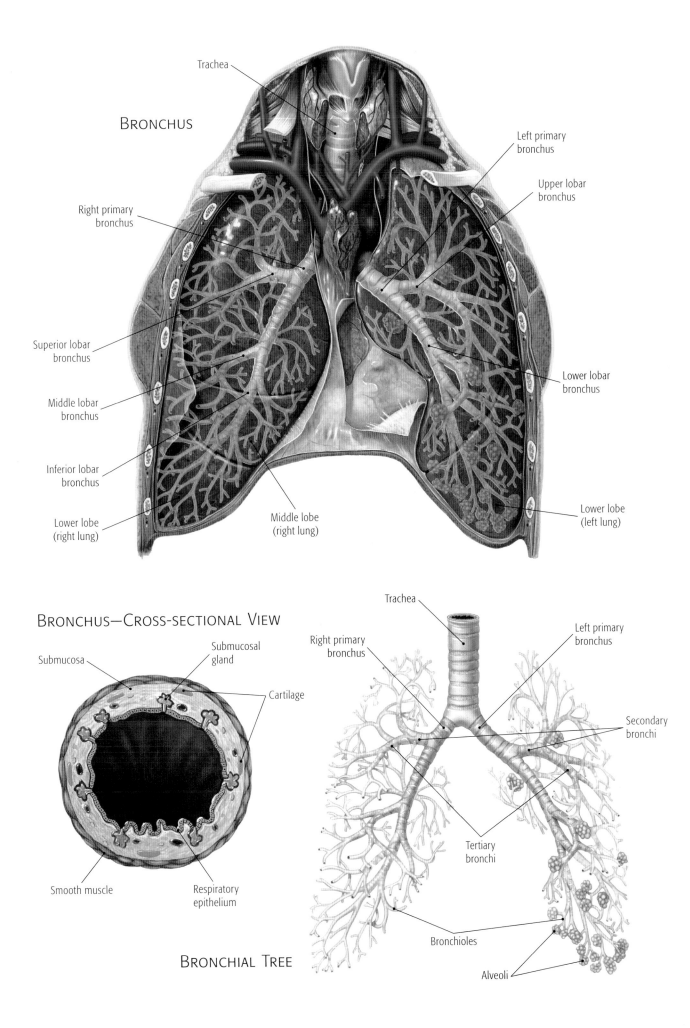

Bronchus

Trachea

Left primary bronchus

Upper lobar bronchus

Right primary bronchus

Superior lobar bronchus

Middle lobar bronchus

Inferior lobar bronchus

Lower lobe (right lung)

Middle lobe (right lung)

Lower lobar bronchus

Lower lobe (left lung)

Bronchus—Cross-sectional View

Submucosal gland

Submucosa

Cartilage

Smooth muscle

Respiratory epithelium

Bronchial Tree

Trachea

Right primary bronchus

Left primary bronchus

Secondary bronchi

Tertiary bronchi

Bronchioles

Alveoli

Lungs

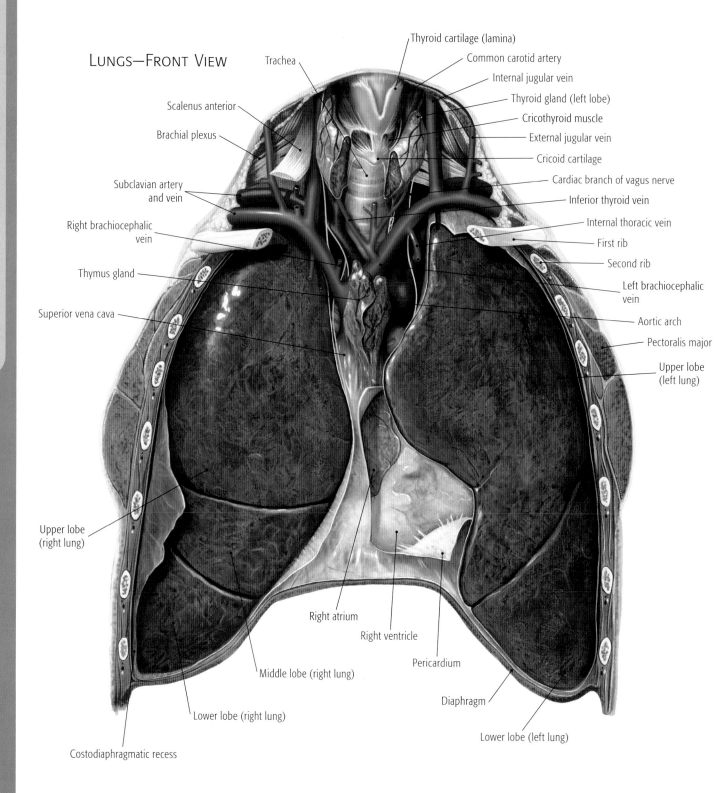

LUNGS—FRONT VIEW

Thyroid cartilage (lamina)

Common carotid artery

Internal jugular vein

Trachea

Thyroid gland (left lobe)

Cricothyroid muscle

Scalenus anterior

External jugular vein

Brachial plexus

Cricoid cartilage

Cardiac branch of vagus nerve

Inferior thyroid vein

Subclavian artery and vein

Internal thoracic vein

First rib

Right brachiocephalic vein

Second rib

Left brachiocephalic vein

Thymus gland

Aortic arch

Superior vena cava

Pectoralis major

Upper lobe (left lung)

Upper lobe (right lung)

Right atrium

Right ventricle

Pericardium

Middle lobe (right lung)

Diaphragm

Lower lobe (right lung)

Lower lobe (left lung)

Costodiaphragmatic recess

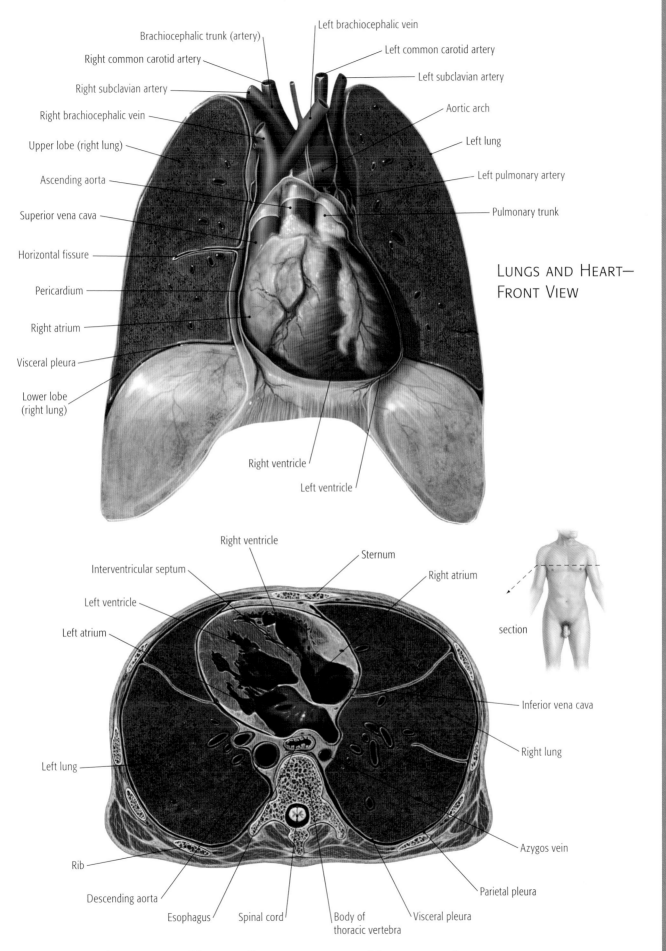

Brachiocephalic trunk (artery)

Left brachiocephalic vein

Right common carotid artery

Left common carotid artery

Right subclavian artery

Left subclavian artery

Right brachiocephalic vein

Aortic arch

Upper lobe (right lung)

Left lung

Ascending aorta

Left pulmonary artery

Superior vena cava

Pulmonary trunk

Horizontal fissure

Pericardium

Right atrium

Visceral pleura

Lower lobe
(right lung)

LUNGS AND HEART—
FRONT VIEW

Right ventricle

Left ventricle

Right ventricle

Sternum

Interventricular septum

Right atrium

Left ventricle

Left atrium

section

Inferior vena cava

Right lung

Left lung

Azygos vein

Rib

Descending aorta

Esophagus

Spinal cord

Body of
thoracic vertebra

Visceral pleura

Parietal pleura

LUNGS AND HEART—CROSS-SECTIONAL VIEW FROM ABOVE

Breathing

HOW WE BREATHE

Respiratory centers in the brain control the rate and depth of breathing, depending on oxygen and carbon dioxide levels in the blood. Contraction of the diaphragm and chest muscles draws air into the lungs via the nasal passage and trachea; the lungs transfer oxygen into the bloodstream.

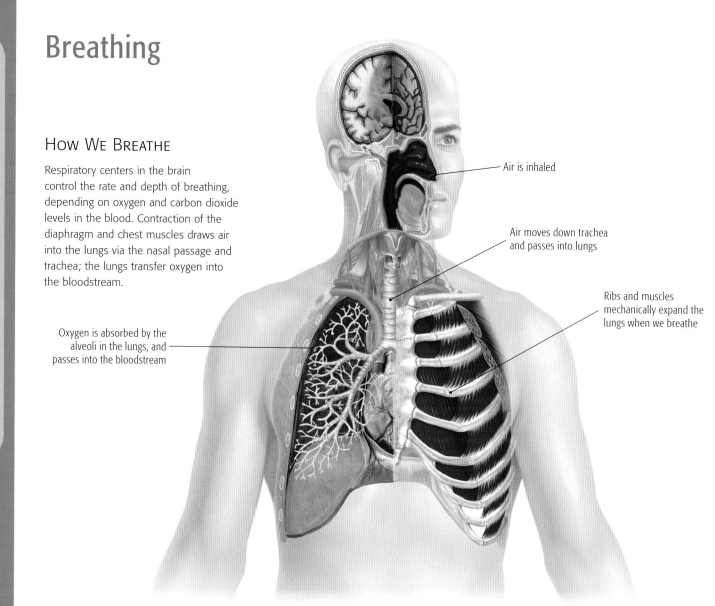

Air is inhaled

Air moves down trachea and passes into lungs

Ribs and muscles mechanically expand the lungs when we breathe

Oxygen is absorbed by the alveoli in the lungs, and passes into the bloodstream

RESPIRATORY CENTERS IN THE BRAIN

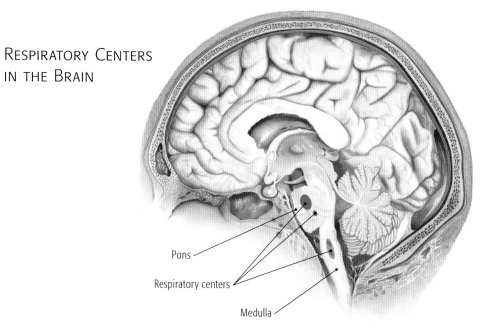

Pons

Respiratory centers

Medulla

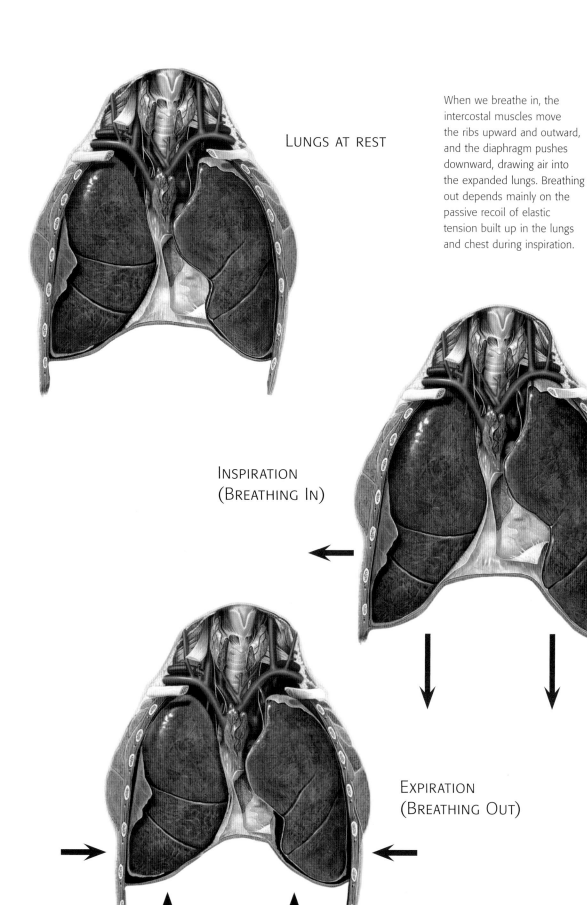

LUNGS AT REST

When we breathe in, the intercostal muscles move the ribs upward and outward, and the diaphragm pushes downward, drawing air into the expanded lungs. Breathing out depends mainly on the passive recoil of elastic tension built up in the lungs and chest during inspiration.

INSPIRATION
(BREATHING IN)

EXPIRATION
(BREATHING OUT)

Breathing

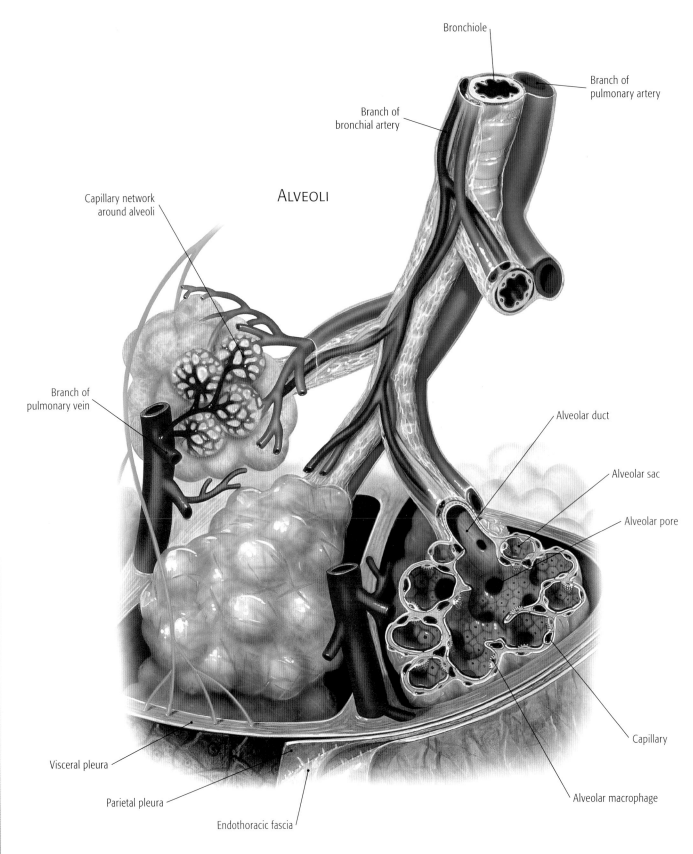

Bronchiole

Branch of
pulmonary artery

Branch of
bronchial artery

Capillary network
around alveoli

ALVEOLI

Branch of
pulmonary vein

Alveolar duct

Alveolar sac

Alveolar pore

Capillary

Visceral pleura

Parietal pleura

Endothoracic fascia

Alveolar macrophage

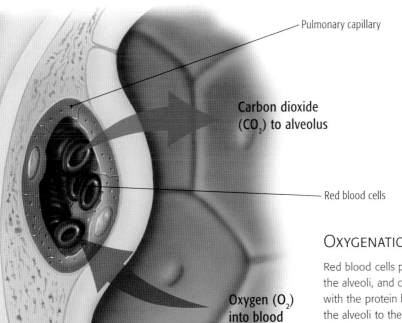

Pulmonary capillary

Carbon dioxide
(CO_2) to alveolus

Red blood cells

Oxygen (O_2)
into blood

Alveolar epithelium

OXYGENATION AT CELL LEVEL

Red blood cells pass carbon dioxide to
the alveoli, and carry oxygen (combined
with the protein hemoglobin) away from
the alveoli to the tissues. When oxygen
reaches the tissues it is released,
absorbed by the cells, and used in
cellular metabolism.

MOVING OXYGEN AROUND THE BODY

Blood travels continuously through two
circulatory systems: the pulmonary (lung)
and the systemic (body) circulations. The
heart pumps oxygen-poor blood from the
systemic circulation into the pulmonary
circulation. This blood is oxygenated by
the lungs and then pumped by the
heart into the systemic circulation.

Note: Part of the lungs has been
removed to reveal the pleura
covering the diaphragm.

Oxygen-rich blood flows
out of the lungs to the left
side of the heart and is
pumped out into the body

Oxygen-poor blood is
pumped into the lungs by
the right side of the heart

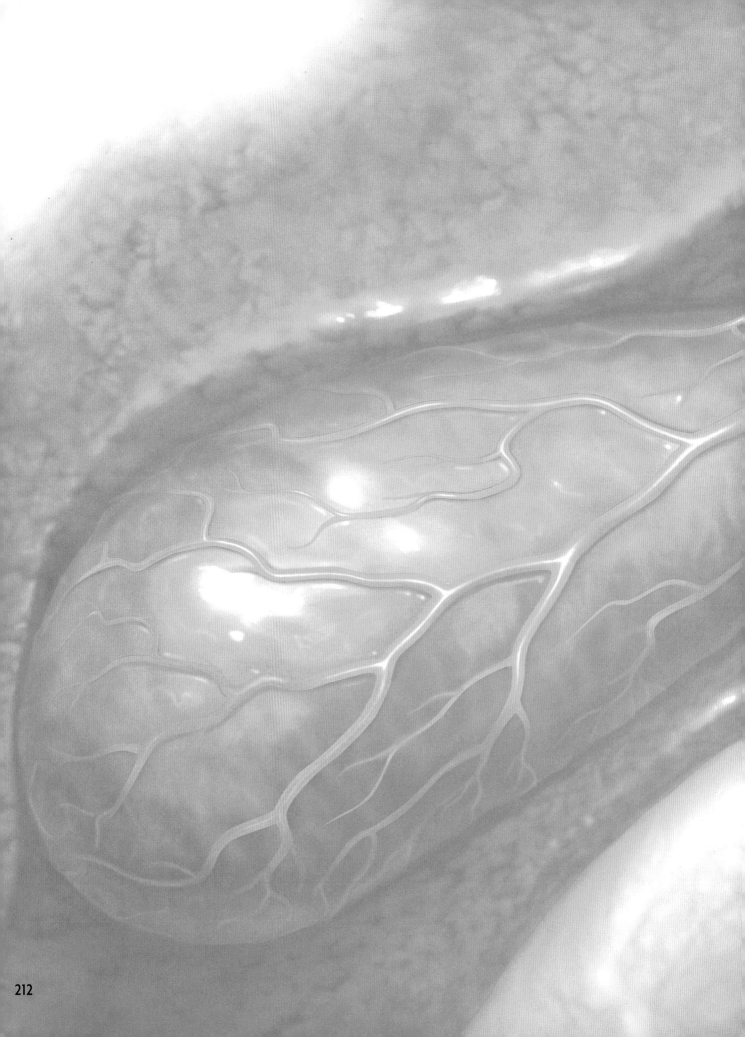

The Digestive System

The Digestive System

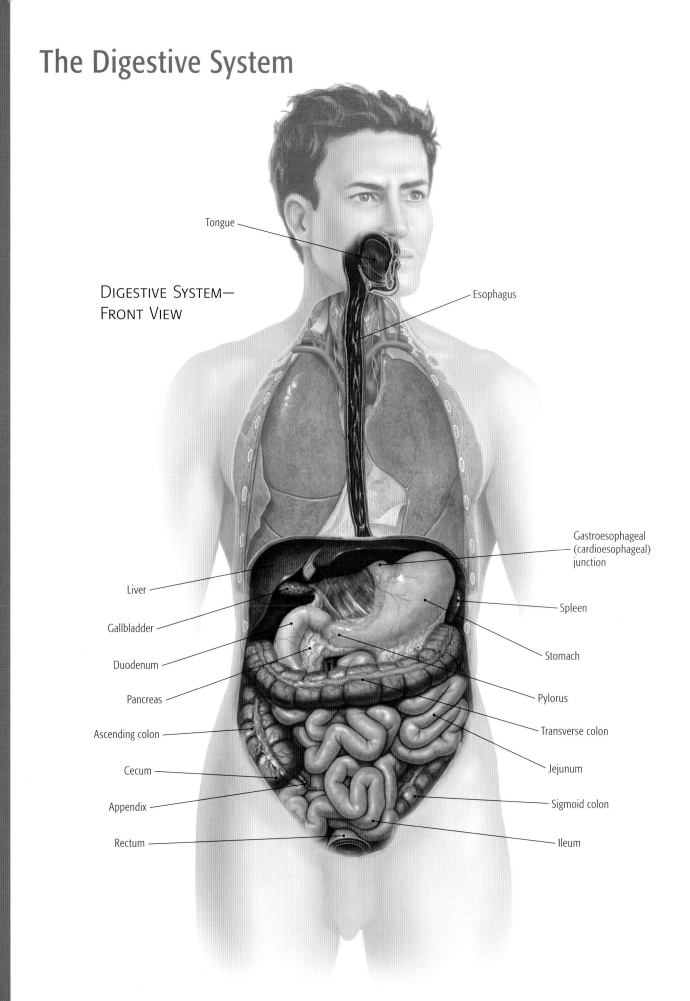

DIGESTIVE SYSTEM—
FRONT VIEW

Tongue

Esophagus

Gastroesophageal
(cardioesophageal)
junction

Liver

Spleen

Gallbladder

Stomach

Duodenum

Pylorus

Pancreas

Transverse colon

Ascending colon

Jejunum

Cecum

Sigmoid colon

Appendix

Rectum

Ileum

UPPER PART OF THE ABDOMEN—CROSS-SECTIONAL VIEW

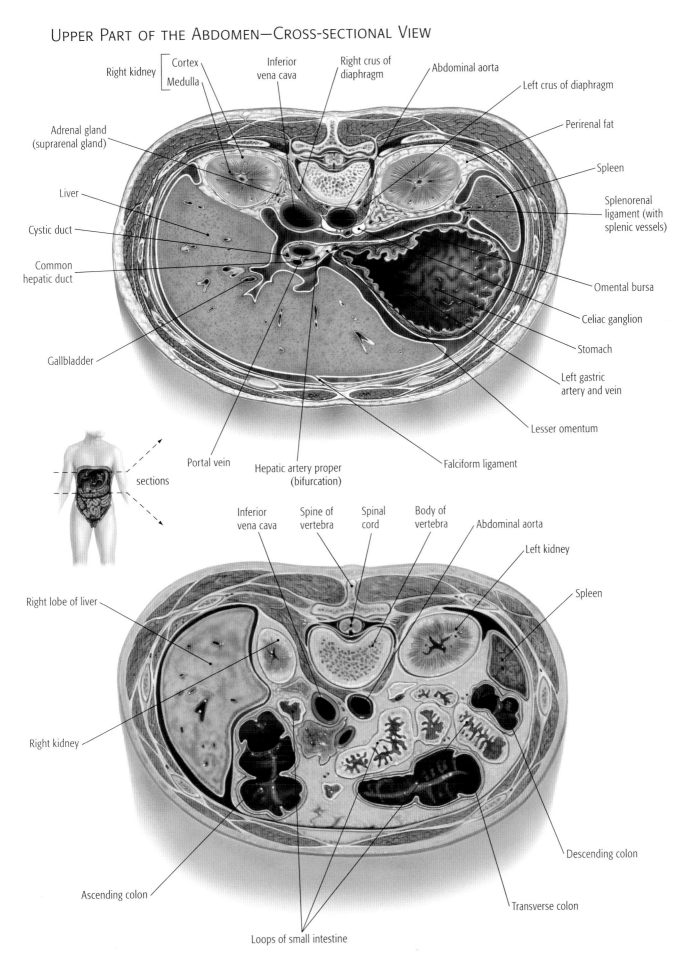

Right kidney [Cortex / Medulla]

Inferior vena cava

Right crus of diaphragm

Abdominal aorta

Left crus of diaphragm

Perirenal fat

Adrenal gland (suprarenal gland)

Spleen

Liver

Splenorenal ligament (with splenic vessels)

Cystic duct

Common hepatic duct

Omental bursa

Celiac ganglion

Stomach

Left gastric artery and vein

Gallbladder

Lesser omentum

Portal vein

Hepatic artery proper (bifurcation)

Falciform ligament

sections

Inferior vena cava

Spine of vertebra

Spinal cord

Body of vertebra

Abdominal aorta

Left kidney

Right lobe of liver

Spleen

Right kidney

Ascending colon

Loops of small intestine

Transverse colon

Descending colon

MIDDLE PART OF THE ABDOMEN—CROSS-SECTIONAL VIEW

The Digestive System

DIGESTIVE ORGANS AND GREATER OMENTUM

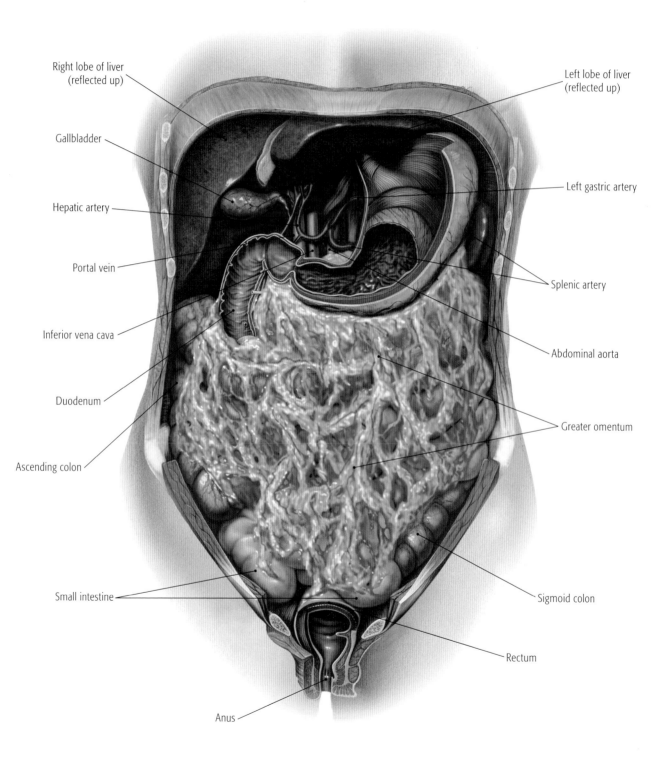

Right lobe of liver (reflected up)

Gallbladder

Hepatic artery

Portal vein

Inferior vena cava

Duodenum

Ascending colon

Small intestine

Anus

Left lobe of liver (reflected up)

Left gastric artery

Splenic artery

Abdominal aorta

Greater omentum

Sigmoid colon

Rectum

ABDOMINAL ORGANS

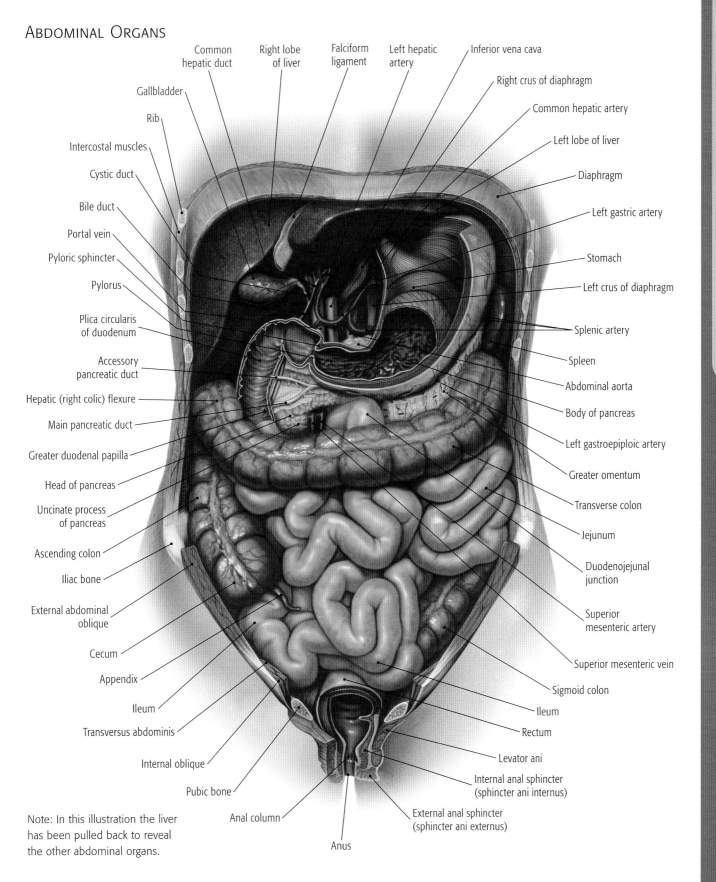

Common hepatic duct

Right lobe of liver

Falciform ligament

Left hepatic artery

Inferior vena cava

Right crus of diaphragm

Common hepatic artery

Left lobe of liver

Diaphragm

Left gastric artery

Stomach

Left crus of diaphragm

Splenic artery

Spleen

Abdominal aorta

Body of pancreas

Left gastroepiploic artery

Greater omentum

Transverse colon

Jejunum

Duodenojejunal junction

Superior mesenteric artery

Superior mesenteric vein

Sigmoid colon

Ileum

Rectum

Levator ani

Internal anal sphincter (sphincter ani internus)

External anal sphincter (sphincter ani externus)

Gallbladder

Rib

Intercostal muscles

Cystic duct

Bile duct

Portal vein

Pyloric sphincter

Pylorus

Plica circularis of duodenum

Accessory pancreatic duct

Hepatic (right colic) flexure

Main pancreatic duct

Greater duodenal papilla

Head of pancreas

Uncinate process of pancreas

Ascending colon

Iliac bone

External abdominal oblique

Cecum

Appendix

Ileum

Transversus abdominis

Internal oblique

Pubic bone

Anal column

Anus

Note: In this illustration the liver has been pulled back to reveal the other abdominal organs.

Digestion and Absorption of Nutrients

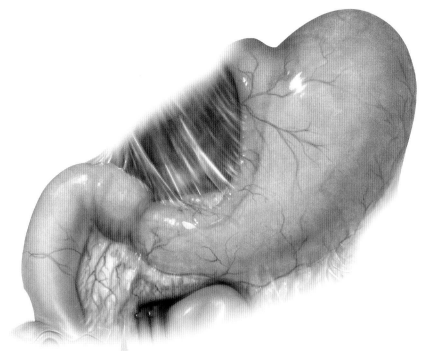

STOMACH

Food is swallowed via the mouth, travels down through the esophagus, and enters the stomach, where it is mixed with acid and pepsin (an enzyme that breaks down proteins into amino acids).

SMALL INTESTINE

From the stomach, semiliquid food matter (known as chyme) passes into the small intestine, where it is broken down into simple sugars, amino acids, and fatty acids that can be absorbed through the lining of the small intestine.

Vasa recta

Mesentery

Nerve

Muscularis externa

Submucosa

Serosa

Mucosa

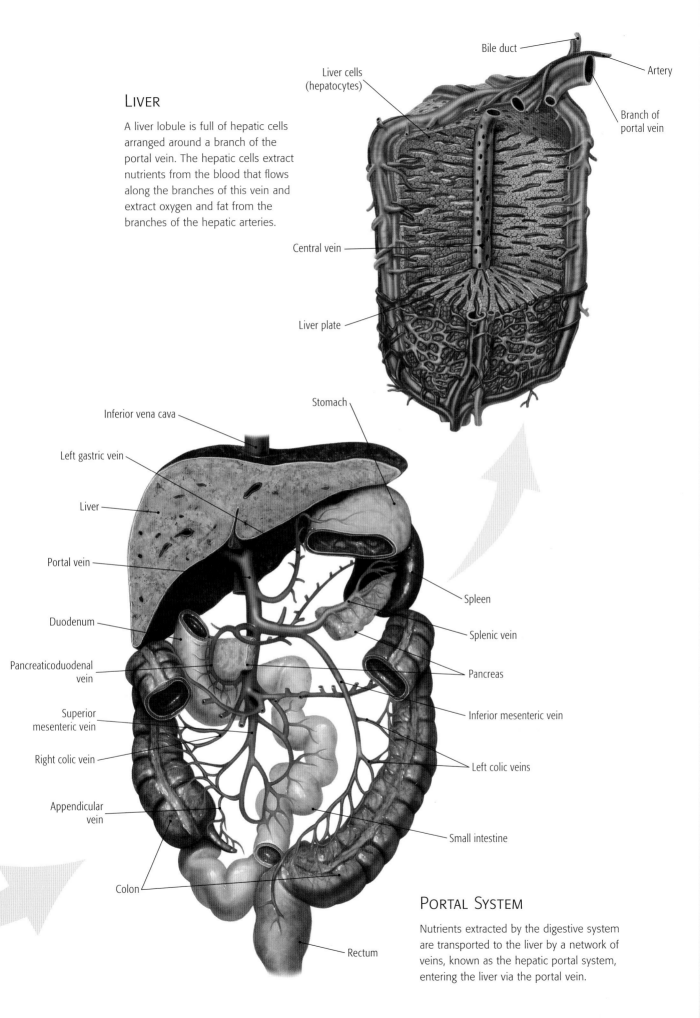

Bile duct

Artery

Liver cells
(hepatocytes)

Branch of
portal vein

LIVER

A liver lobule is full of hepatic cells
arranged around a branch of the
portal vein. The hepatic cells extract
nutrients from the blood that flows
along the branches of this vein and
extract oxygen and fat from the
branches of the hepatic arteries.

Central vein

Liver plate

Inferior vena cava

Stomach

Left gastric vein

Liver

Portal vein

Spleen

Splenic vein

Duodenum

Pancreaticoduodenal
vein

Pancreas

Superior
mesenteric vein

Inferior mesenteric vein

Right colic vein

Left colic veins

Appendicular
vein

Small intestine

Colon

PORTAL SYSTEM

Nutrients extracted by the digestive system
are transported to the liver by a network of
veins, known as the hepatic portal system,
entering the liver via the portal vein.

Rectum

Mouth and Tongue

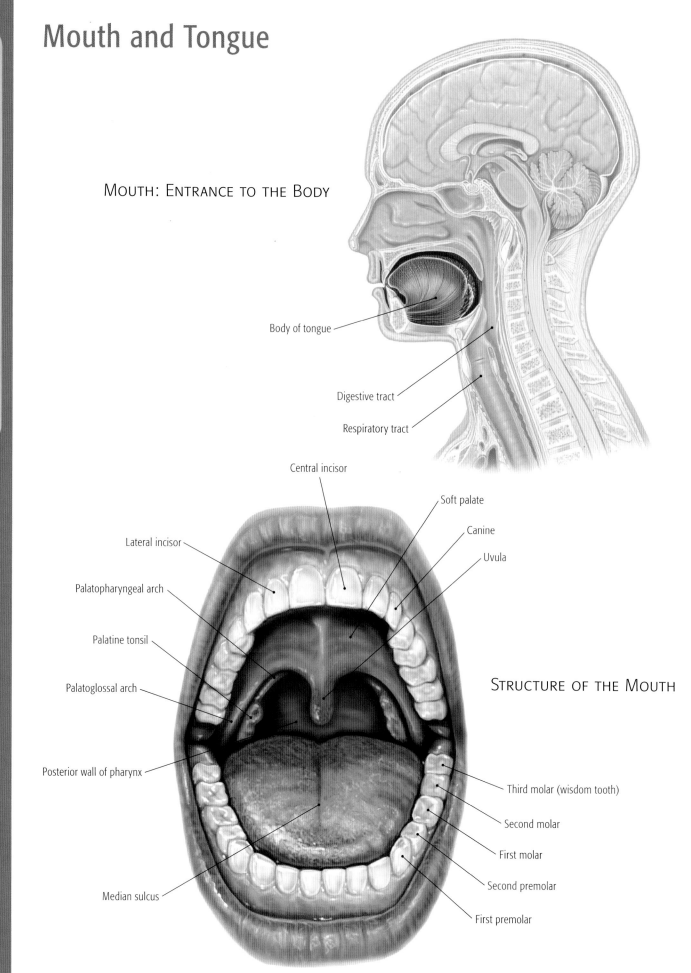

MOUTH: ENTRANCE TO THE BODY

Body of tongue

Digestive tract

Respiratory tract

Central incisor

Lateral incisor

Palatopharyngeal arch

Palatine tonsil

Palatoglossal arch

Posterior wall of pharynx

Median sulcus

Soft palate

Canine

Uvula

STRUCTURE OF THE MOUTH

Third molar (wisdom tooth)

Second molar

First molar

Second premolar

First premolar

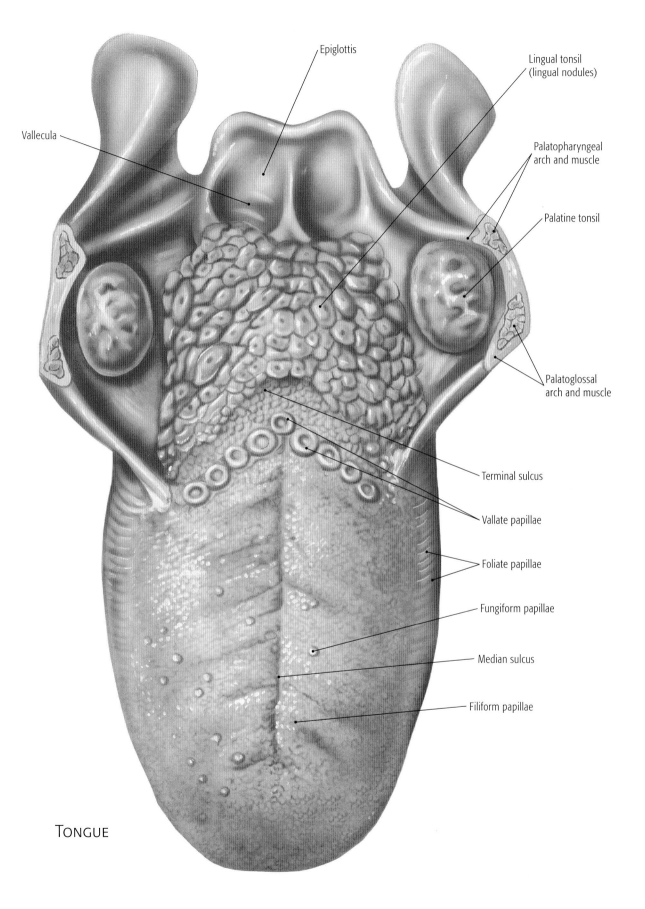

Epiglottis

Lingual tonsil
(lingual nodules)

Vallecula

Palatopharyngeal
arch and muscle

Palatine tonsil

Palatoglossal
arch and muscle

Terminal sulcus

Vallate papillae

Foliate papillae

Fungiform papillae

Median sulcus

Filiform papillae

TONGUE

Teeth

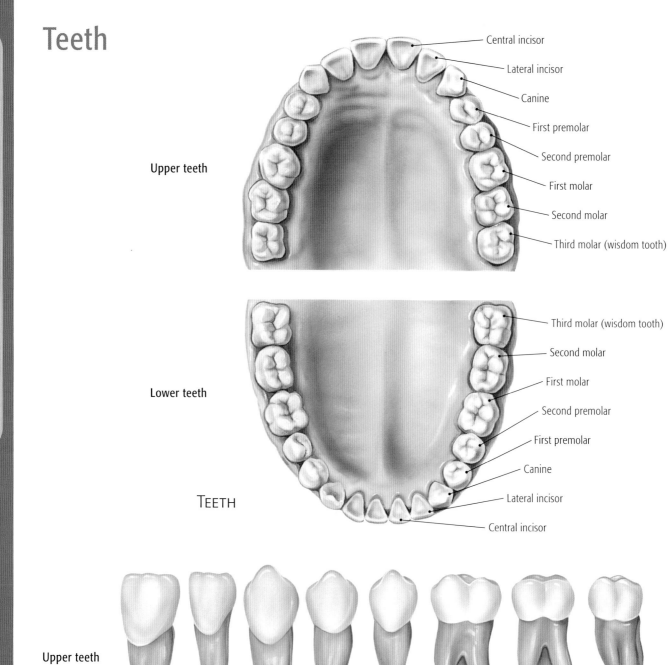

Upper teeth

- Central incisor
- Lateral incisor
- Canine
- First premolar
- Second premolar
- First molar
- Second molar
- Third molar (wisdom tooth)

Lower teeth

- Third molar (wisdom tooth)
- Second molar
- First molar
- Second premolar
- First premolar
- Canine
- Lateral incisor
- Central incisor

TEETH

Upper teeth

Lower teeth

Central incisor | Lateral incisor | Canine | First premolar | Second premolar | First molar | Second molar | Third molar (wisdom tooth)

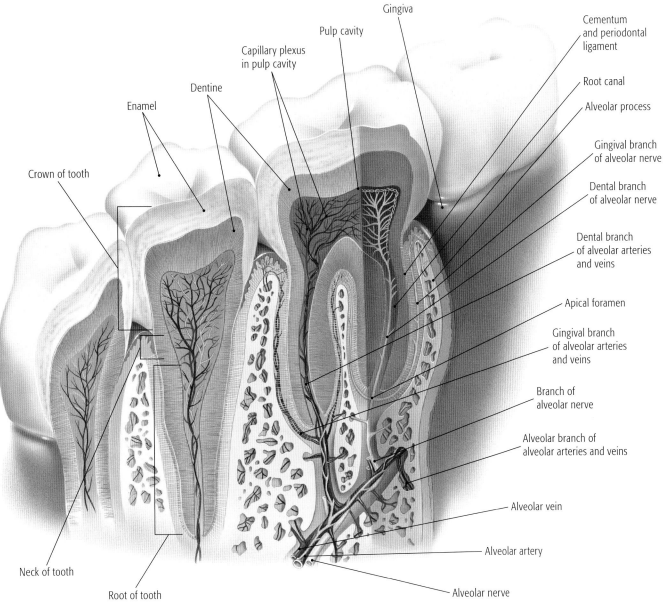

Gingiva

Pulp cavity

Capillary plexus
in pulp cavity

Cementum
and periodontal
ligament

Root canal

Alveolar process

Gingival branch
of alveolar nerve

Dentine

Dental branch
of alveolar nerve

Enamel

Dental branch
of alveolar arteries
and veins

Crown of tooth

Apical foramen

Gingival branch
of alveolar arteries
and veins

Branch of
alveolar nerve

Alveolar branch of
alveolar arteries and veins

Alveolar vein

Alveolar artery

Neck of tooth

Root of tooth

Alveolar nerve

STRUCTURE OF TEETH—CROSS-SECTIONAL VIEW

Salivary Glands

ORAL CAVITY AND SALIVARY GLANDS

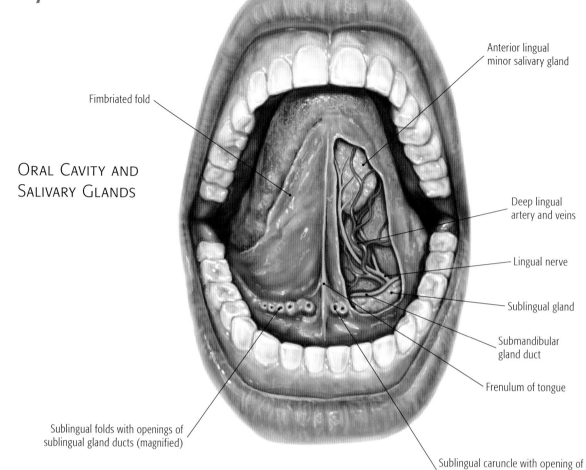

Fimbriated fold

Anterior lingual minor salivary gland

Deep lingual artery and veins

Lingual nerve

Sublingual gland

Submandibular gland duct

Frenulum of tongue

Sublingual folds with openings of sublingual gland ducts (magnified)

Sublingual caruncle with opening of submandibular gland duct (magnified)

SALIVARY GLANDS

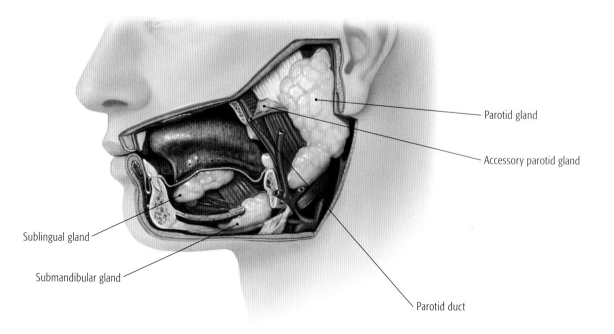

Parotid gland

Accessory parotid gland

Sublingual gland

Submandibular gland

Parotid duct

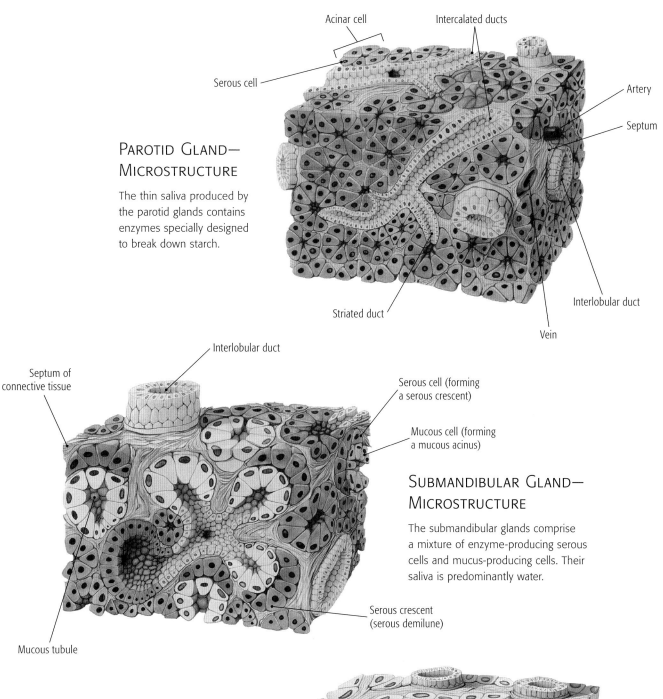

PAROTID GLAND— MICROSTRUCTURE

The thin saliva produced by the parotid glands contains enzymes specially designed to break down starch.

Acinar cell

Serous cell

Intercalated ducts

Artery

Septum

Interlobular duct

Vein

Striated duct

Interlobular duct

Septum of connective tissue

Serous cell (forming a serous crescent)

Mucous cell (forming a mucous acinus)

SUBMANDIBULAR GLAND— MICROSTRUCTURE

The submandibular glands comprise a mixture of enzyme-producing serous cells and mucus-producing cells. Their saliva is predominantly water.

Serous crescent (serous demilune)

Mucous tubule

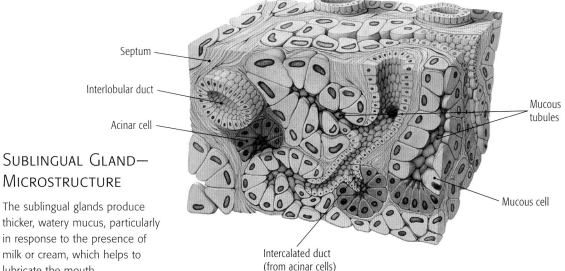

Septum

Interlobular duct

Acinar cell

Mucous tubules

Mucous cell

SUBLINGUAL GLAND— MICROSTRUCTURE

The sublingual glands produce thicker, watery mucus, particularly in response to the presence of milk or cream, which helps to lubricate the mouth.

Intercalated duct (from acinar cells)

Liver and Gallbladder

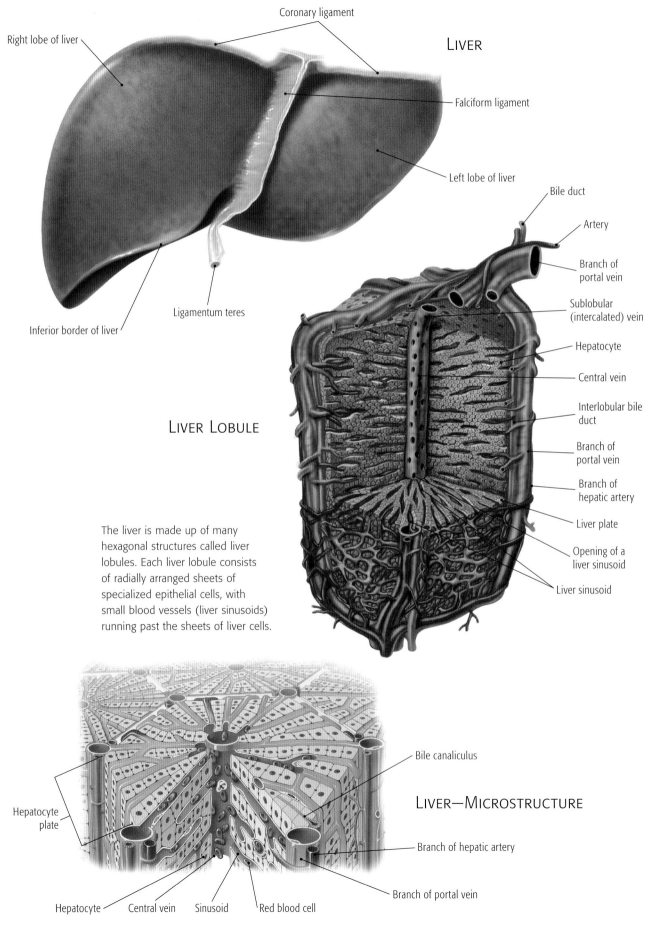

LIVER

Coronary ligament

Right lobe of liver

Falciform ligament

Left lobe of liver

Ligamentum teres

Inferior border of liver

Bile duct

Artery

Branch of portal vein

Sublobular (intercalated) vein

Hepatocyte

Central vein

Interlobular bile duct

Branch of portal vein

Branch of hepatic artery

Liver plate

Opening of a liver sinusoid

Liver sinusoid

LIVER LOBULE

The liver is made up of many hexagonal structures called liver lobules. Each liver lobule consists of radially arranged sheets of specialized epithelial cells, with small blood vessels (liver sinusoids) running past the sheets of liver cells.

Bile canaliculus

LIVER—MICROSTRUCTURE

Hepatocyte plate

Branch of hepatic artery

Branch of portal vein

Hepatocyte   Central vein   Sinusoid   Red blood cell

226

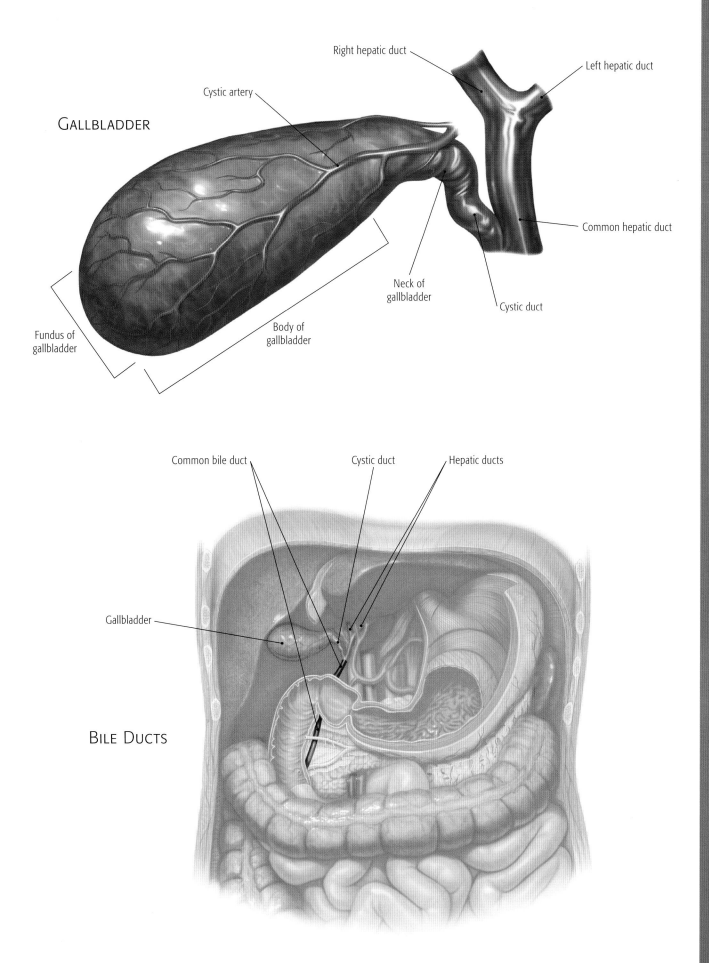

Gallbladder

Right hepatic duct

Cystic artery

Left hepatic duct

Common hepatic duct

Neck of gallbladder

Cystic duct

Fundus of gallbladder

Body of gallbladder

Common bile duct

Cystic duct

Hepatic ducts

Gallbladder

Bile Ducts

Stomach and Pancreas

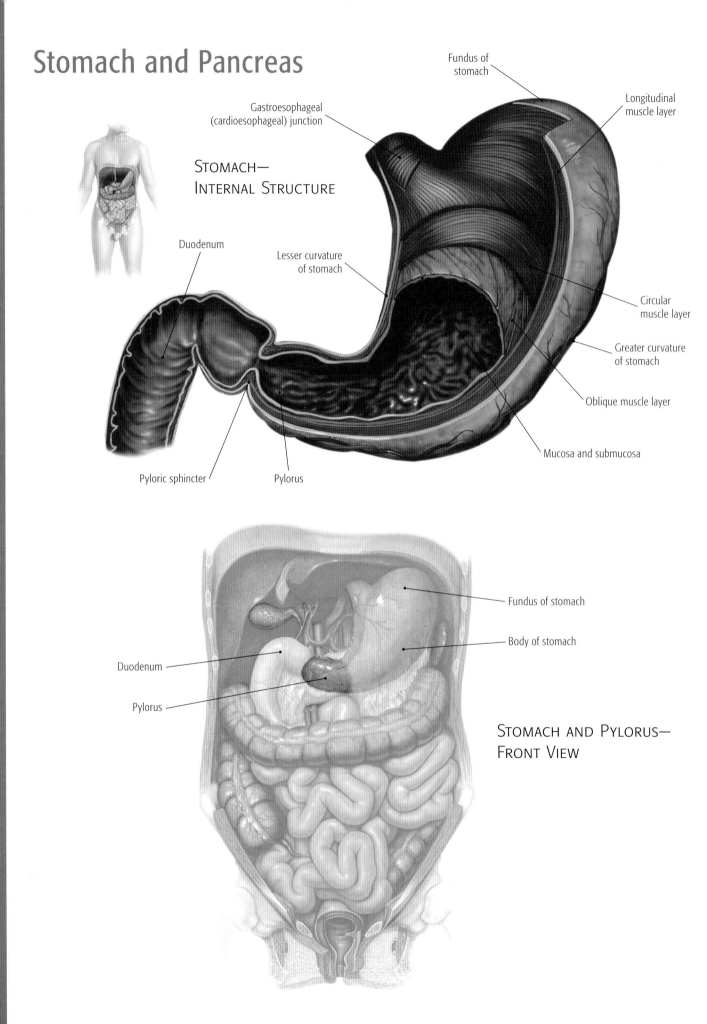

Fundus of stomach

Gastroesophageal (cardioesophageal) junction

Longitudinal muscle layer

STOMACH— INTERNAL STRUCTURE

Duodenum

Lesser curvature of stomach

Circular muscle layer

Greater curvature of stomach

Oblique muscle layer

Mucosa and submucosa

Pyloric sphincter

Pylorus

Duodenum

Fundus of stomach

Body of stomach

Pylorus

STOMACH AND PYLORUS— FRONT VIEW

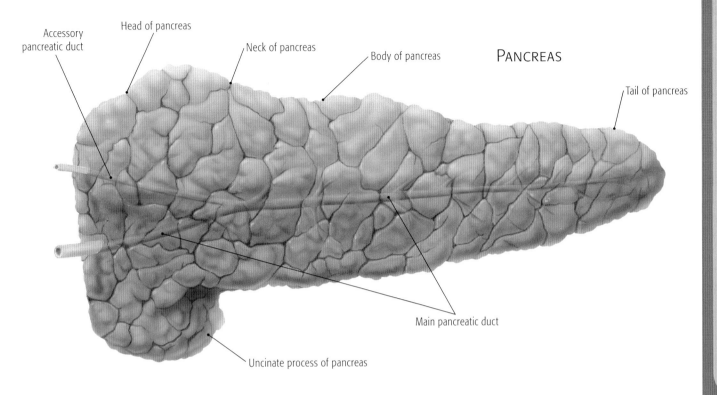

Accessory pancreatic duct

Head of pancreas

Neck of pancreas

Body of pancreas

PANCREAS

Tail of pancreas

Main pancreatic duct

Uncinate process of pancreas

PANCREAS: EXOCRINE CELLS

Most of the pancreas consists of acinar cells, which secrete digestive enzymes that aid in food processing. The enzymes flow from the cells into the small intestine along a network of attached ducts.

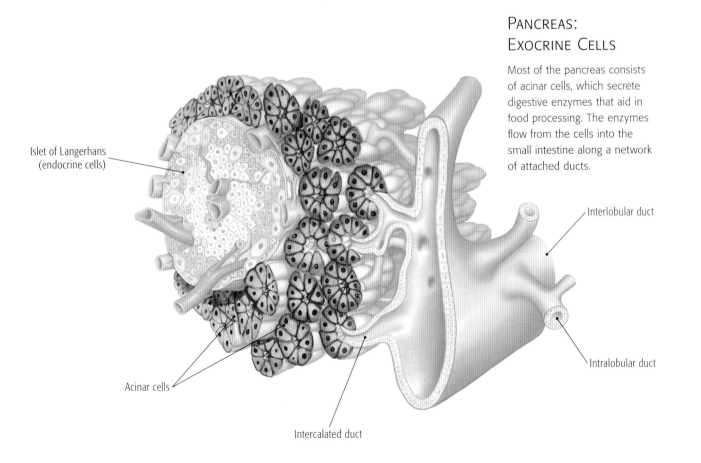

Islet of Langerhans (endocrine cells)

Interlobular duct

Intralobular duct

Acinar cells

Intercalated duct

Alimentary Canal and Peristalsis

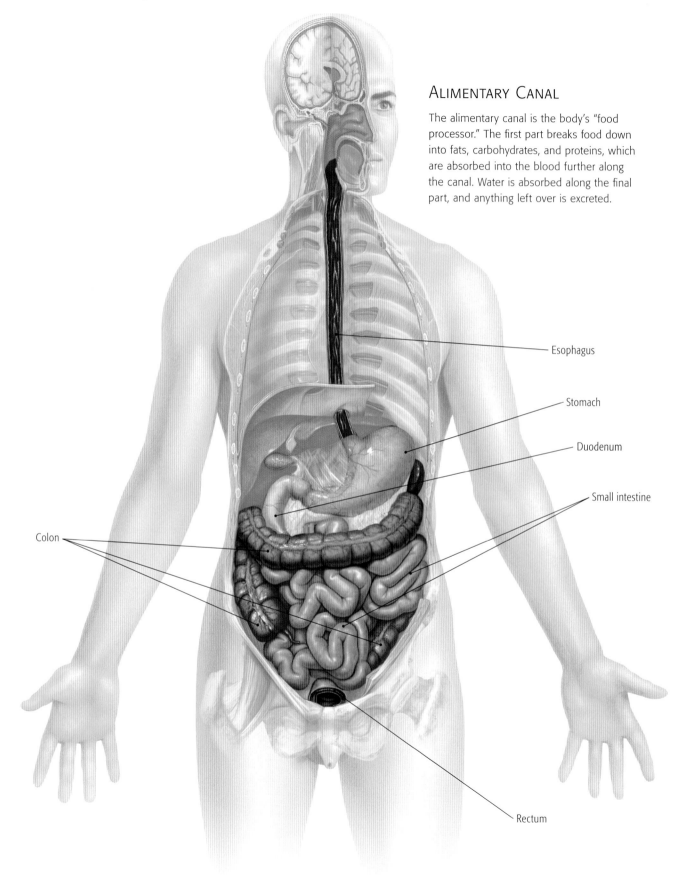

ALIMENTARY CANAL

The alimentary canal is the body's "food processor." The first part breaks food down into fats, carbohydrates, and proteins, which are absorbed into the blood further along the canal. Water is absorbed along the final part, and anything left over is excreted.

Esophagus

Stomach

Duodenum

Small intestine

Colon

Rectum

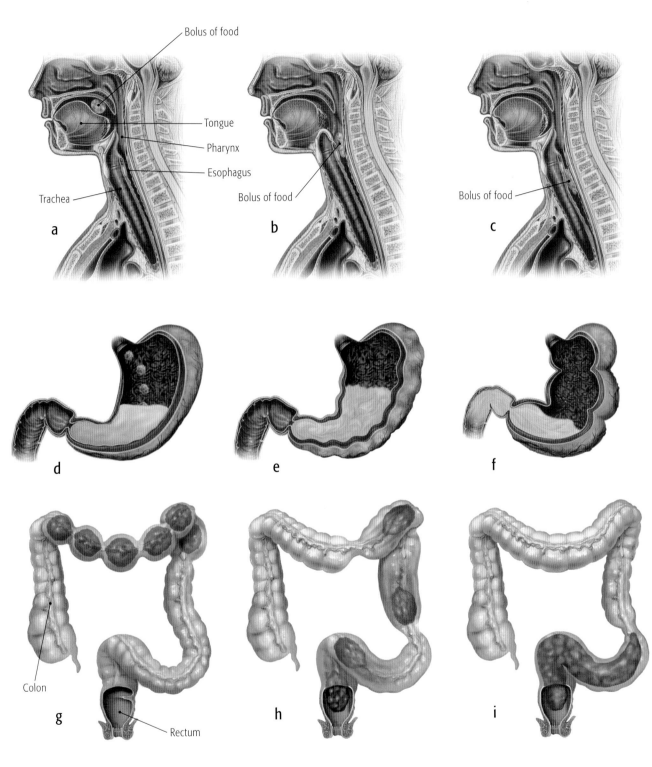

Bolus of food

Tongue

Pharynx

Esophagus

Trachea

Bolus of food

Bolus of food

a

b

c

d

e

f

Colon

g

Rectum

h

i

PERISTALSIS

Peristalsis consists of wavelike contractions in the muscular walls of the esophagus, stomach, and intestines that propel the contents along. After food is swallowed, it enters the esophagus (**a, b, c**) and travels toward the stomach (**d, e, f**) before moving to the small intestine and then the colon. Water and bile salts are absorbed from the colon before peristaltic contractions push the waste matter along to the rectum (**g, h, i**).

Intestines

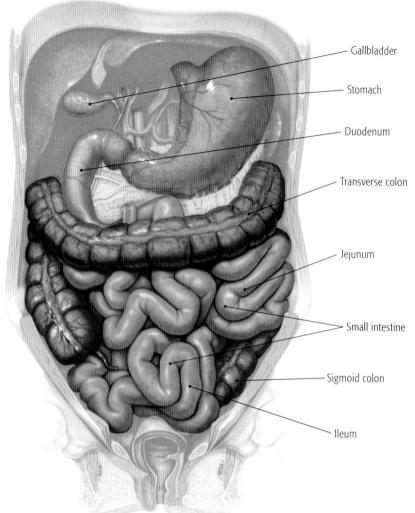

STOMACH AND INTESTINES

Gallbladder

Stomach

Duodenum

Transverse colon

Jejunum

Small intestine

Sigmoid colon

Ileum

DUODENUM

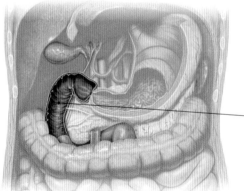

Duodenum

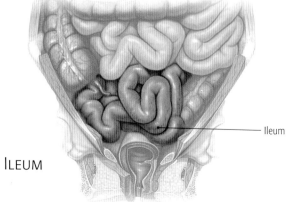

Jejunum

JEJUNUM

Ileum

ILEUM

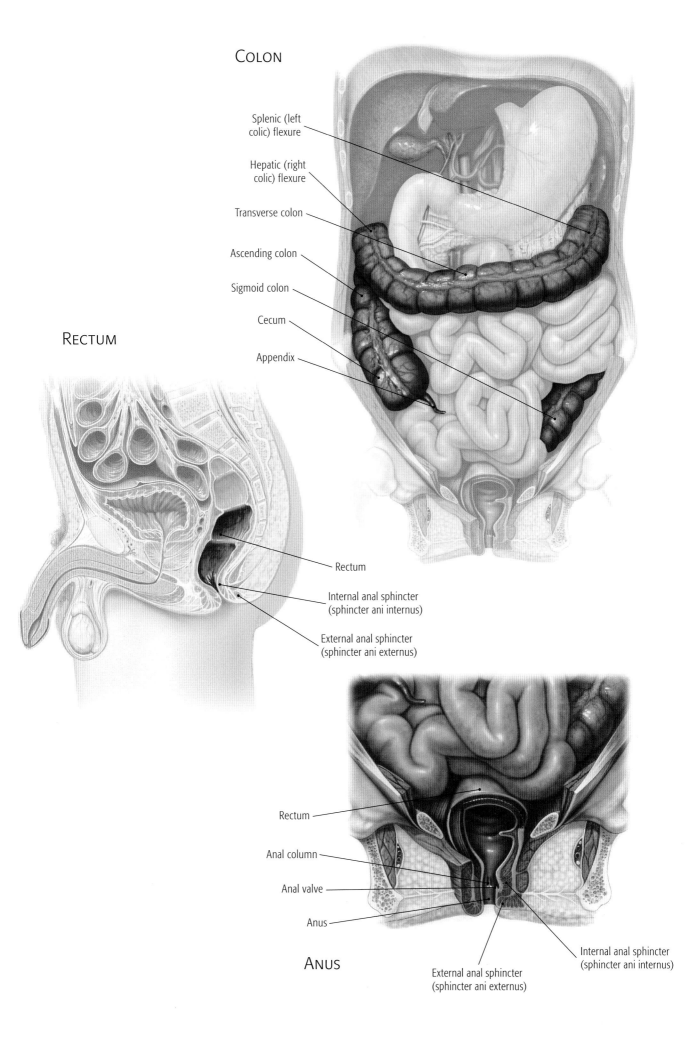

Colon

Splenic (left colic) flexure

Hepatic (right colic) flexure

Transverse colon

Ascending colon

Sigmoid colon

Cecum

Appendix

Rectum

Rectum

Internal anal sphincter (sphincter ani internus)

External anal sphincter (sphincter ani externus)

Rectum

Anal column

Anal valve

Anus

Internal anal sphincter (sphincter ani internus)

External anal sphincter (sphincter ani externus)

Anus

Intestines

Mesentery

INTESTINAL JEJUNUM—CUT-AWAY VIEW

The jejunum is the part of the small intestine between the duodenum and the ileum. It digests and absorbs food, sending nutrients to the lymphatic vessels and liver.

Nerve

Mesentery

Inner circular layer of muscularis externa

Outer longitudinal layer of muscularis externa

Plicae circulares

Nerves of myenteric plexus

Serosa (mesothelium)

Serosa (connective tissue)

Muscularis mucosae

Submucosa

Mucosa

Outer longitudinal fibers of muscularis externa

INTESTINAL JEJUNUM PLICA—CROSS-SECTIONAL VIEW

The lining of the jejunum has many small folds (known as plicae circulares) that feature tiny fingerlike projections called villi. The plicae circulares and villi greatly increase the surface area available for the absorption of nutrients.

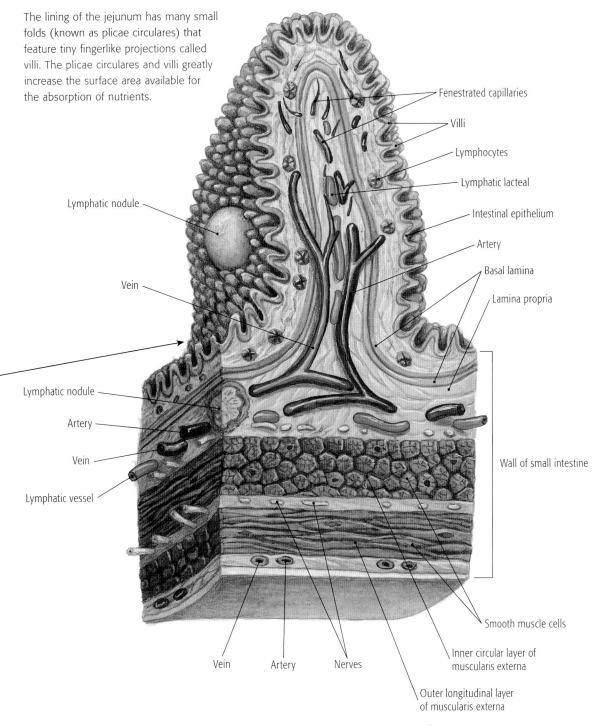

Fenestrated capillaries

Villi

Lymphocytes

Lymphatic lacteal

Intestinal epithelium

Artery

Basal lamina

Lamina propria

Lymphatic nodule

Vein

Lymphatic nodule

Artery

Vein

Lymphatic vessel

Wall of small intestine

Smooth muscle cells

Inner circular layer of muscularis externa

Outer longitudinal layer of muscularis externa

Vein   Artery   Nerves

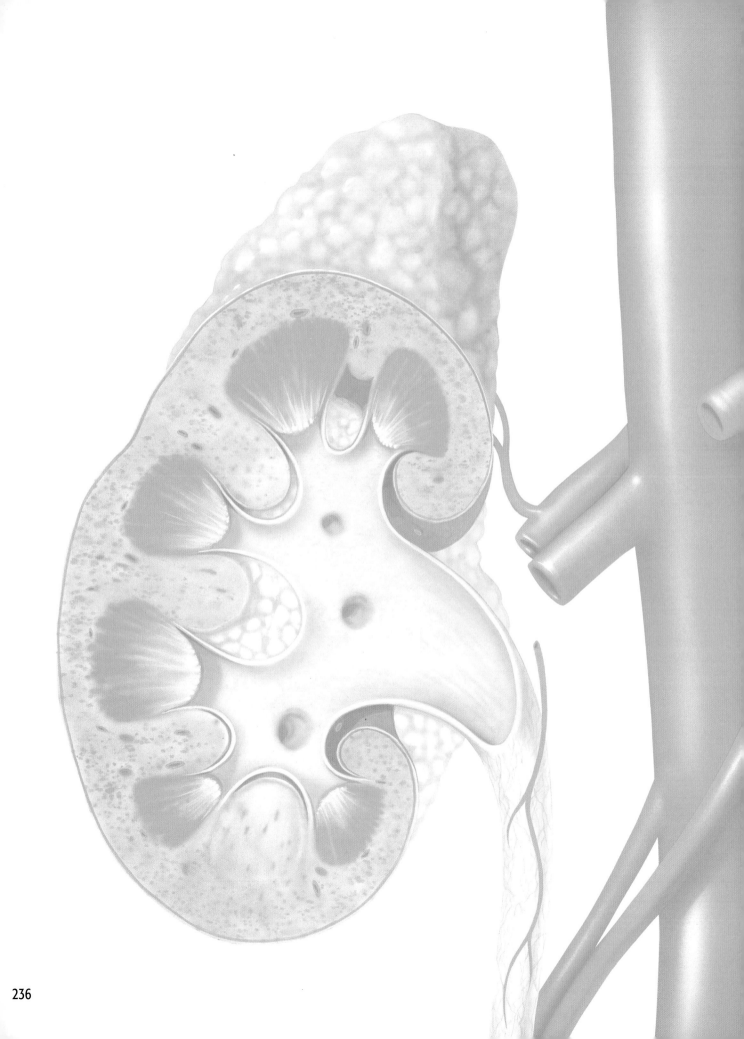

The Urinary System

The Urinary System

MALE URINARY SYSTEM—
FRONT VIEW

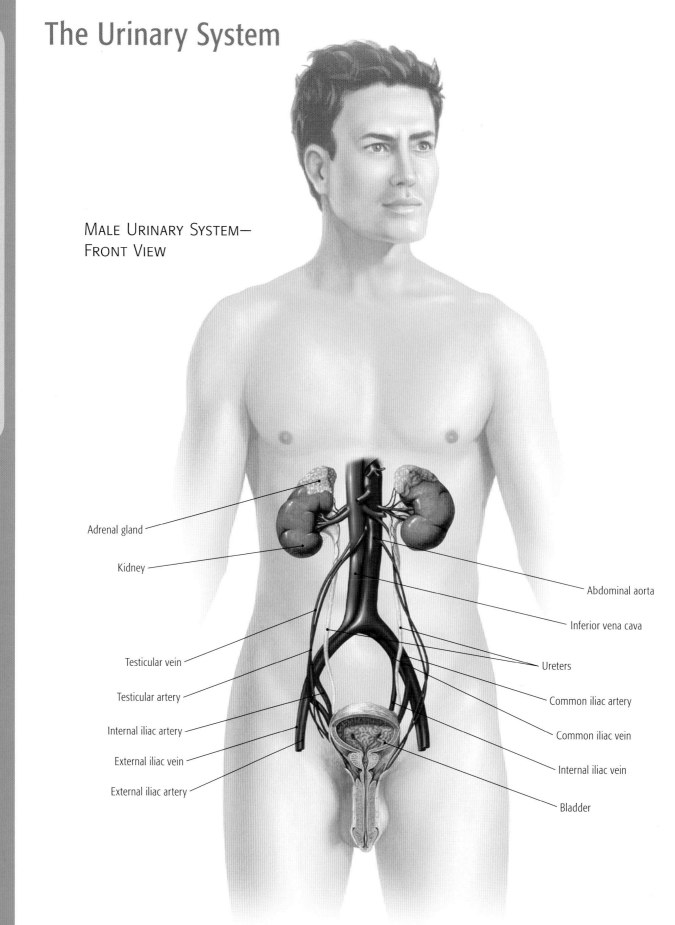

Adrenal gland

Kidney

Testicular vein

Testicular artery

Internal iliac artery

External iliac vein

External iliac artery

Abdominal aorta

Inferior vena cava

Ureters

Common iliac artery

Common iliac vein

Internal iliac vein

Bladder

FEMALE URINARY SYSTEM—
FRONT VIEW

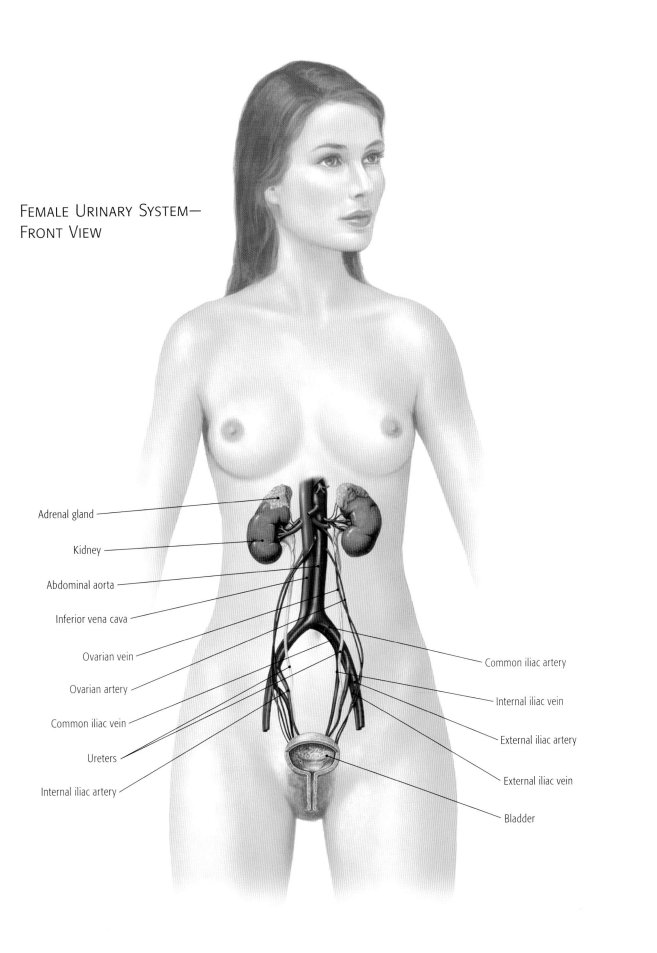

Adrenal gland

Kidney

Abdominal aorta

Inferior vena cava

Ovarian vein

Ovarian artery

Common iliac vein

Ureters

Internal iliac artery

Common iliac artery

Internal iliac vein

External iliac artery

External iliac vein

Bladder

Urinary Tract and Bladder

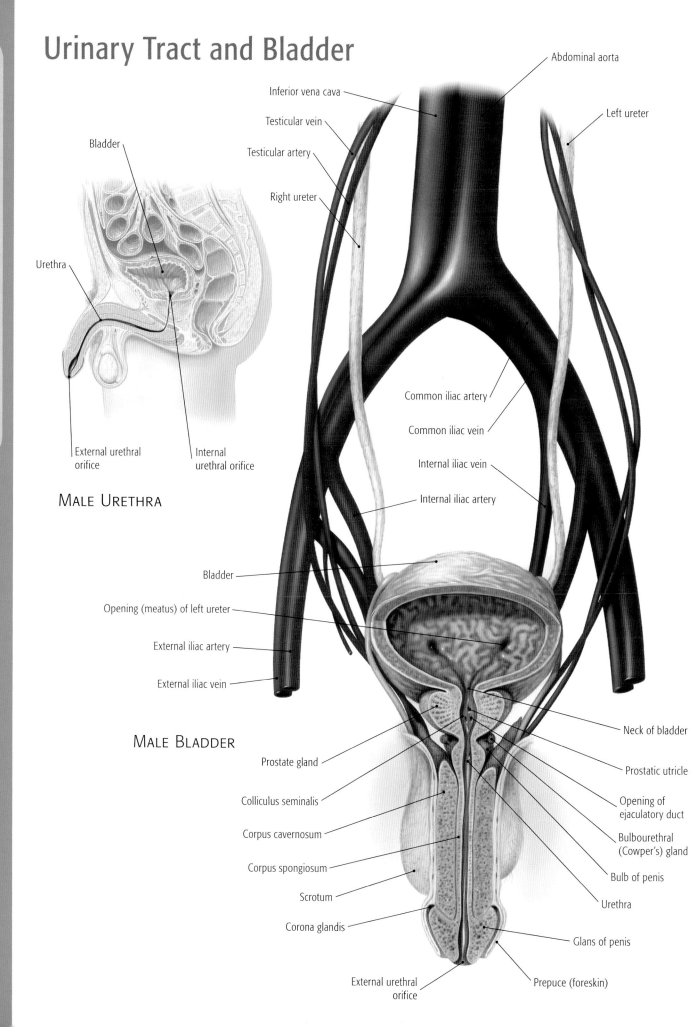

Bladder

Urethra

External urethral orifice

Internal urethral orifice

MALE URETHRA

Inferior vena cava

Testicular vein

Testicular artery

Right ureter

Abdominal aorta

Left ureter

Common iliac artery

Common iliac vein

Internal iliac vein

Internal iliac artery

Bladder

Opening (meatus) of left ureter

External iliac artery

External iliac vein

MALE BLADDER

Prostate gland

Colliculus seminalis

Corpus cavernosum

Corpus spongiosum

Scrotum

Corona glandis

External urethral orifice

Neck of bladder

Prostatic utricle

Opening of ejaculatory duct

Bulbourethral (Cowper's) gland

Bulb of penis

Urethra

Glans of penis

Prepuce (foreskin)

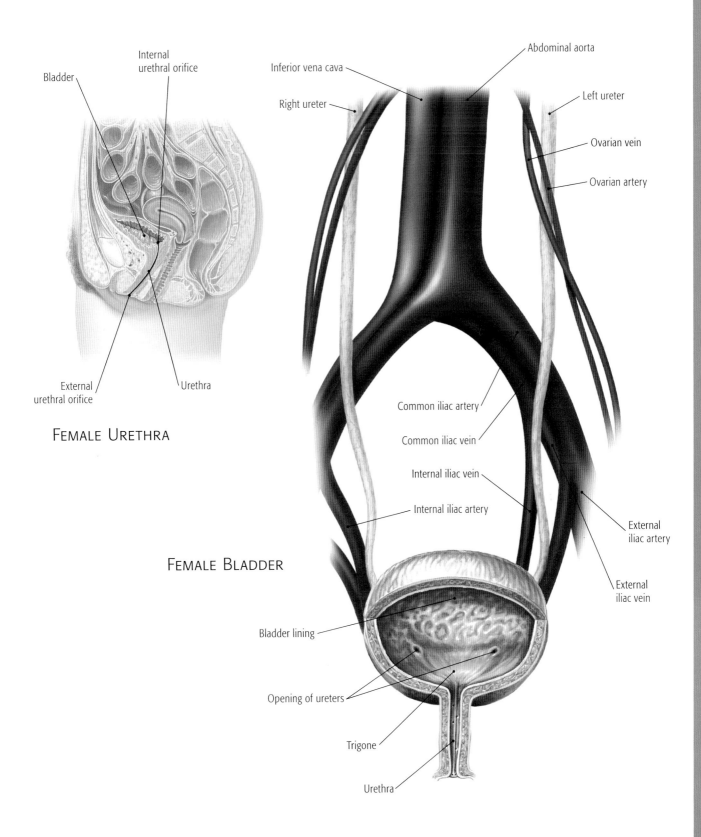

Internal
urethral orifice

Bladder

Abdominal aorta

Inferior vena cava

Right ureter

Left ureter

Ovarian vein

Ovarian artery

External
urethral orifice

Urethra

FEMALE URETHRA

Common iliac artery

Common iliac vein

Internal iliac vein

FEMALE BLADDER

Internal iliac artery

External
iliac artery

External
iliac vein

Bladder lining

Opening of ureters

Trigone

Urethra

Kidneys

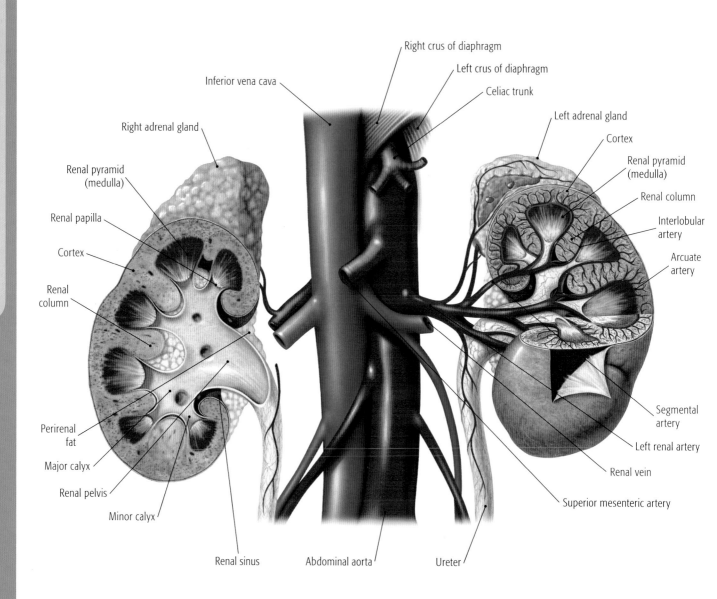

Right crus of diaphragm

Left crus of diaphragm

Celiac trunk

Inferior vena cava

Left adrenal gland

Right adrenal gland

Cortex

Renal pyramid
(medulla)

Renal pyramid
(medulla)

Renal column

Renal papilla

Interlobular
artery

Cortex

Arcuate
artery

Renal
column

Segmental
artery

Perirenal
fat

Left renal artery

Major calyx

Renal vein

Renal pelvis

Superior mesenteric artery

Minor calyx

Renal sinus   Abdominal aorta   Ureter

KIDNEYS AND ADRENAL GLANDS

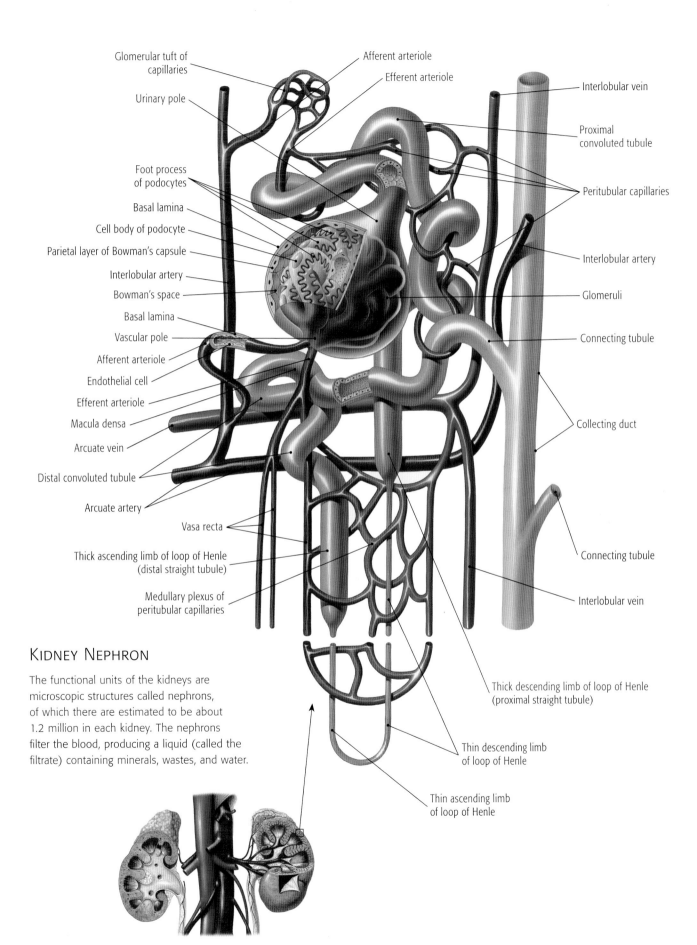

Glomerular tuft of capillaries

Afferent arteriole

Efferent arteriole

Urinary pole

Interlobular vein

Proximal convoluted tubule

Foot process of podocytes

Peritubular capillaries

Basal lamina

Cell body of podocyte

Parietal layer of Bowman's capsule

Interlobular artery

Interlobular artery

Bowman's space

Glomeruli

Basal lamina

Vascular pole

Connecting tubule

Afferent arteriole

Endothelial cell

Efferent arteriole

Macula densa

Arcuate vein

Collecting duct

Distal convoluted tubule

Arcuate artery

Vasa recta

Connecting tubule

Thick ascending limb of loop of Henle (distal straight tubule)

Interlobular vein

Medullary plexus of peritubular capillaries

Thick descending limb of loop of Henle (proximal straight tubule)

KIDNEY NEPHRON

The functional units of the kidneys are microscopic structures called nephrons, of which there are estimated to be about 1.2 million in each kidney. The nephrons filter the blood, producing a liquid (called the filtrate) containing minerals, wastes, and water.

Thin descending limb of loop of Henle

Thin ascending limb of loop of Henle

Controlling Fluid Balance

The hypothalamus monitors water levels in the blood

The posterior pituitary gland works with the kidneys to control water balance

MAINTAINING FLUID BALANCE IN THE BODY

When water levels in the blood drop too low, the hypothalamus instructs the posterior pituitary gland to release antidiuretic hormone (ADH). This makes the kidneys retain water and reabsorb it into the blood, and decreases urine production. When the body has returned to a normal state of hydration, the hypothalamus tells the pituitary to slow ADH secretion, the kidneys keep less water in the blood, and the bladder releases urine again.

The amount of antidiuretic hormone (ADH) secreted by the posterior pituitary gland affects the volume of water that the kidneys retain

When the body is dehydrated, the bladder discharges less urine than normal

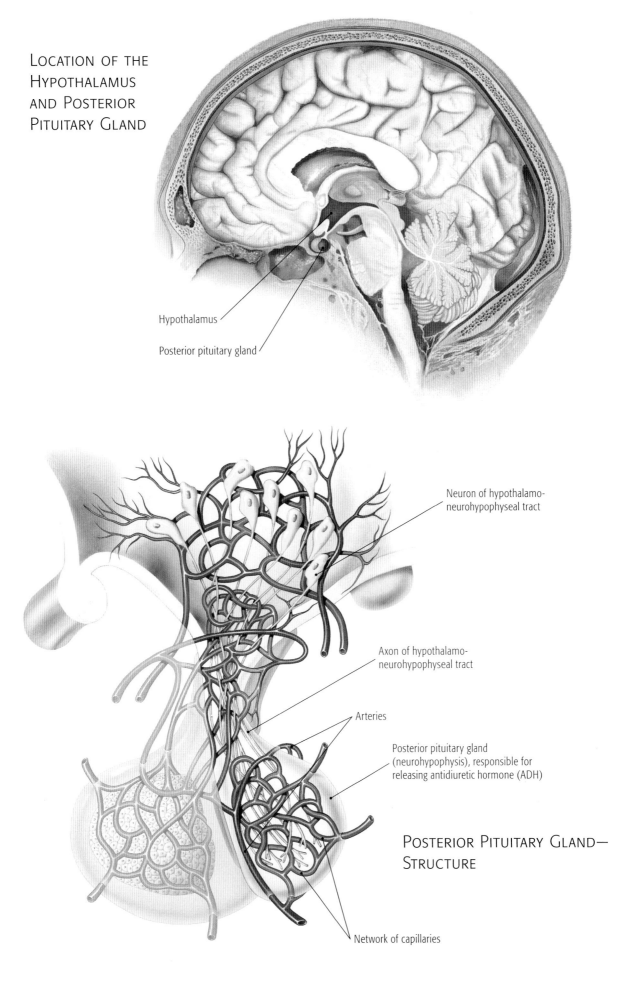

LOCATION OF THE
HYPOTHALAMUS
AND POSTERIOR
PITUITARY GLAND

Hypothalamus

Posterior pituitary gland

Neuron of hypothalamo-
neurohypophyseal tract

Axon of hypothalamo-
neurohypophyseal tract

Arteries

Posterior pituitary gland
(neurohypophysis), responsible for
releasing antidiuretic hormone (ADH)

POSTERIOR PITUITARY GLAND—
STRUCTURE

Network of capillaries

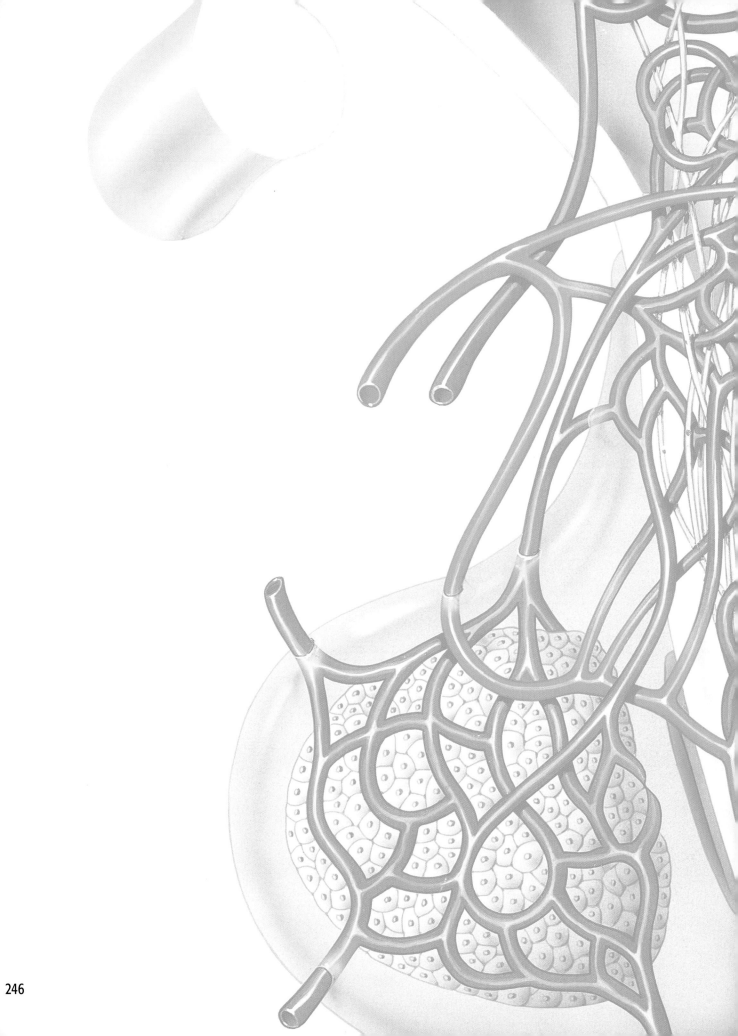

The Endocrine System

The Endocrine System

MALE ENDOCRINE SYSTEM—
FRONT VIEW

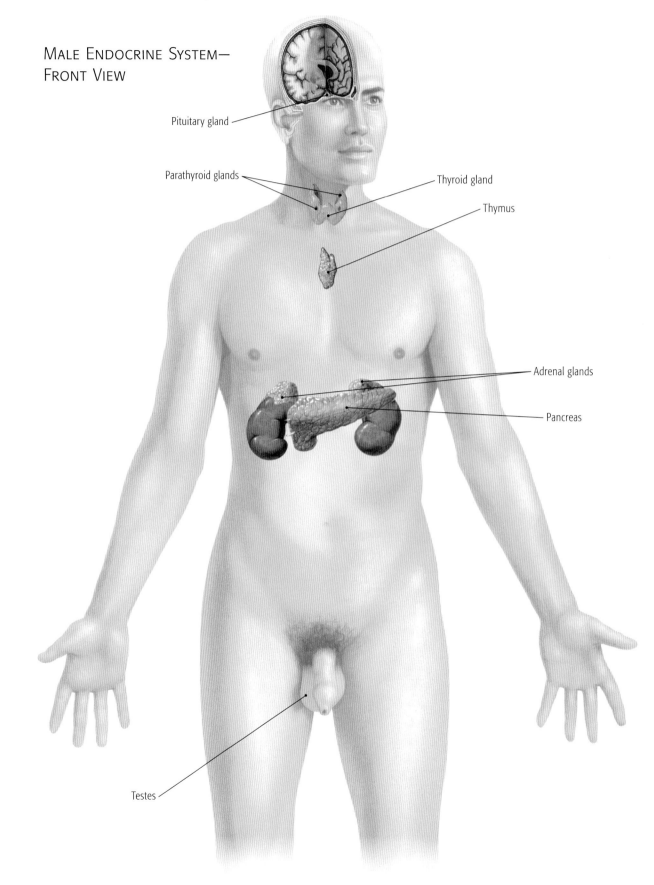

Pituitary gland

Parathyroid glands

Thyroid gland

Thymus

Adrenal glands

Pancreas

Testes

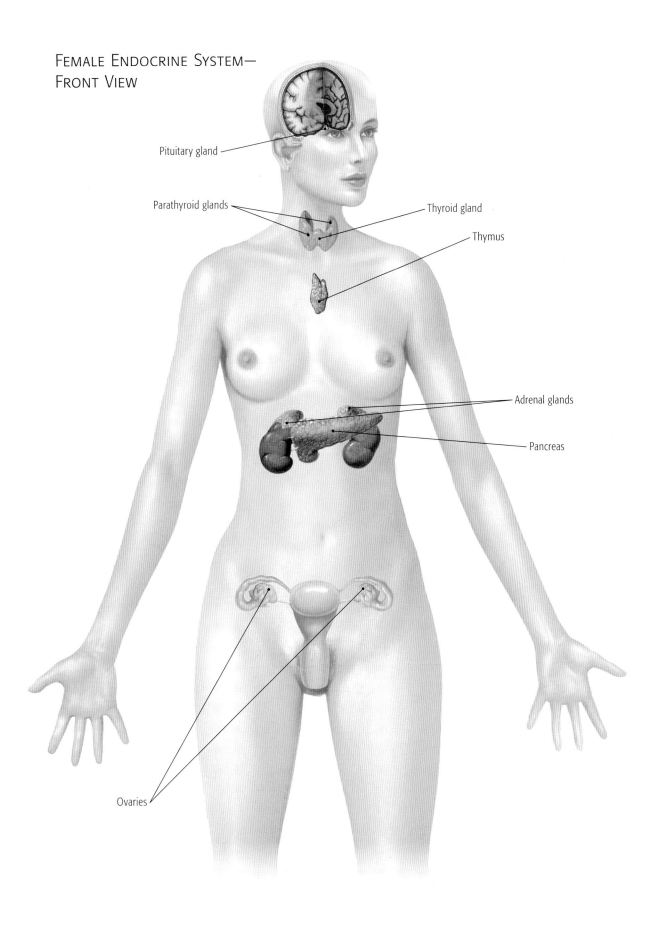

FEMALE ENDOCRINE SYSTEM— FRONT VIEW

Pituitary gland

Parathyroid glands

Thyroid gland

Thymus

Adrenal glands

Pancreas

Ovaries

Pituitary Gland

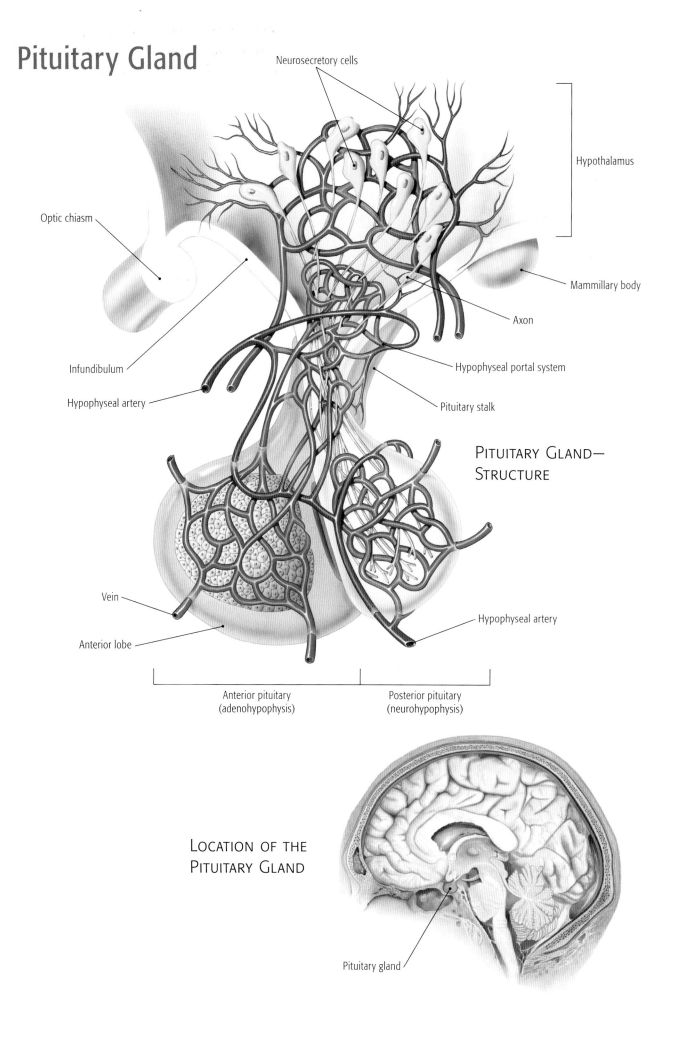

Neurosecretory cells

Hypothalamus

Optic chiasm

Mammillary body

Axon

Infundibulum

Hypophyseal portal system

Hypophyseal artery

Pituitary stalk

PITUITARY GLAND—
STRUCTURE

Vein

Hypophyseal artery

Anterior lobe

Anterior pituitary
(adenohypophysis)

Posterior pituitary
(neurohypophysis)

LOCATION OF THE
PITUITARY GLAND

Pituitary gland

GLANDS AND ORGANS AFFECTED BY THE PITUITARY GLAND

The pituitary gland exerts its effects on organs and tissues throughout the body by means of organic chemicals called hormones. This illustration shows the organs and tissues affected by the pituitary gland, and the specific hormones involved.

Kidney tubules
Antidiuretic hormone (ADH)

Bone and muscle growth
Growth hormone (GH)

Thyroid gland
Thyroid-stimulating hormone (TSH)

Posterior pituitary

Anterior pituitary

Adrenal cortex
Adrenocorticotropic hormone (ACTH)

Uterus smooth muscle
Oxytocin (OT)

Skin
Melanocyte-stimulating hormone (MSH)

Mammary glands
Oxytocin (OT)

Mammary glands
Prolactin (PRL)

Testis and Ovary
Follicle-stimulating hormone (FSH) and luteinizing hormone (LH)

Endocrine Glands

LOCATION OF THE PINEAL GLAND

The pineal gland is found deep inside the brain. It produces melatonin, thought to be involved in regulating the body's sleep–wake "clock"— melatonin production is highest during a person's normal sleeping hours, and drops off as the body begins to wake.

Corpus callosum

Thalamus

Pineal gland

Superior and inferior colliculi

LOCATION OF THE THYROID GLAND

The largest of the endocrine glands, the thyroid is situated at the front of the trachea in the neck. It secretes thyroid hormone; the main function of this hormone is to determine the metabolic rate of the body's tissues.

Thyroid gland

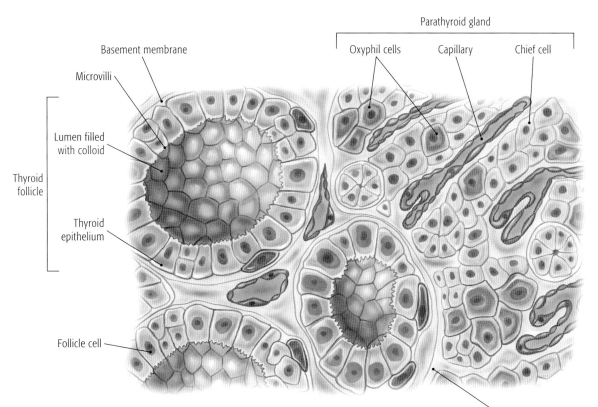

Basement membrane

Microvilli

Lumen filled with colloid

Thyroid follicle

Thyroid epithelium

Follicle cell

Parathyroid gland

Oxyphil cells

Capillary

Chief cell

Capsule of parathyroid

THYROID AND PARATHYROID GLANDS—MICROSTRUCTURE

Thyroid gland cells are separated from the cells of the parathyroid glands by a dense capsule of fibers. The thyroid gland comprises many follicles, each consisting of thyroid epithelium cells arranged around a cavity (lumen). The parathyroid glands contain two different cells: chief cells and oxyphil cells.

LOCATION OF THE PARATHYROID GLANDS

The parathyroid glands are four (or occasionally three) pea-sized endocrine glands that lie just behind the thyroid gland in the neck. They secrete parathyroid hormone, which controls calcium levels in the blood.

Parathyroid glands

Endocrine Glands

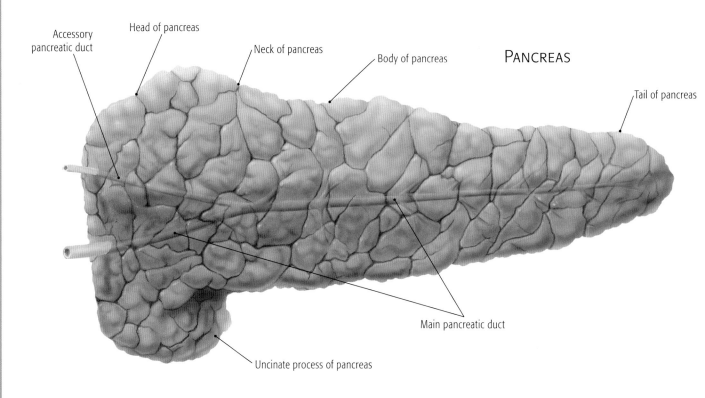

PANCREAS

Accessory pancreatic duct

Head of pancreas

Neck of pancreas

Body of pancreas

Tail of pancreas

Main pancreatic duct

Uncinate process of pancreas

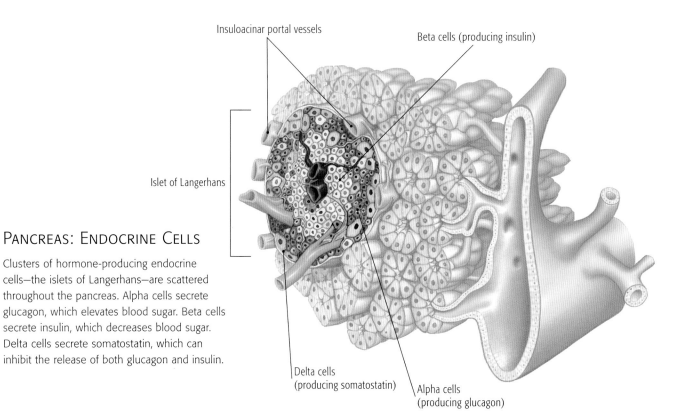

Insuloacinar portal vessels

Beta cells (producing insulin)

Islet of Langerhans

Delta cells (producing somatostatin)

Alpha cells (producing glucagon)

PANCREAS: ENDOCRINE CELLS

Clusters of hormone-producing endocrine cells—the islets of Langerhans—are scattered throughout the pancreas. Alpha cells secrete glucagon, which elevates blood sugar. Beta cells secrete insulin, which decreases blood sugar. Delta cells secrete somatostatin, which can inhibit the release of both glucagon and insulin.

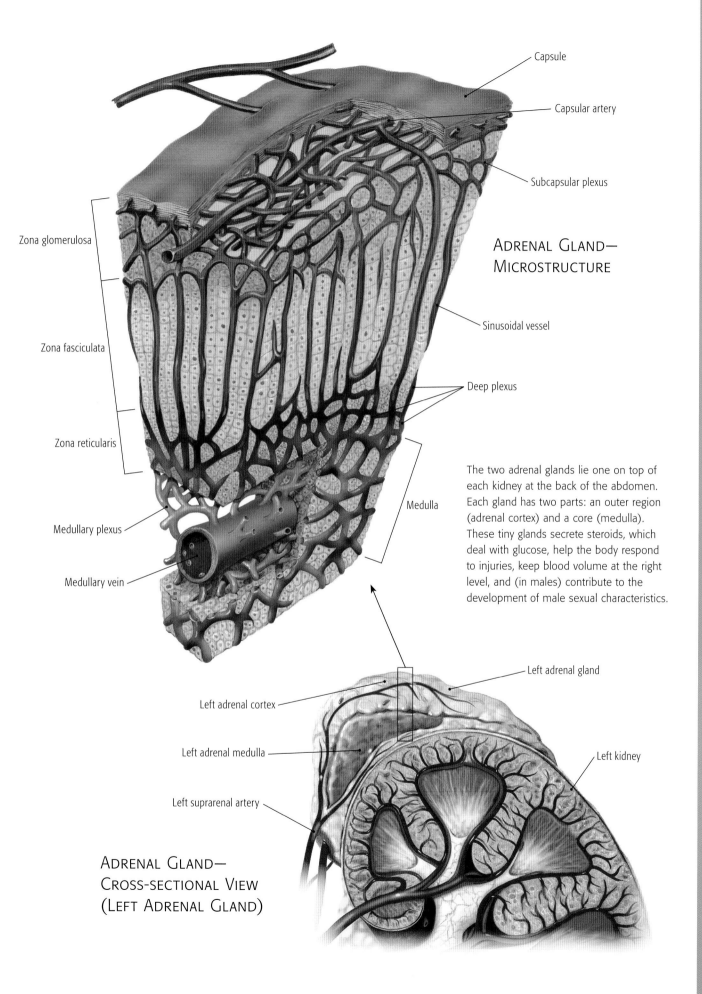

Capsule

Capsular artery

Subcapsular plexus

ADRENAL GLAND— MICROSTRUCTURE

Zona glomerulosa

Sinusoidal vessel

Zona fasciculata

Deep plexus

Zona reticularis

Medullary plexus

Medulla

The two adrenal glands lie one on top of each kidney at the back of the abdomen. Each gland has two parts: an outer region (adrenal cortex) and a core (medulla). These tiny glands secrete steroids, which deal with glucose, help the body respond to injuries, keep blood volume at the right level, and (in males) contribute to the development of male sexual characteristics.

Medullary vein

Left adrenal gland

Left adrenal cortex

Left adrenal medulla

Left kidney

Left suprarenal artery

ADRENAL GLAND— CROSS-SECTIONAL VIEW (LEFT ADRENAL GLAND)

Male and Female Endocrine Glands

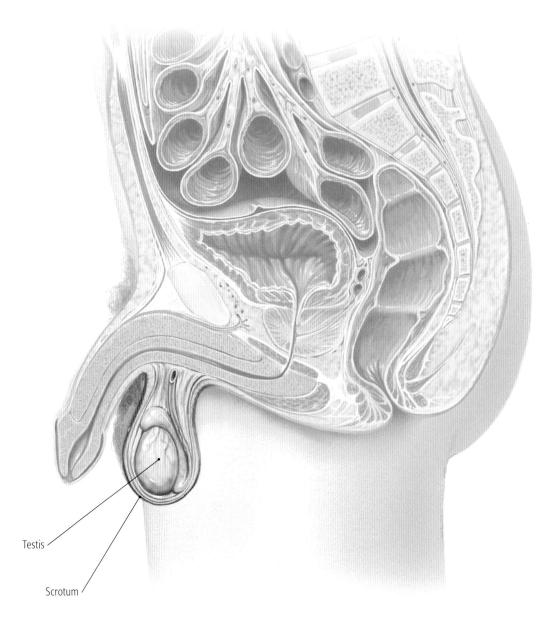

Testis

Scrotum

TESTES: ENDOCRINE FUNCTION

The testes are two ovoid organs contained in the scrotum, a sac that lies directly behind and beneath the penis. They produce testosterone, which is responsible for the development of secondary sexual characteristics in the male—it stimulates the growth of facial and pubic hair, deepens the voice, and increases muscle tone.

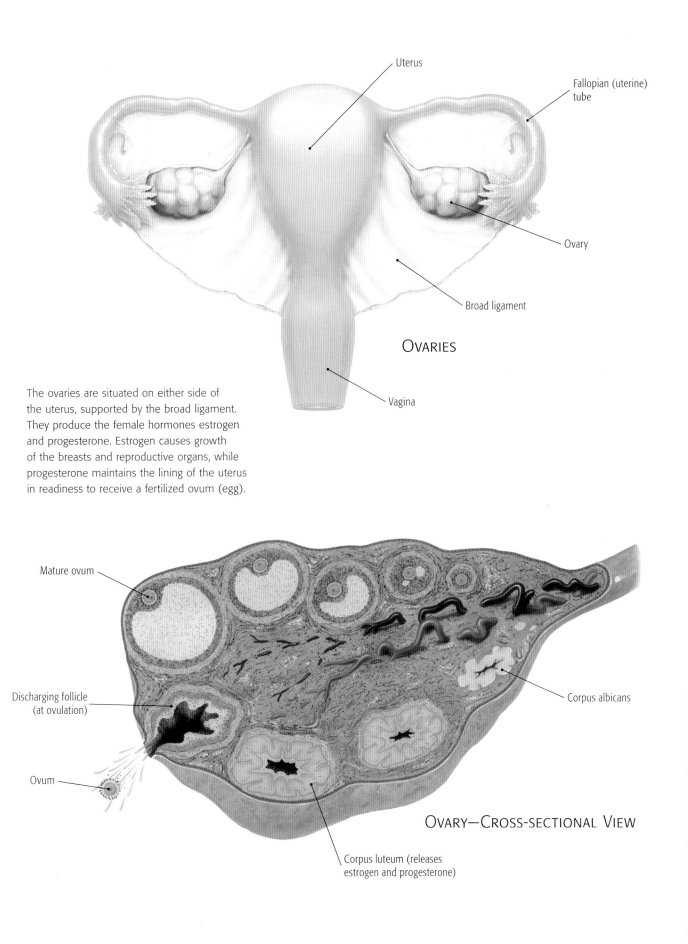

Uterus

Fallopian (uterine) tube

Ovary

Broad ligament

OVARIES

Vagina

The ovaries are situated on either side of the uterus, supported by the broad ligament. They produce the female hormones estrogen and progesterone. Estrogen causes growth of the breasts and reproductive organs, while progesterone maintains the lining of the uterus in readiness to receive a fertilized ovum (egg).

Mature ovum

Corpus albicans

Discharging follicle (at ovulation)

Ovum

OVARY—CROSS-SECTIONAL VIEW

Corpus luteum (releases estrogen and progesterone)

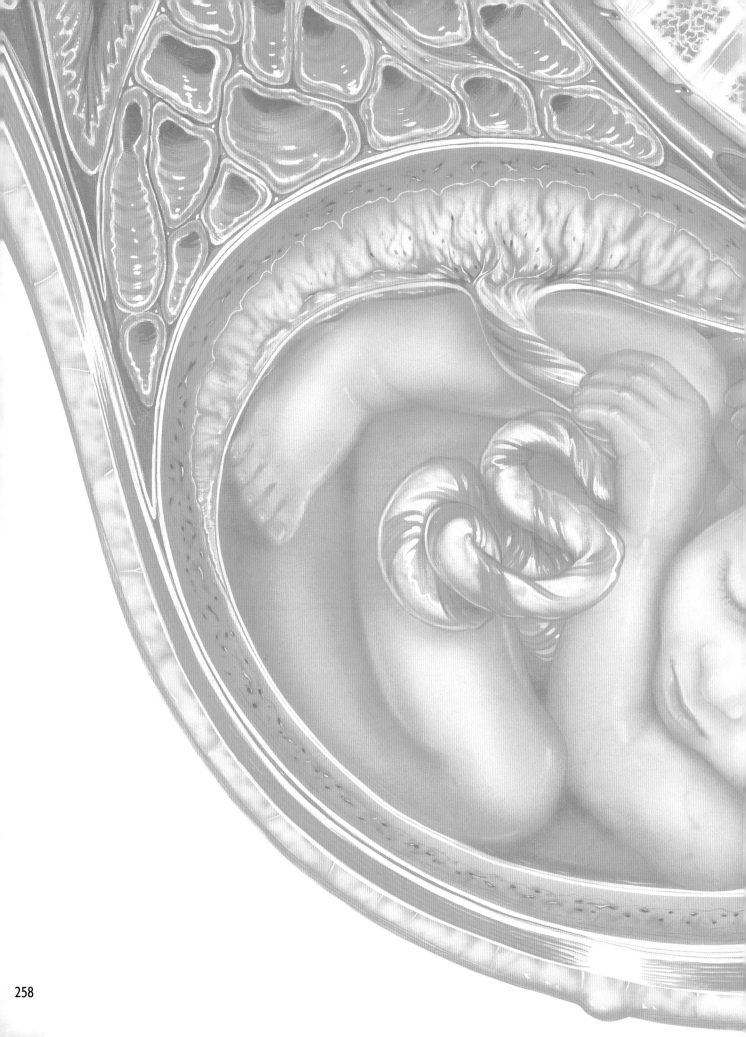

The Reproductive System

Male Reproductive System

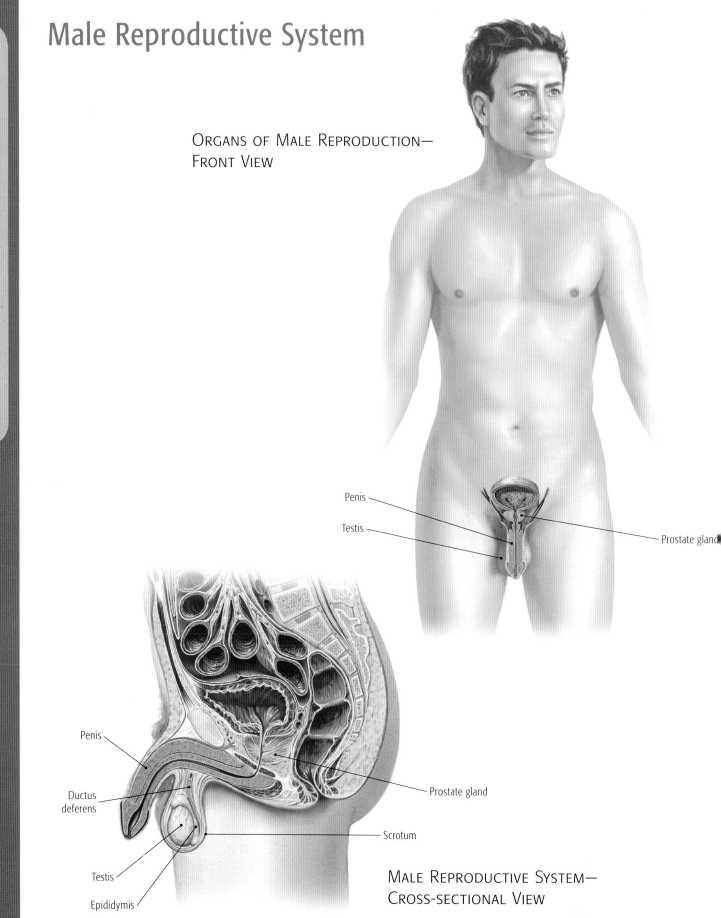

ORGANS OF MALE REPRODUCTION—
FRONT VIEW

Penis

Testis

Prostate gland

Penis

Ductus
deferens

Prostate gland

Scrotum

Testis

Epididymis

MALE REPRODUCTIVE SYSTEM—
CROSS-SECTIONAL VIEW

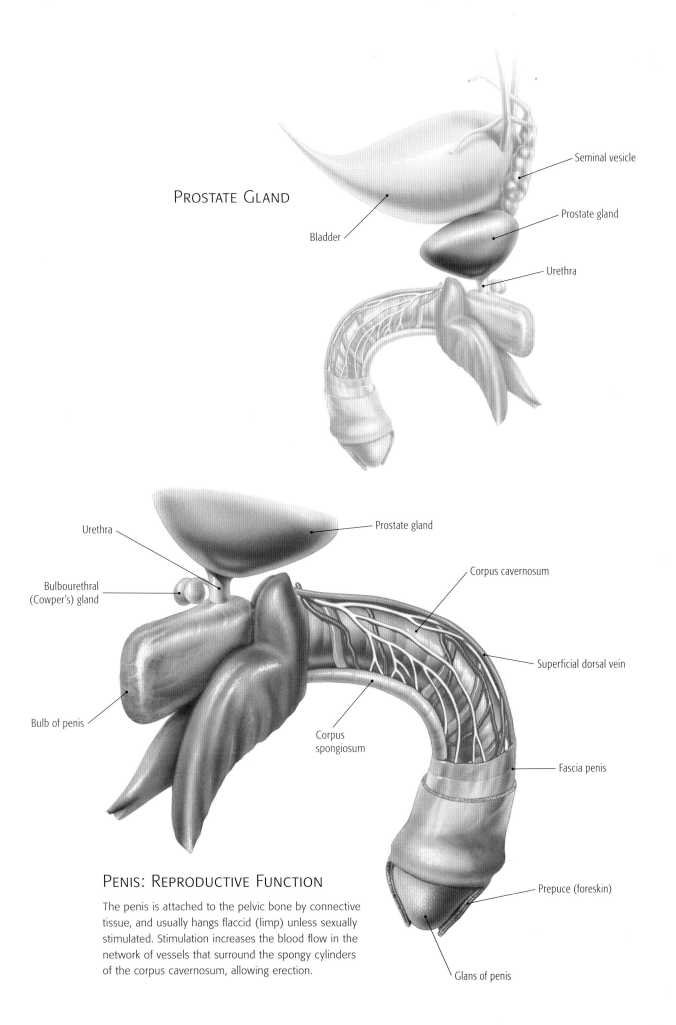

PROSTATE GLAND

Seminal vesicle

Prostate gland

Urethra

Bladder

Urethra

Prostate gland

Bulbourethral
(Cowper's) gland

Corpus cavernosum

Superficial dorsal vein

Bulb of penis

Corpus
spongiosum

Fascia penis

Prepuce (foreskin)

PENIS: REPRODUCTIVE FUNCTION

The penis is attached to the pelvic bone by connective
tissue, and usually hangs flaccid (limp) unless sexually
stimulated. Stimulation increases the blood flow in the
network of vessels that surround the spongy cylinders
of the corpus cavernosum, allowing erection.

Glans of penis

Male Reproductive System

Peritoneum

Bladder (detrusor muscle)

Ureter

Ductus deferens

Seminal vesicle

Ampulla of ductus deferens

PROSTATE AND BLADDER—
REAR VIEW

Ejaculatory duct

Prostate gland

Prostatic urethra

Bulbourethral
(Cowper's) gland

Membranous urethra

Superficial inguinal ring

Testicular artery

Pampiniform
(venous) plexus

Ductus deferens
(vas deferens)

Genital branch of
genitofemoral nerve

Artery to ductus deferens

Head of epididymis

Cremaster muscle
and fascia

Body of epididymis

Testis (covered by visceral
layer of tunica vaginalis)

External
spermatic fascia

Septum of scrotum

Parietal layer of tunica vaginalis

Scrotal skin

Superficial fascia
of scrotum

TESTES—REAR VIEW

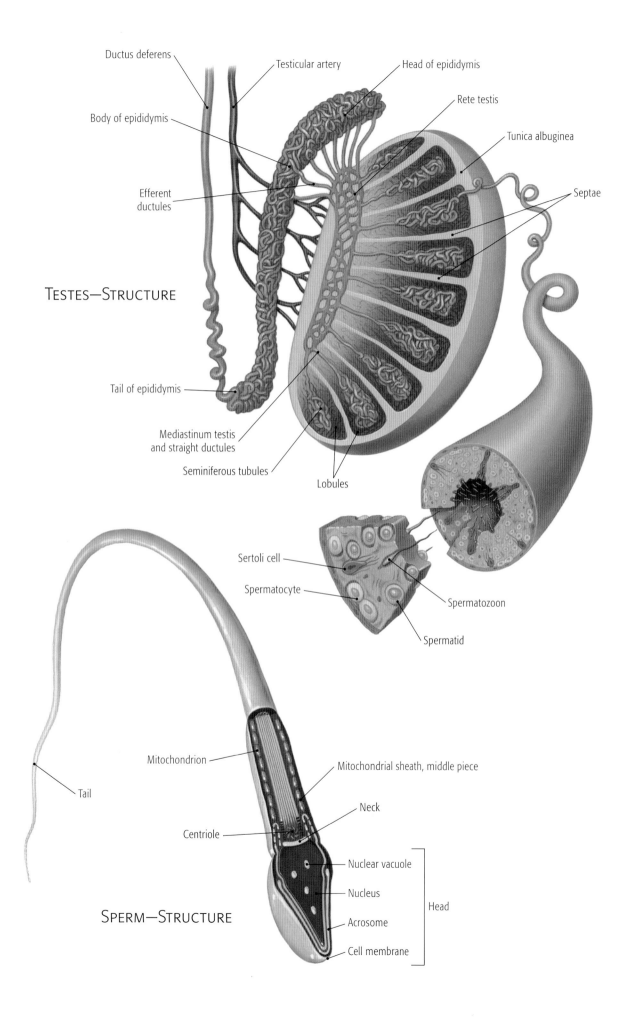

Ductus deferens

Testicular artery

Head of epididymis

Rete testis

Body of epididymis

Tunica albuginea

Efferent ductules

Septae

TESTES—STRUCTURE

Tail of epididymis

Mediastinum testis and straight ductules

Seminiferous tubules

Lobules

Sertoli cell

Spermatocyte

Spermatozoon

Spermatid

Mitochondrion

Mitochondrial sheath, middle piece

Neck

Tail

Centriole

Nuclear vacuole

Nucleus

SPERM—STRUCTURE

Head

Acrosome

Cell membrane

Female Reproductive System

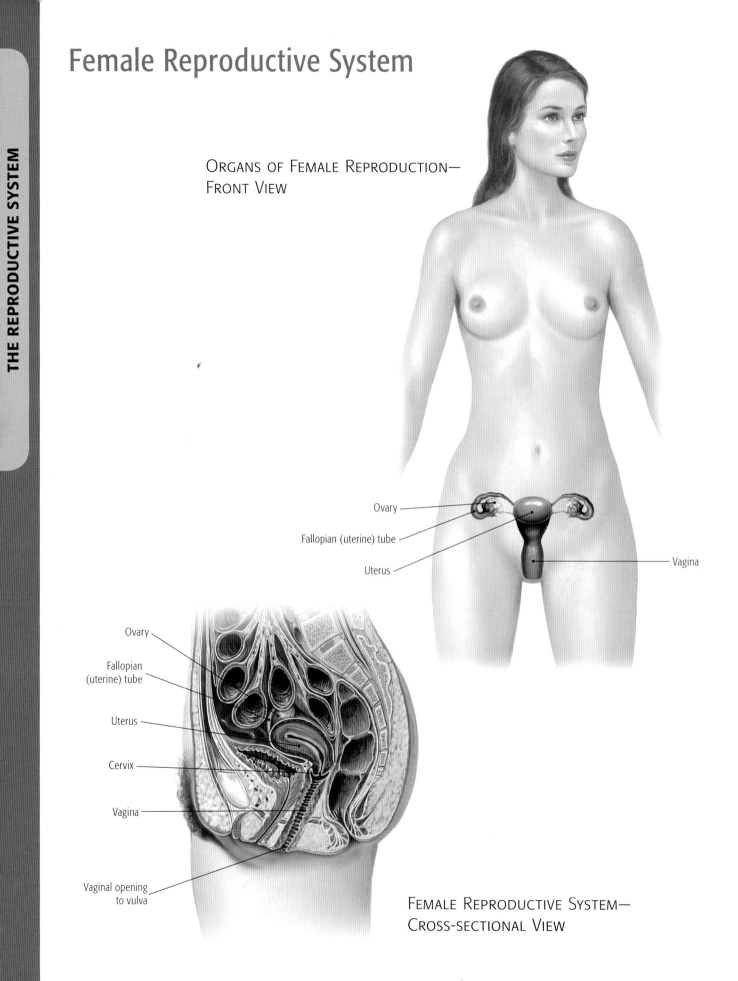

ORGANS OF FEMALE REPRODUCTION—
FRONT VIEW

Ovary

Fallopian (uterine) tube

Uterus

Vagina

Ovary

Fallopian
(uterine) tube

Uterus

Cervix

Vagina

Vaginal opening
to vulva

FEMALE REPRODUCTIVE SYSTEM—
CROSS-SECTIONAL VIEW

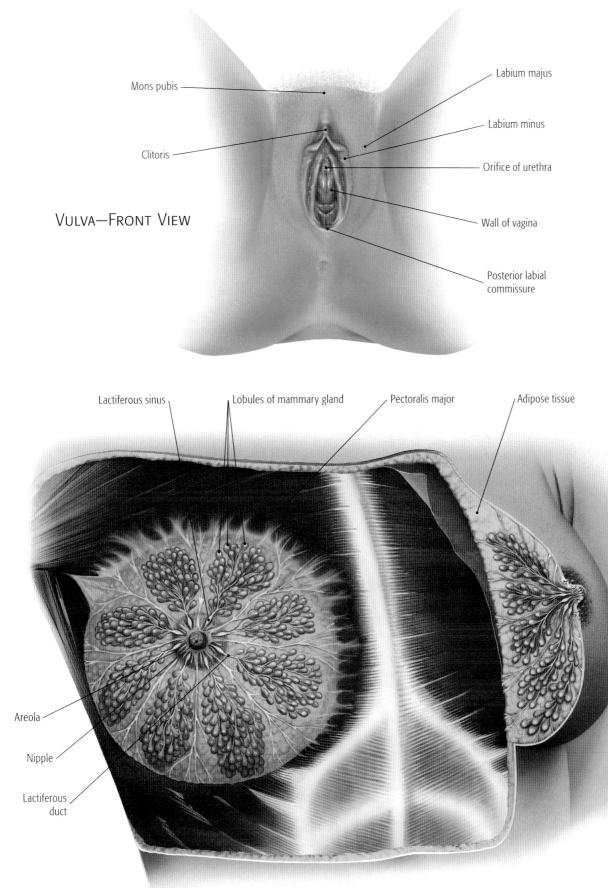

Mons pubis

Clitoris

Labium majus

Labium minus

Orifice of urethra

Wall of vagina

Posterior labial
commissure

VULVA—FRONT VIEW

Lactiferous sinus

Lobules of mammary gland

Pectoralis major

Adipose tissue

Areola

Nipple

Lactiferous
duct

MAMMARY GLANDS

Menstrual Cycle

CYCLE REGULATION

The hypothalamus and the anterior pituitary gland regulate the menstrual cycle. During each cycle the anterior pituitary gland releases follicle-stimulating hormone (FSH) and luteinizing hormone (LH), which trigger follicles (egg sacs) in the ovaries to mature and release estrogen and progesterone.

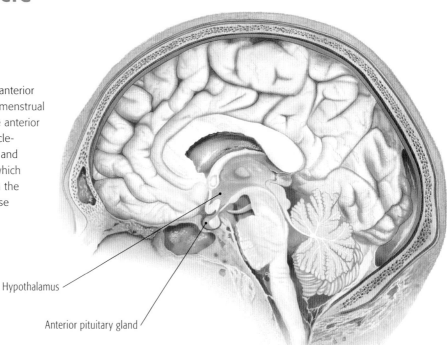

Hypothalamus

Anterior pituitary gland

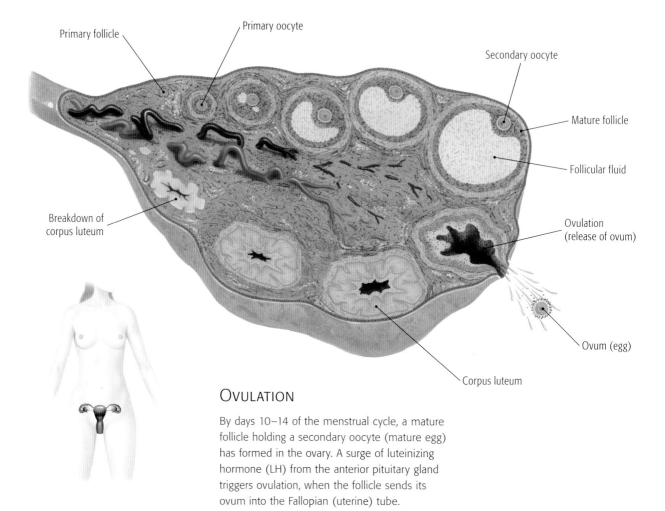

Primary follicle

Primary oocyte

Secondary oocyte

Mature follicle

Follicular fluid

Breakdown of corpus luteum

Ovulation (release of ovum)

Ovum (egg)

Corpus luteum

OVULATION

By days 10–14 of the menstrual cycle, a mature follicle holding a secondary oocyte (mature egg) has formed in the ovary. A surge of luteinizing hormone (LH) from the anterior pituitary gland triggers ovulation, when the follicle sends its ovum into the Fallopian (uterine) tube.

a Days 1-6
Menstruation

During menstruation, the lining of the uterus (endometrium) breaks down and is discharged.

b Days 7–13
Proliferative phase

At the start of the proliferative phase, cells begin to repair the lining of the uterus, and follicles in the ovary begin to form an ovum (egg).

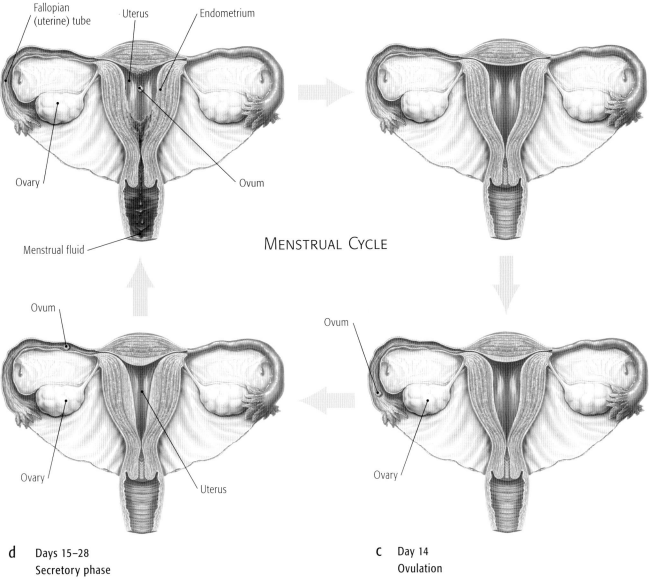

MENSTRUAL CYCLE

Fallopian (uterine) tube · Uterus · Endometrium

Ovary

Ovum

Menstrual fluid

Ovum

Ovary

Uterus

Ovum

Ovary

d Days 15–28
Secretory phase

During the secretory phase, the ovum travels along the Fallopian (uterine) tube toward the uterus, and hormones thicken the uterus lining in readiness to support a fertilized ovum. If the ovum is not fertilized, hormone levels fall and blood vessels in the uterus constrict.

c Day 14
Ovulation

Ovulation takes place on around day 14 of the cycle, and the ovary releases its ovum into the Fallopian (uterine) tube.

Conception and Early Pregnancy

Fertilization

Blastocyst implants in uterine wall

EARLY STAGES OF PREGNANCY

Once fertilized, an ovum (egg) is called a zygote and begins to divide immediately. This developing mass moves along the Fallopian (uterine) tube and reaches the uterus 5–6 days after fertilization. The mass of cells (now called a blastocyst) implants in the uterine wall and begins to develop into an embryo. From eight weeks, the embryo is described as a fetus.

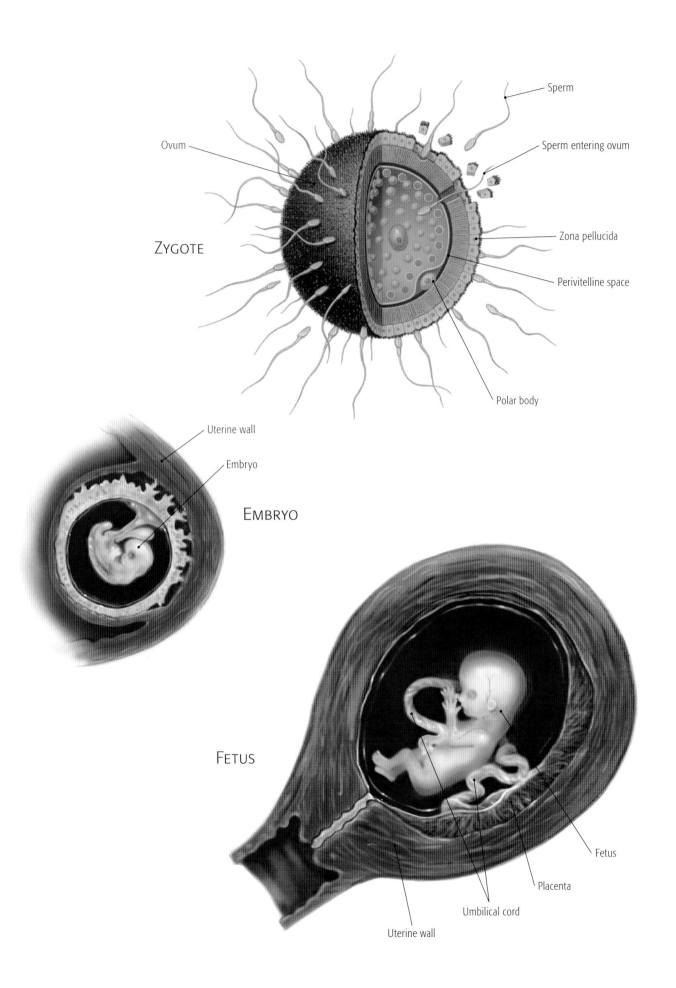

Sperm

Ovum

ZYGOTE

Sperm entering ovum

Zona pellucida

Perivitelline space

Polar body

Uterine wall

Embryo

EMBRYO

FETUS

Fetus

Placenta

Umbilical cord

Uterine wall

Fetal Development Cycle

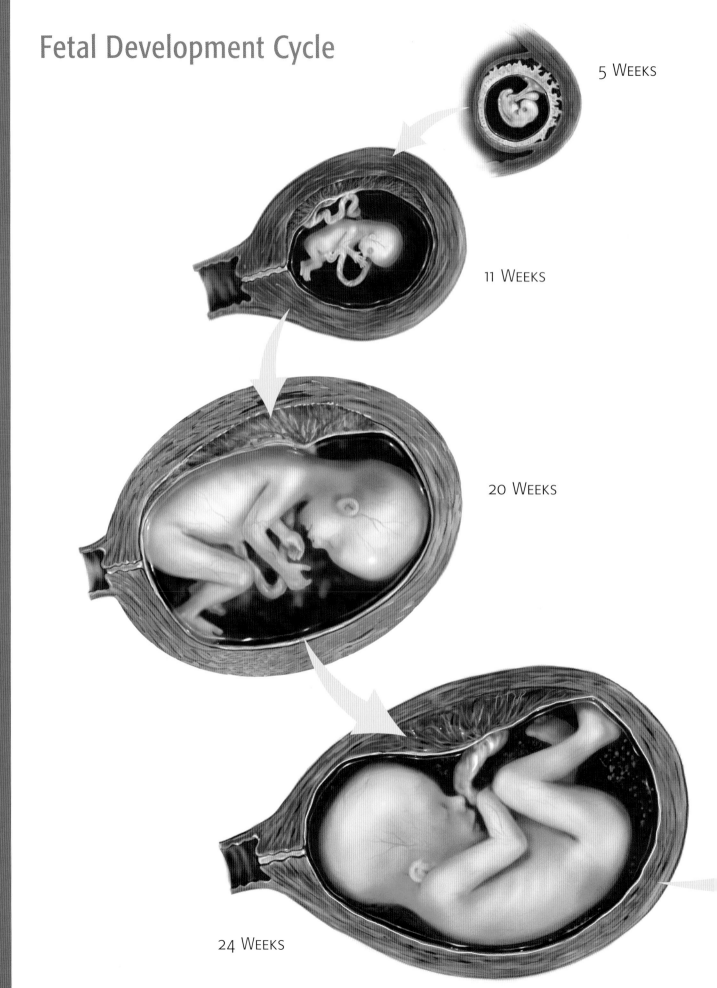

5 Weeks

11 Weeks

20 Weeks

24 Weeks

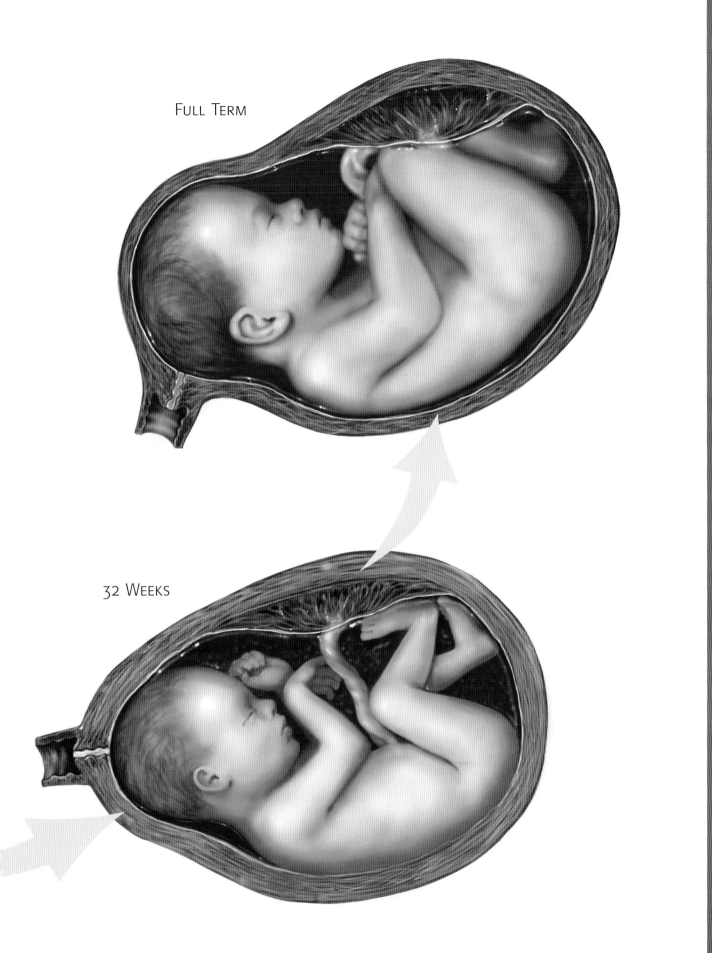

FULL TERM

32 WEEKS

Fetal Skull and Bone Development

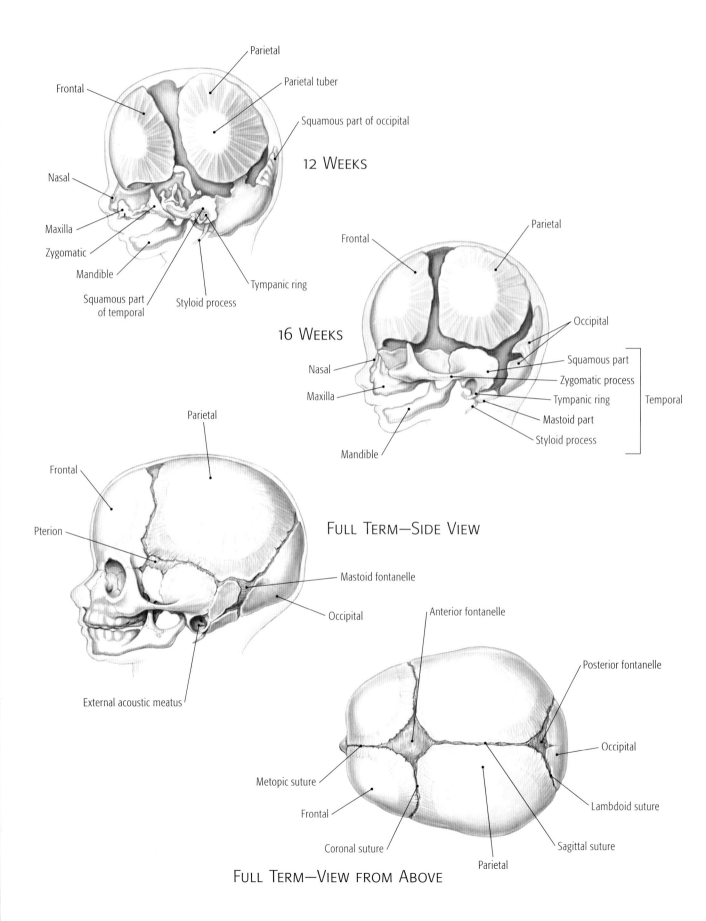

Parietal

Frontal

Parietal tuber

Squamous part of occipital

12 WEEKS

Nasal

Maxilla

Zygomatic

Mandible

Squamous part of temporal

Styloid process

Tympanic ring

16 WEEKS

Frontal

Parietal

Nasal

Maxilla

Occipital

Squamous part

Zygomatic process

Tympanic ring

Temporal

Mastoid part

Styloid process

Mandible

Parietal

Frontal

Pterion

FULL TERM—SIDE VIEW

Mastoid fontanelle

Occipital

External acoustic meatus

Anterior fontanelle

Posterior fontanelle

Occipital

Metopic suture

Frontal

Lambdoid suture

Sagittal suture

Coronal suture

Parietal

FULL TERM—VIEW FROM ABOVE

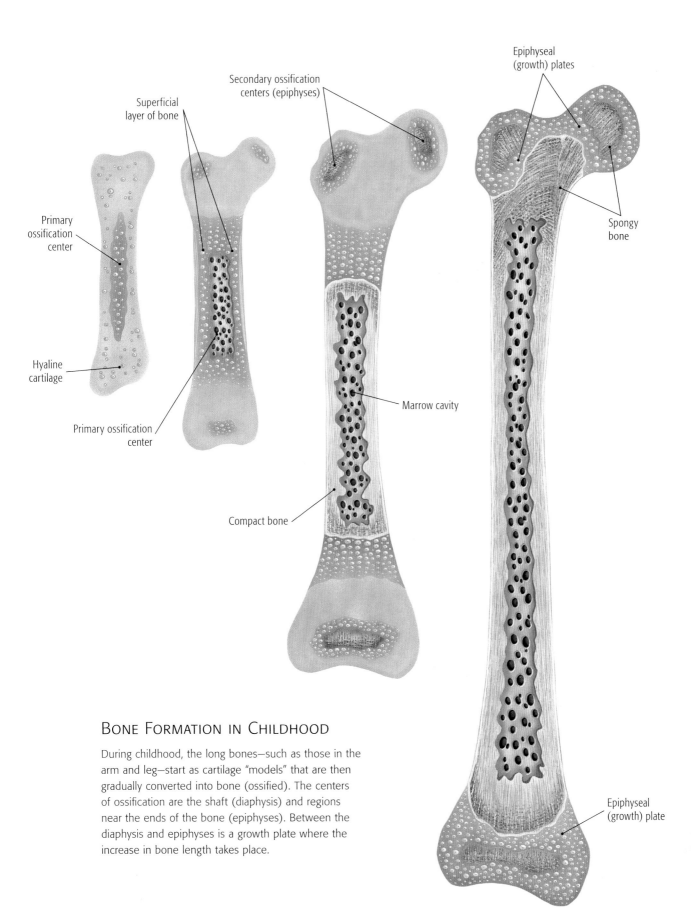

Primary ossification center

Superficial layer of bone

Secondary ossification centers (epiphyses)

Epiphyseal (growth) plates

Primary ossification center

Hyaline cartilage

Primary ossification center

Marrow cavity

Spongy bone

Compact bone

Epiphyseal (growth) plate

BONE FORMATION IN CHILDHOOD

During childhood, the long bones—such as those in the arm and leg—start as cartilage "models" that are then gradually converted into bone (ossified). The centers of ossification are the shaft (diaphysis) and regions near the ends of the bone (epiphyses). Between the diaphysis and epiphyses is a growth plate where the increase in bone length takes place.

Fetal Brain Development

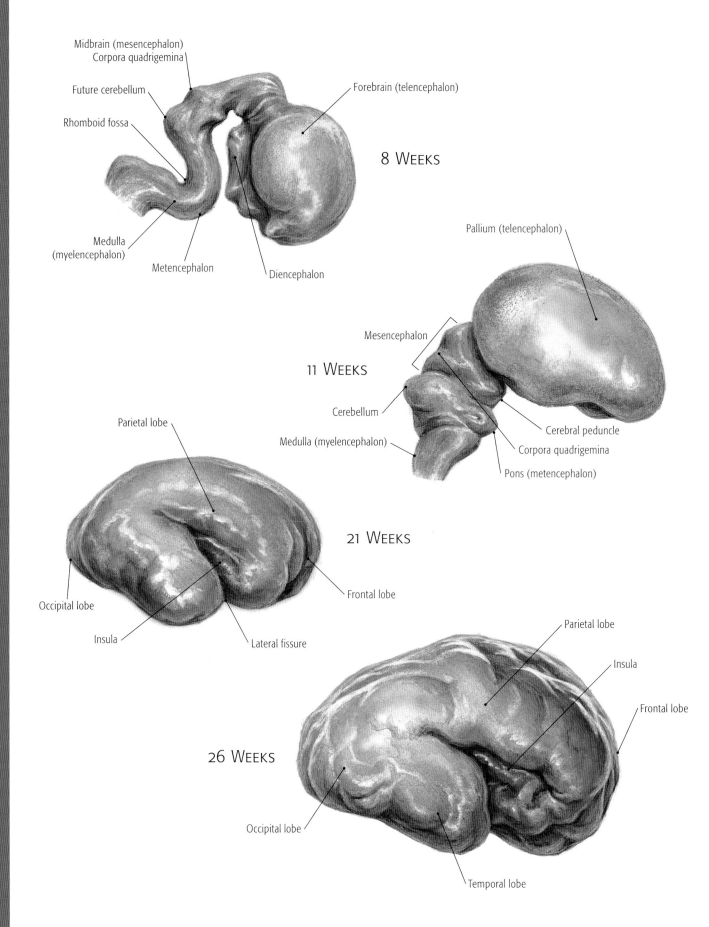

Midbrain (mesencephalon)
Corpora quadrigemina

Future cerebellum

Rhomboid fossa

Forebrain (telencephalon)

8 Weeks

Medulla
(myelencephalon)

Metencephalon

Diencephalon

Pallium (telencephalon)

Mesencephalon

11 Weeks

Cerebellum

Medulla (myelencephalon)

Cerebral peduncle

Corpora quadrigemina

Pons (metencephalon)

Parietal lobe

21 Weeks

Frontal lobe

Occipital lobe

Insula

Lateral fissure

Parietal lobe

Insula

Frontal lobe

26 Weeks

Occipital lobe

Temporal lobe

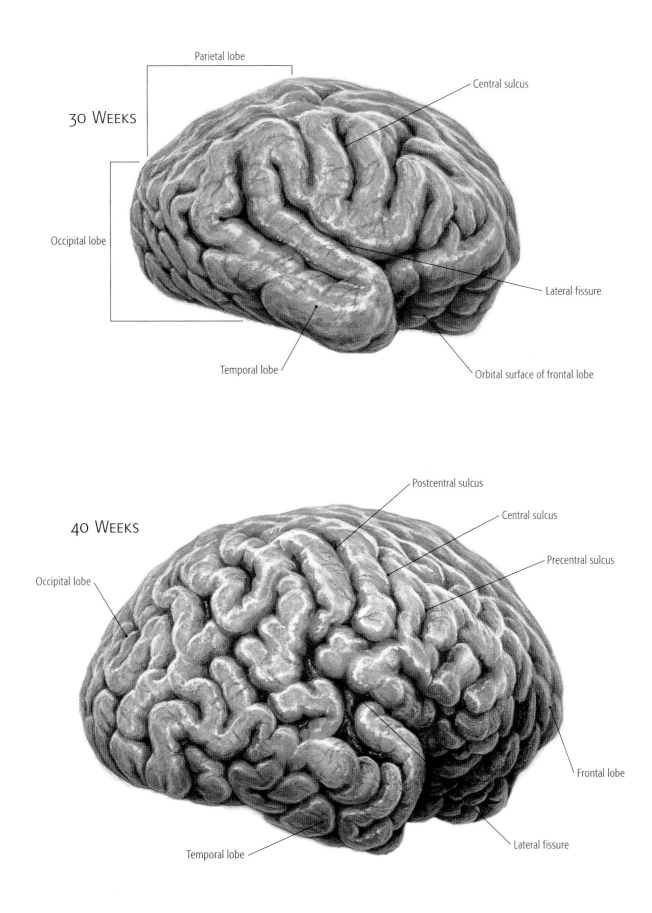

30 WEEKS

Parietal lobe

Central sulcus

Occipital lobe

Lateral fissure

Temporal lobe

Orbital surface of frontal lobe

40 WEEKS

Postcentral sulcus

Central sulcus

Precentral sulcus

Occipital lobe

Frontal lobe

Temporal lobe

Lateral fissure

Fetal Sex Differentiation

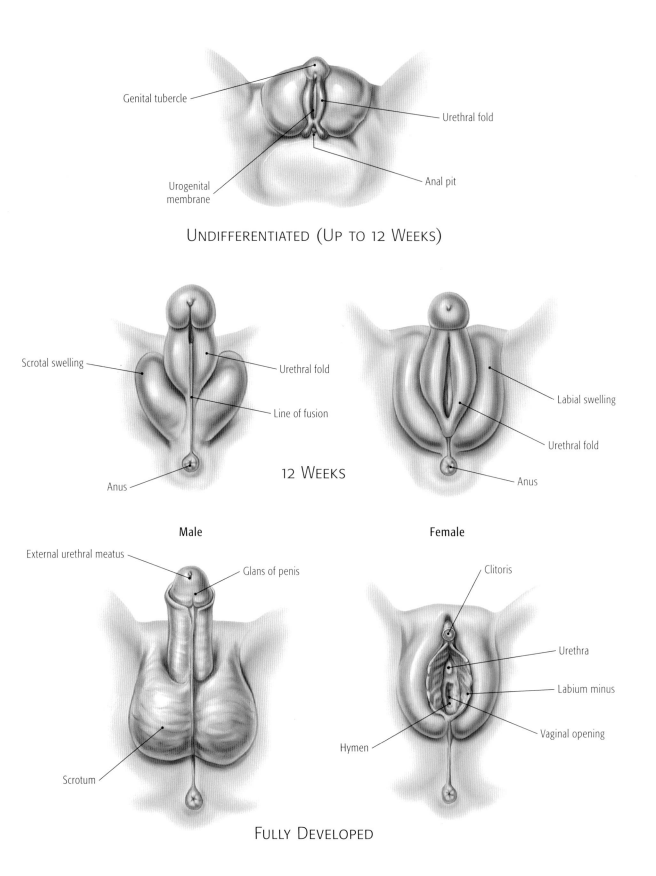

Genital tubercle

Urethral fold

Urogenital membrane

Anal pit

UNDIFFERENTIATED (UP TO 12 WEEKS)

Scrotal swelling

Urethral fold

Line of fusion

Anus

Labial swelling

Urethral fold

Anus

12 WEEKS

Male

Female

External urethral meatus

Glans of penis

Clitoris

Urethra

Labium minus

Vaginal opening

Hymen

Scrotum

FULLY DEVELOPED

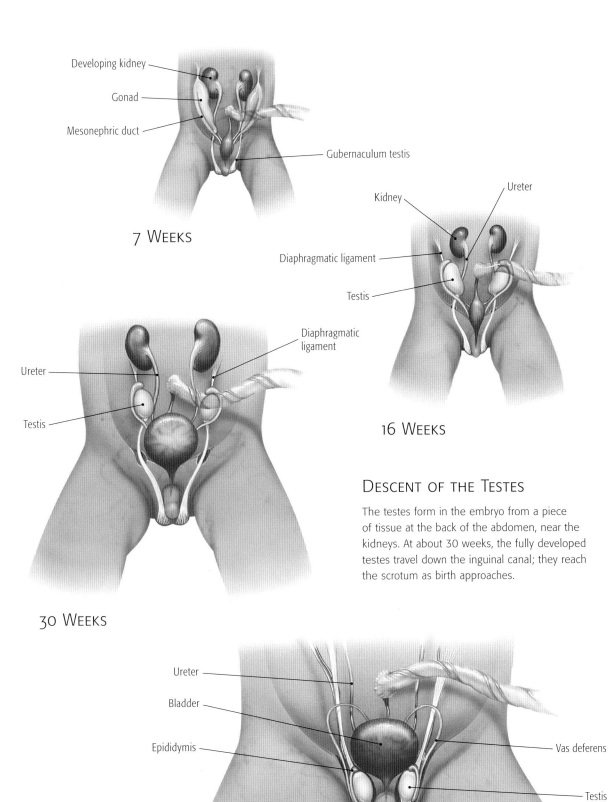

Developing kidney

Gonad

Mesonephric duct

Gubernaculum testis

7 Weeks

Kidney

Ureter

Diaphragmatic ligament

Testis

16 Weeks

Ureter

Diaphragmatic ligament

Testis

30 Weeks

Descent of the Testes

The testes form in the embryo from a piece of tissue at the back of the abdomen, near the kidneys. At about 30 weeks, the fully developed testes travel down the inguinal canal; they reach the scrotum as birth approaches.

Ureter

Bladder

Epididymis

Vas deferens

Testis

Fully Developed

Late Pregnancy

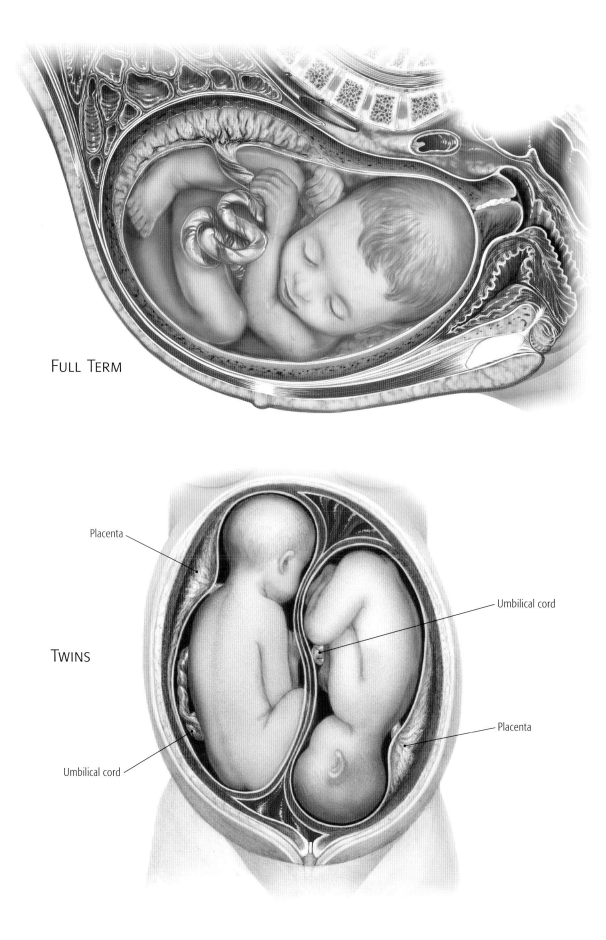

FULL TERM

Placenta

Umbilical cord

TWINS

Umbilical cord

Placenta

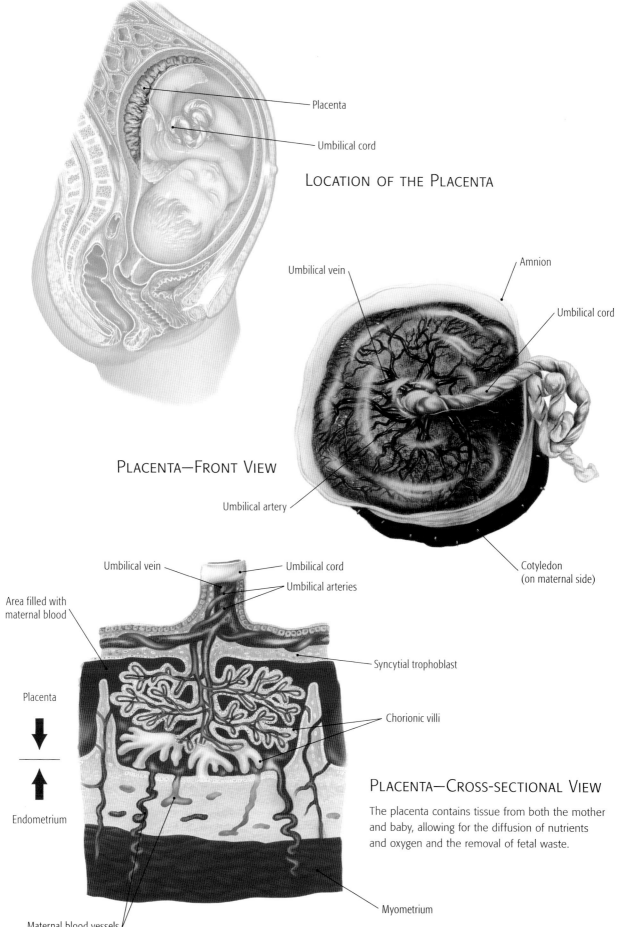

Placenta

Umbilical cord

LOCATION OF THE PLACENTA

Umbilical vein

Amnion

Umbilical cord

PLACENTA—FRONT VIEW

Umbilical artery

Cotyledon
(on maternal side)

Umbilical vein

Umbilical cord

Umbilical arteries

Area filled with
maternal blood

Syncytial trophoblast

Placenta

Chorionic villi

Endometrium

PLACENTA—CROSS-SECTIONAL VIEW

The placenta contains tissue from both the mother
and baby, allowing for the diffusion of nutrients
and oxygen and the removal of fetal waste.

Myometrium

Maternal blood vessels

Childbirth

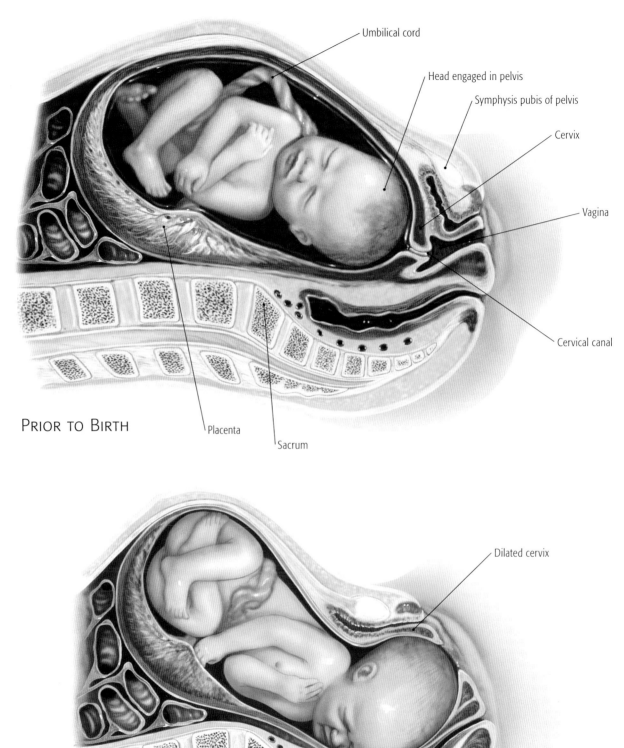

Umbilical cord

Head engaged in pelvis

Symphysis pubis of pelvis

Cervix

Vagina

Cervical canal

Placenta

Sacrum

PRIOR TO BIRTH

Dilated cervix

DILATION

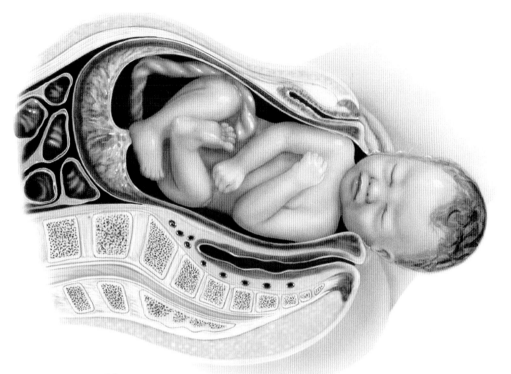

PRESENTATION OF THE HEAD

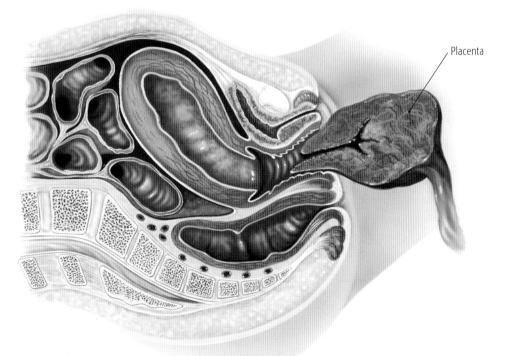

Placenta

EXPULSION OF THE PLACENTA

Time of Your Life: Female

At about 10 years of age, girls have a growth spurt, and pubic hair and underarm hair start to grow a year or two later. Soon the reproductive system develops, with the first period arriving around the age of 13. By 18 the body is approaching maturity and from there it continues to change, but not grow. From the late 40s the production of eggs and sex hormones decreases, culminating in menopause at around the age of 50. Without the hormonal effects, the breasts and skin lose firmness, fat distribution changes, bones lose minerals, and height decreases.

BIRTH–6 MONTHS

6–12 MONTHS

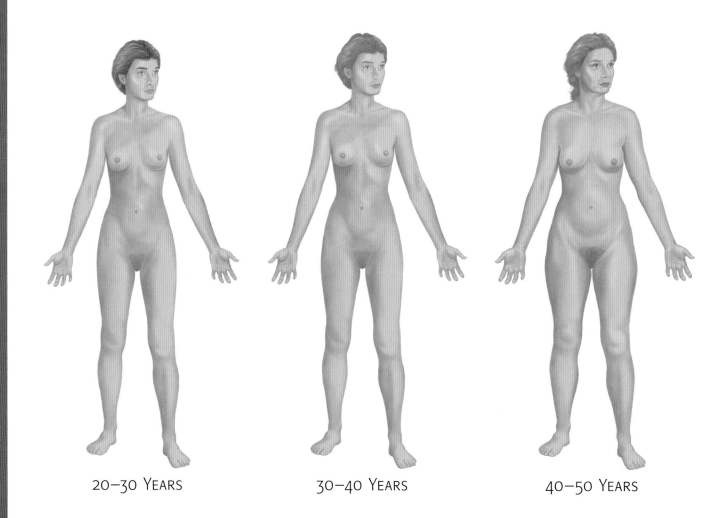

20–30 YEARS

30–40 YEARS

40–50 YEARS

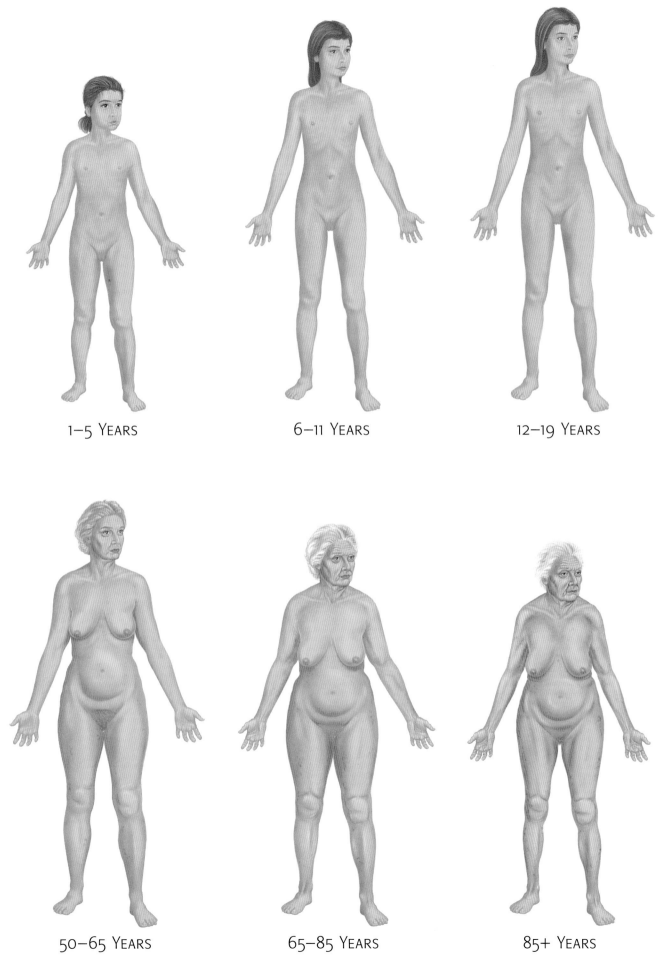

1–5 YEARS

6–11 YEARS

12–19 YEARS

50–65 YEARS

65–85 YEARS

85+ YEARS

Time of Your Life: Male

Boys' growth spurt occurs at around 13 or 14 years of age. Muscles begin to bulk up and body hair grows. The testes grow and produce sperm, and the voice deepens. As men mature the body reaches full muscular development, then starts to decline. The skin and muscles become softer, fat may increase, the prostate enlarges, production of male hormones and sperm reduces, and hair loss occurs.

BIRTH–6 MONTHS   6–12 MONTHS

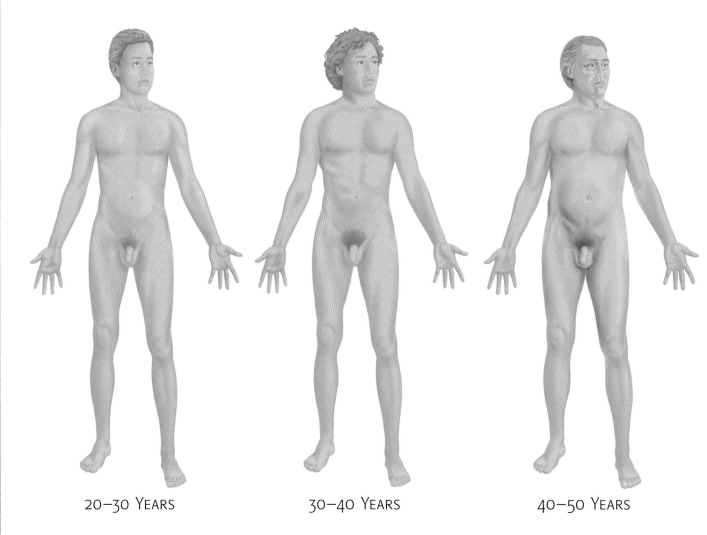

20–30 YEARS   30–40 YEARS   40–50 YEARS

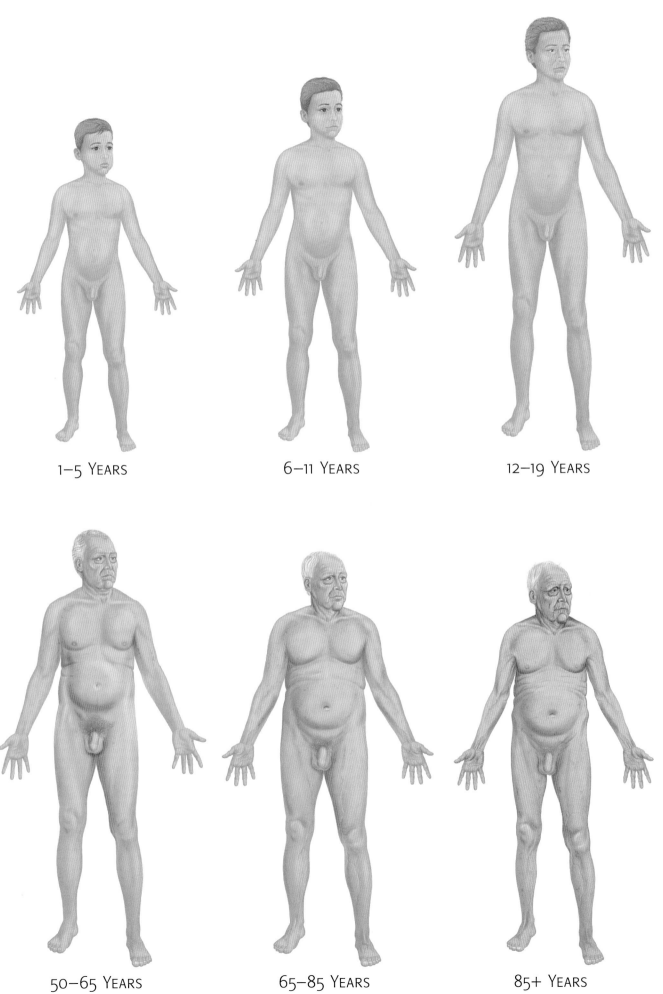

1–5 YEARS

6–11 YEARS

12–19 YEARS

50–65 YEARS

65–85 YEARS

85+ YEARS

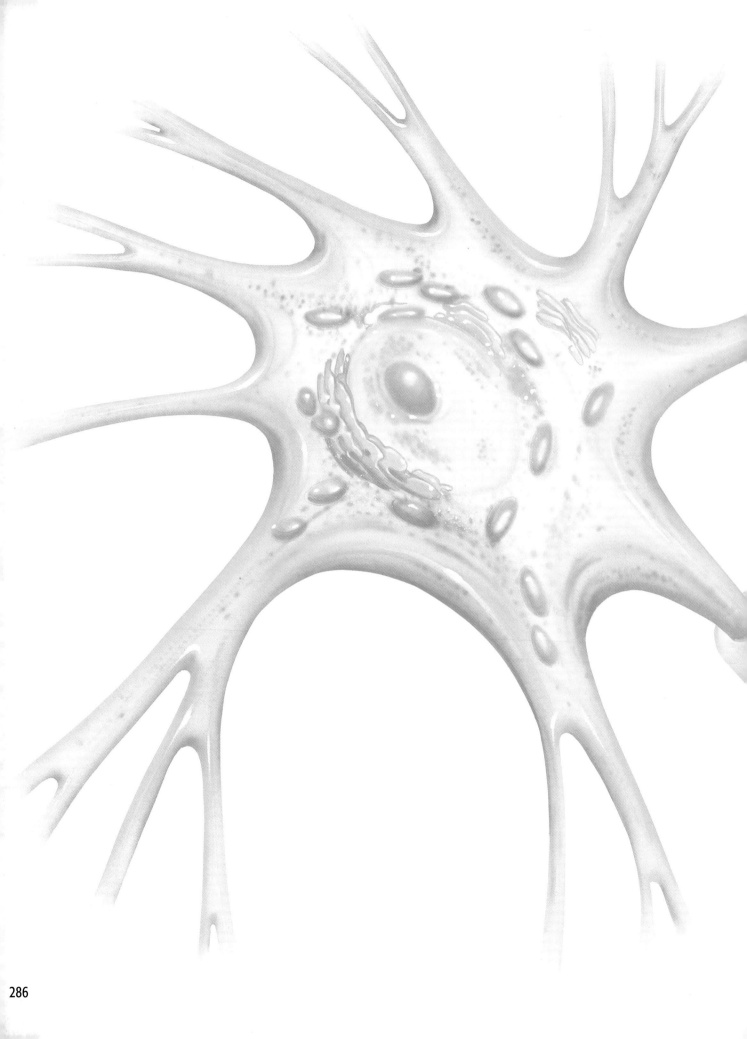

Reference

Glossary

Abduction A movement that pulls a structure or part away from the midline of the body.

Adduction A movement that returns a structure or part toward the midline of the body.

Adenohypophysis Another name for the anterior pituitary gland.

Adipose Tissue A specialized connective tissue that stores fat.

Alimentary Canal Another name for the digestive tract; the long muscular tube extending from the mouth to the anus.

Allergen A substance that will produce an allergic reaction, such as pollen, dust mites, and fur.

Antigen A molecule that is recognized by the immune system as foreign to the body.

Artery A flexible, thick-walled, tube-shaped blood vessel that carries blood away from the heart to the rest of the body.

Atrium *(plural: atria)* One of the two upper chambers in the heart.

B Lymphocyte A type of white blood cell that produces antibodies to help fight bacteria and viruses in the body.

Bacterium *(plural: bacteria)* A simple organism of microscopic size; some bacteria are beneficial to humans, while others cause and spread infections.

Blastocyst An early, hollow, spherical embryo comprising 150–300 cells.

Bronchus *(plural: bronchi)* A tube that conducts air from the trachea (windpipe) to the lung tissue.

Bursa A small, fluid-filled, saclike structure, found mainly around the joints, that protects bones and tendons from friction.

Carpal Of or relating to the carpus (the bones of the wrist).

Cartilage A tough, semitransparent, elastic, flexible connective tissue that covers the surface of joints, acts as a shock absorber, and joins the ribs to the sternum (breastbone).

Cerebral Cortex A highly folded sheet of nerve cells that forms the outer surface of the brain, and accounts for 40 percent of the brain's mass.

Cervical Of or relating to the neck or uterine cervix.

Chromosome A threadlike structure in the nucleus of a cell, consisting of a double strand of DNA and containing many hundreds of genes.

Circle of Willis The circuit of arteries at the base of the brain; the most common site for a brain aneurysm to form.

Circulatory System Comprises the heart and blood vessels of the body.

Clavicle Also known as the collar bone; it is attached to the sternum (breastbone) and the scapula (shoulder blade), and stabilizes the shoulder joint.

Coccygeal Of or relating to the coccyx.

Cochlea A small, spiral-shaped structure in the inner ear containing fluid and special hair cells that serve as sound sensors.

Condyle A rounded projection on the end of a bone where it joins another bone.

Connective Tissue The framework that supports, connects, and fills out body structures.

Crus An anatomical structure that resembles the shape of a leg.

Cytoplasm All the parts that make up a cell except the nucleus.

Dermatome An area of skin that is innervated by a particular pair of spinal nerves.

Diaphragm The muscular layer that separates the chest cavity from the abdominal cavity.

Diaphysis The central shaft of a mature long bone.

Diastole The rest phase of the cardiac cycle; usually used to refer to the resting of the ventricles, when the mitral and tricuspid valves of the heart open, allowing blood to fill the left and right ventricles.

Digestive System The process of breaking down foods into small, simple molecules for absorption and use as building blocks for human cells.

DNA A shortened form of the term "deoxyribonucleic acid"; molecules of DNA, found in the chromosomes of every cell, carry genetic information that determines inherited traits.

Dorsal Of or relating to the back, or toward the back.

Embryo A mass of multiplying cells during early pregnancy, from fertilization of the ovum (egg) to the end of week eight.

Endocrine System Coordinates the activities of tissues throughout the body, and acts by means of organic chemicals called hormones.

Epicondyle A projection on the end of a bone where muscles and ligaments attach.

Epiglottis A flap of elastic cartilage found in the larynx (voice box) that folds down during swallowing but remains upright during speaking and breathing.

Epiphysis *(plural: epiphyses)* The end of a mature long bone; it is the site of the growth plate during development.

Epithelial Tissue The outermost layer of the skin and the lining of hollow internal organs.

Eversion (of the foot) Moving the sole of the foot away from the other leg.

Exocrine Relating to a secretion that is released through a duct to an epithelial surface.

Extension A straightening movement that increases the angle between two parts.

Fetal Of or relating to a fetus.

Fetus A developing baby, from week eight of the pregnancy until birth.

Fibrin A white, fibrous protein that is formed during blood clotting.

Flexion A bending movement that decreases the angle between two parts.

Fontanelle A natural gap between three or four bones in a baby's skull.

Foramen *(plural: foramina)* A natural hole or opening in a bone or membrane.

Gene A unit of genetic information, passed from parent to offspring, which is found in a chromosome within the nucleus of a cell.

Gland A type of tissue made up of specialized cells that produce fluid secretions.

Gyrus *(plural: gyri)* A ridge on the surface of the cerebral cortex.

Hepatic Of or relating to the liver.

Histamine A chemical messenger found in body tissues that reacts with receptors on cell surfaces, causing changes in certain bodily functions.

Hormone A chemical substance produced by an endocrine organ that is released into the bloodstream and carried to a target organ, where it alters the activity of target cells.

Hypothalamus A small, but vital, region at the base of the brain, it regulates the heart, blood pressure, body temperature, water balance, food intake, growth, and sexual reproduction.

Intervertebral Disk A pad of fibrocartilage sitting between two vertebrae in the spine to provide mobility and shock absorption.

Inversion (of the foot) Moving the sole of the foot toward the other leg.

Larynx Also known as the voice box; it is the part of the throat that leads from the pharynx to the trachea (windpipe) and lungs.

Leukocyte A white blood cell.

Ligament A tough, white, fibrous, slightly elastic tissue that mainly supports and strengthens the joints of the body.

Lobe A rounded projection or section of a part or organ of the body.

Lumbar Of or relating to the lower back.

Lymphatic System A network of lymphoid tissue (lymph nodes), lymphatic vessels, and lymphoid organs that brings back to the heart much of the cells' interstitial fluid, and uses lymphocytes and macrophages to sweep up foreign bacteria, viruses, and cancer cells.

Lymphatic Tissue Acts as a first line of defense against infection in the respiratory system and digestive and urogenital tracts.

Lymphocyte A type of white blood cell that plays an important role in the immune response.

Macrophage A scavenging type of white blood cell that fights infection by engulfing foreign organisms and debris.

Mammary Of or relating to the milk-producing glands in the female breast.

Mandible The lower jaw.

Manubrium The upper part of the sternum (breastbone).

Maxilla The upper jaw.

Meninges Three layers that cover and protect the brain and spinal cord: the fibrous outside layer (dura mater), the middle layer of collagen and elastin (arachnoid mater), and the inner pia mater.

mRNA A shortened form of the term "messenger ribonucleic acid"; used by DNA to carry the information required by a cell to make proteins.

Muscular System Comprises the muscles of the body.

Myofibril One of the threads of a muscle fiber, consisting of contractile protein myofilaments that are arranged in regular arrays.

Nephron A tiny filtering unit found in the kidney.

Nervous System Comprises the central nervous system (the brain and spinal cord) and the peripheral nervous system (the nerves and ganglion cells distributed throughout the body).

Neural Tissue Nervous system tissue that transmits messages to and from the brain.

Neurohypophysis Another name for the posterior pituitary gland.

Neuron A specialized cell that conducts nerve impulses.

Nucleotide Base Adenine, thymine, cytosine, and guanine, which bind together in limited combinations to produce the "rungs" of a DNA ladder.

Olecranon The part of the ulna bone that forms the outer bulge of the elbow.

Olfactory Of or relating to the sense of smell.

Omentum *(plural: omenta)* A membrane of fatty tissue that covers and supports the organs of the abdomen.

Oocyte An immature ovum (egg) in the ovary.

Ossification The process whereby cartilage or other connective tissue changes into bone.

Osteon Found in compact bone, it is a canal with a blood vessel running through it, which is surrounded by rings of bone tissue.

Palmar Of or relating to the palm of the hand.

Papilla *(plural: papillae)* A small, nipple-shaped projection on a tissue surface.

Peduncle A stalklike structure joining one part of the body to another.

Peristalsis Wavelike contractions in the muscular walls of the esophagus, stomach, and intestines that propel the contents along.

Peritoneum A thin, lubricating membrane that lines the abdominal cavity and covers the organs within it.

Phalanx *(plural: phalanges)* One of the bones that forms the fingers and toes.

Pharynx A vertically elongated tube that lies behind, and has openings to, the nose, mouth, and larynx (voice box), and is a common passage for air, water, and food.

Platelet The smallest structural unit in the blood, formed in the bone marrow from the cytoplasm of giant cells known as megakaryocytes; it is concerned with blood coagulation.

Plexus A network of intersecting blood vessels, nerves, or lymph vessels.

Plica *(plural: plicae)* A fold of skin or other tissue.

Pronation (of the forearm) In the anatomical position: moving the palm from a front-facing position to a rear-facing position; with the elbow flexed: facing the palm downward.

Pulmonary Of or relating to the lungs.

Reproductive System Comprises (in the female) the ovaries, Fallopian (uterine) tubes, uterus, and vagina, and (in the male) the testes, ducts to convey spermatozoa (sperm), glands, scrotum, and penis.

Respiratory System A group of organs concerned with providing gas exchange with the external environment; it includes the nose, pharynx, larynx (voice box), trachea (windpipe), bronchi, lungs, and pleural sacs.

Ribosome The part of a cell responsible for creating proteins from amino acids.

Sacral Of or relating to the sacrum.

Salivary Glands Located around the beginning of the digestive tract, they produce saliva, which aids chewing, tasting, swallowing, and digestion.

Sebaceous Glands Located in the lower layer of skin (dermis) throughout most of the body's surface, they produce sebum, which protects the skin from water loss and controls the spread of bacteria and fungi.

Sinus A small passage or cavity relatively wide in relation to its length, which contains air (paranasal sinuses) or blood (venous sinuses).

Skeletal System Comprises the bones of the body.

Spermatozoon *(plural: spermatozoa)* Also known as a sperm cell; a mature male reproductive cell produced in the testes.

Sphincter A ring of muscle that controls the opening and closing of a passageway in the body.

Spinous Process The bony projection from the rear of a vertebra.

Sulcus *(plural: sulci)* A shallow groove on the surface of the cerebral cortex.

Supination (of the forearm) In the anatomical position: moving the palm from a rear-facing position to a front-facing position; with the elbow flexed: facing the palm upward.

Suture A joint between two bones of the skull, which is bound together by fibrous connective tissue and is immobile.

Systemic Of or relating to the body as a whole.

Systole The phase of the cardiac cycle when the ventricles of the heart contract, pushing blood into the aorta and pulmonary artery.

T Lymphocyte A type of white blood cell that helps the body fight certain infections as well as cancer.

Tendon A bundle of aligned and tightly packed collagen fibers that provides the strength to attach muscle to bone.

Thoracic Of or relating to the chest (thorax).

Trachea Also known as the windpipe; it is a tube for the passage of air, beginning at the end of the larynx (voice box) and ending at the bronchi of the lungs.

Transverse Process One of the two bony projections on either side of a vertebral arch.

Tympanic Membrane Also known as the eardrum; it is a thin, semitransparent membrane that separates the external ear from the middle ear, and transmits sound vibrations from the ear canal to the ossicles (the three bones of the middle ear).

Urinary System Excretes waste products from the body and maintains the balance of water and electrolytes in the blood.

Vein A thin-walled, low-pressure blood vessel that returns blood to the heart.

Ventricle One of the two lower chambers in the heart, or one of the four cavities in the brain that are connected via passageways and contain cerebrospinal fluid.

Villus *(plural: villi)* A fingerlike projection from the lining of the small intestine that greatly increases the surface area available for the absorption of nutrients.

Virus A tiny organism that can cause a recurring or chronic disease, or an acute disease lasting only a short time.

Zygote A cell created when a spermatozoon (sperm) enters and fertilizes an ovum (egg), before it begins the process of division that leads to the development of an embryo.

Index

Bold numbers indicate chapter names and subject titles. Plain numbers indicate illustration names and labels. *Italicized* numbers indicate references in captions.

digestion *149, 234*
digestion and absorption of nutrients
  218–19
digestive enzymes *229*
digestive organs and greater omentum 216
digestive system 16, **212–35,** *219*, 288
digestive system—front view 214
digestive tract *41*, 220
digital arteries *176*, 194, 195
digital nerve 128
digital veins *176*, 194, 195
dilated cervix 280
diploic vein 133
discharging follicle (at ovulation) 257
disease *36*
distal convoluted tubule 243
distal interphalangeal joint 79
distal phalanges 78, 86
distal phalanx 78
distal phalanx of thumb 78
distal radioulnar joint 77
DNA **30–31,** *37*, 288
DNA ladder *30,* 31, *31, 32*
DNA replication 30
dominant and recessive genes 33, *33*
dorsal 289
dorsal arch *176*, 180, 195
dorsal branch to corpus callosum (artery)
  183
dorsal calcaneocuboid ligament 87
dorsal cavity 19
dorsal cuboideonavicular ligament 87
dorsal cuneocuboid ligament 87
dorsal cuneonavicular ligaments 87
dorsal funiculus 142
dorsal horn (spinal cord) 142
dorsal intercuneiform ligament 87
dorsal interosseous muscles 118, 125
dorsal median sulcus 141
dorsal metatarsal ligaments 87
dorsal plexus 168
dorsal rootlets 142
dorsal spinocerebellar tract 142
dorsal tarsometatarsal ligaments 87
dorsal tubercle of radius 78
dorsal venous arch *176*, 181, 195
dorsalis pedis artery 176
dorsiflexion 91, *103*
dorsolateral sulcus 142
dorsum of tongue 201
ducts (pancreas) *229*
ductus deferens (vas deferens) 260,
  262, 263, 277
duodenojejunal junction 217
duodenum 192, 214, 216, 219, 228,
  230, 232, *234*
dura 107
dura mater 133, *133,* 142

E

E. coli (food poisoning) 34
ear canal *158*
ear (otic) 18, 156, **156–57**
eardrum 65, 156, 158, *158,* 291
early stages of pregnancy 268
Ebner's gland (serous gland) 161
Ebola virus 36
ectomorph female 20
ectomorph male 21
efferent arteriole 243
efferent ductules 263
efferent lymphatic vessel 169
eighth rib 70
ejaculatory duct 262
elastic cartilage *43*
elbow (antecubital) 18, *102*

elbow extension 91
elbow flexion 91
elbow joint 76, 94
elbow/olecranon (olecranal) 18
ellipsoidal joint 92
embryo *43, 268,* 269, *277,* 289
emotion *162*
emotional responses *165*
emotional states *136*
enamel 223
endocrine glands *252,* **252–55,** *253*
endocrine organs *179*
endocrine system 17, **246–57,** 289
endolymph 159
endolymphatic duct 157
endometrium 267, *267,* 279
endomorph female 20
endomorph male 21
endoneurium 142
endoplasmic reticulum 24
endosteal layer of dura mater 133
endosteum 56
endothelial cell 169, 243
endothoracic fascia 210
enzymes *225*
eosinophil 27
epicondyle 289
epidermis 46, 47, 51
epididymis 260, 277
epidural fat 107
epiglottis *43,* 160, 161, 201, 202, 203,
  203, 221, 289
epiglottis: breathing 203
epiglottis: speaking 203
epiglottis: swallowing 203
epineurium 142
epiphyseal (growth) plates 273
epiphyseal line 56
epiphyses 273, 289
epithelial cells 161, *173,* 226
epithelial tissue 41, *41,* 289
erection *261*
erector pili muscle (arrector pili) 51
erector spinae 110
erythrocytes (red blood cells) 26, 177
esophagus 107, 112, 199, 201, 202,
  207, 214, *218,* 230, 231, *231*
estrogen *257, 266*
ethmoid bone 58, 64
ethmoid sinuses 64, 200
eustachian (auditory) tube 65, 157
eversion 90, 289
exercising muscles 102
exocrine 289
expiration (breathing out) 208
extension (body movement) 91, 289
extension (muscles) *102*
extensor carpi radialis brevis 117, 118
extensor carpi radialis longus 99, 114,
  116, 118
extensor carpi ulnaris 99, 116
extensor digiti minimi 115, 118
extensor digitorum 99, 115, 116, 118
extensor digitorum brevis 123
extensor digitorum brevis tendons 123
extensor digitorum longus 98, 99, 120,
  122, 123
extensor digitorum longus tendons 123
extensor hallucis longus 98, 120, 123
extensor hallucis longus tendon 123
extensor indicis 118
extensor pollicis brevis 99, 115, 118
extensor pollicis longus 115, 118
extensor retinaculum 99, 115
external abdominal oblique 98, 99, 110, 217
external acoustic meatus 58, 272
external anal sphincter (sphincter ani
  externus) 217, 233

external carotid artery 184
external ear canal (meatus) 156, 158
external iliac artery 176, 180, 192, 195,
  238, 239, 240, 241
external iliac nodes 168
external iliac vein 176, 181, 192, 195,
  238, 239, 240, 241
external intercostals 110, 112, 199
external jugular vein 176, 181, 184, 206
external occipital crest 62
external occipital protuberance 58, 61, 62
external root sheath 51
external spermatic fascia 262
external urethral meatus 276
external urethral orifice 240, 241
eye 18, *42,* 148, 149, **152–53,** *155*
eye color *33*
eyeball 64, 152
eye—front view 152
eye—side view 153

F

face (facial) 18, *144*
facet for head of first rib 67
facial artery 176, 180, 184
facial colliculus 141
facial nerve (VII) 140, 141
facial nerves 146
facial vein 184
falciform ligament 215, 217, 226
Fallopian (uterine) tube 257, 264,
  266, 267, *267, 268*
false rib 54, 55
false ribs (pairs 8–10) 70
falx cerebri 133
fascia penis 261
fat *40, 219*
fat distribution *282*
fat pad 117
fats *230*
fatty acids *218*
female: 1–5 years 283
female: 6–11 years 283
female: 6–12 months 282
female: 12–19 years 283
female: 20–30 years 282
female: 30–40 years 282
female: 40–50 years 282
female: 50–65 years 283
female: 65–85 years 283
female: 85+ years 283
female: birth–6 months 282
female bladder 241
female endocrine system—front view 249
female pelvis—front view 80
female reproductive system **264–65**
female reproductive system—cross-sectional
  view 264
female sex hormones *282*
female urethra 241
female urinary system—front view 239
femoral artery 122, 176, 180, 195
femoral condyle 55
femoral lateral condyle 55, 84
femoral nerve 128, 147
femoral vein 122, 176, 181, 195
femur 54, 55, 80, 81, 82, 83, 84, 85, 95
fenestrated capillaries 179, *179,* 235
fenestrations 179
fertilization 268, *268*
fertilized ovum (egg) *257*
fetal 289
fetal brain development **274–75**
fetal brain development: 8 weeks 274
fetal brain development: 11 weeks 274
fetal brain development: 21 weeks 274